Basic Engineering METALLURGY

Theories, Principles, and Applications

Basic Engineering

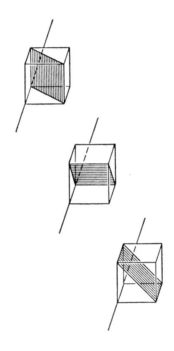

SECOND EDITION

Englewood Cliffs, N.J.

METALLURGY

Theories, Principles, and Applications

CARL A. KEYSER

Professor of Metallurgical Engineering, University of Massachusetts; Consulting Engineer; Registered Engineer, Commonwealth of Massachusetts

PRENTICE-HALL, INC.

Basic Engineering METALLURGY, 2nd ed.

Library of Congress Catalog Card Number: 59–12428

Current printing (last digit):
14 13 12 11 10 9 8

PRINTED IN THE UNITED STATES OF AMERICA

06053—C

To Annie and Louis . . .
    last of the Algonkin and Shoshone

Preface to the Second Edition

This book is intended to serve all persons who are interested in learning more about metals. It contains general metallurgical information of interest to engineers and students of metallurgy.

The second edition differs from the first mainly in that an attempt has been made to introduce new topics, bring old ones up to date, and eliminate or deemphasize those the importance of which has diminished. I hope that users of the first edition will feel comfortable using the second edition. They will be pleased to discover that no change has been made in the general organization of the book.

The first six chapters approach the subject from a theory viewpoint. In these chapters are presented the concepts and principles of behavior common to most metals. Discussed in this connection are the mechanism of metal failure and the steps that can be taken to improve service behavior.

Chapters 7, 8, and 9 are devoted to the properties and heat-treatment of steel. These topics are probably among the most important phases of engineering metallurgy. Chapters 10, 11, and 12 present a discussion of the properties, applications, and fabrication of some nonferrous metals.

Chapters 13 through 18 discuss the advantages, limitations, and control of the various means of fabricating metals. Casting, electroforming, and powder metallurgy techniques are discussed as primary methods of fabrication; i.e., methods by which formless metal is made into useful shapes. These shapes are further processed into useful objects by secondary methods of fabrication which include mechanical working, joining, machining, finishing, and electroplating.

At this point I should like to express my gratitude to:
my friends, who have given encouragement and support;
my readers, who have made many valuable suggestions;

my students, who are my least diffident critics;

my three sons, who would much rather have had me take them fishing; and

my wife, for being a good sport.

Carl A. Keyser

Amherst, Massachusetts

Contents

CHAPTER 1

The Structure of Metals

1.1. The Atom

An understanding of metal behavior is grounded in knowledge of the nature of atoms and how they are arranged in solid metals. Atoms consist of a massive core, known as the *nucleus*, surrounded by negative electric charges called *electrons*. The nucleus itself contains *protons*, which bear positive charges, and *neutrons*, which are electrically neutral. Protons having a mass of about 1.7×10^{-24} g are almost 2000 times more massive than electrons, which have a mass of about 9.0×10^{-28} g. The mass of the neutron is about the same as that of the proton.

The number of protons in the nucleus is equal to the number of electrons around the nucleus. Since the positive charge of a proton equals the negative charge of an electron, the atom itself is electrically neutral.

A simplified physical picture of the atom portrays the electrons revolving about the nucleus in definite orbits. The centrifugal force of rotation balances the electrostatic attraction between the nucleus and the electrons, keeping the latter in their orbits. There are an infinite number of possible orbits surrounding a nucleus, which orbits, theoretically, can be filled by the electrons. The orbits do not exist as a continuous series. Rather they represent a discontinuous series. Each orbit represents a definite electronic frequency, with frequency gaps between successive orbits. The electrons in orbits close to the nucleus are known as low-energy electrons, because they would liberate only small amounts of potential energy if they fell into the nucleus. The farther the orbit from the nucleus, the greater the potential energy of its electrons. Electrons, if sufficiently excited by electromagnetic energy, such as heat, light, or x-rays, can be knocked from their normal orbits to fill higher-energy orbits further from the nucleus. However, no more than two electrons can occupy any one orbit at a time.[1] If an electron is ejected from its orbit, the atom immediately assumes an unstable high-energy state. The vacancy created by the ejection is quickly filled by an electron from one of the nearby orbits of higher energy. This in turn creates another vacancy, which is filled in the same way as the initial vacancy. Eventually all the vacancies are filled and the atom returns to a low-energy, stable condition. As the initial and subsequent orbital vacancies are filled by successive electrons falling into orbits nearer the nucleus, energy is liberated in such forms as light, heat, and x-rays. The frequency and penetrative power of the radiation is greater, and its wave length shorter, generally speaking, when the vacancies which are filled lie close to the nucleus. The reverse is true for filling of vacancies remote from the nucleus.

It is convenient to consider electron orbits in groups known as electron shells. This is done when the orbits represent nearby or nearly equal energy levels. An energy level diagram for aluminum is shown in Fig. 1.1. The aluminum atom consists of a nucleus and 13 associated electrons. The innermost orbit forms the K-shell

Relative Energy Levels	Energy Level Designation	Number of Electrons in Levels	Shells
————	3p	1	
————	3s	2	*M*
————	2p	6	
————	2s	2	*L*
————	1s	2	*K*

Fig. 1.1. **Schematic energy level diagram for aluminum.** The potential energy of the electrons diminishes as the nucleus is approached or as the column is descended. Conversely, a greater amount of energy is required to eject an electron from a low energy level than from a high energy level.

and contains two electrons. At a somewhat higher energy level, known as the 2s level, there is another orbit also containing two electrons. Close to this are three more orbits all of the same

[1] This is known as the Pauli exclusion principle.

energy level (in this case the $2p$ level) and containing a total of 6 electrons.   The eight electrons in the $2s$ and $2p$ levels form the *L-shell*.   This pattern is repeated in the *M*-shell, which consists of the $3s$ and $3p$ energy levels.   Though the $3p$ level can hold a total of 6 electrons in 3 orbits, in aluminum there is only one electron in one of these orbits.   Aluminum differs chemically from the other elements in the third period of the periodic table by the number of electrons in the *M*-shell.   This is shown by Table 1.1.   In fact, chemical differences arise as a result of the number and arrange-

Table 1.1.   A portion of the periodic table showing the elements of the third period.

Group	I	II	III	IV	V	VI	VII	VIII
Element	Na	Mg	Al	Si	P	S	Cl	A
Energy levels		Numbers	of	electrons	in	various	energy	levels
1s	2	2	2	2	2	2	2	2
2s	2	2	2	2	2	2	2	2
2p	6	6	6	6	6	6	6	6
3s	1	2	2	2	2	2	2	2
3p			1	2	3	4	5	6
Total electrons	11	12	13	14	15	16	17	18
Atomic number	11	12	13	14	15	16	17	18
Atomic weight	22.997	24.32	26.97	28.06	30.98	32.06	35.457	39.944

ment of the outermost electrons.   The atomic number is the same (see Table 1.1) as the number of electrons of the atom.   Since the number of electrons is the same as the number of protons in the nucleus, the atomic number is also the same as the number of protons.

The atomic weight represents the mass of the atom of an element relative to the mass of an oxygen atom arbitrarily assigned the value 16.000.   Most elements actually have more than one atomic weight, the differences being caused by variation in the numbers of neutrons in the nuclei.   Varieties of the same element having different atomic weights are known as **isotopes** of the element.   Since all the isotopes of a given element have the same number of protons and electrons, the isotopes of a given element have identical chemical properties.   In naturally occurring elements, the ratios of the amounts of the isotopes of a given element are fixed.   Thus, the atomic weight of an element actually represents the atomic weights of its various isotopes and the ratios in which the isotopes occur in nature.   For instance, chlorine with an atomic weight of 35.457 consists of two isotopes of chlorine having atomic weights of 35 and 37.   These isotopes represent respectively 77.1 and 22.9 per cent of the total numbers of chlorine atoms normally present in chlorine.

The electrons of the outermost shells of atoms are the electrons which are involved in chemical reactions and thus determine chemical properties.   They are known as valence electrons.   The valence electrons are high-energy electrons, and are least tightly bound to the nucleus.   They determine how atoms of one element react when in close contact with one another or with atoms of other elements.

1.2.   X-Rays

Much of our knowledge of metal structure has been derived from the use of x-rays.   Hence, we shall give here a brief discussion of x-rays—their nature, and how they are produced.

Discovery of x-rays is generally credited to W. K. Röntgen in 1895.   Sir William Crookes had observed previously that a high potential caused fluorescence of gases in evacuated tubes.   [See Fig. 1.2(a).]   He also noted a glow on the glass wall of the tube opposite the cathode, produced by a stream of electrons, or cathode rays, striking the glass.   It was found that by curving the cathode the electron stream could be focused on the tube wall, with the result that the glass could be melted.   Röntgen's observation was made on a Crookes tube similar to the one shown in Fig. 1.2(b).   The tube was shielded with thin cardboard in a darkened room. Röntgen observed that fluorescent material held outside the tube, opposite the cathode, would glow.   He concluded that secondary radiations were emitted from whatever objects were struck by cathode rays.   Objects placed in the path of these radiations cast shadows on the fluorescent spot.   [See Fig. 1.2(c).]   Röntgen proceeded to study this radiation and found that it could not be deflected by a magnetic field (as could the cathode rays), but that it was able to ionize gases; expose photographic plates; pass through dense substances, opaque as well as transparent; and cause fluorescence of some substances.   Between 1895 and 1912 it was discovered that this radiation had wavelengths between 4×10^{-9} cm and 1×10^{-8} cm.   This distance is approximately the same as the spacing between the planes of atoms in solid substances.   These new radiations were called x-rays.

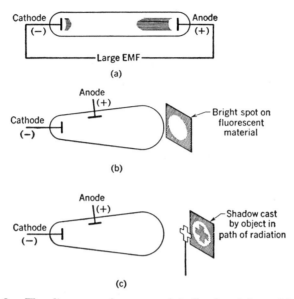

Fig. 1.2. The discovery of x-rays. (a) Crookes tube. (b) Fluorescence noted opposite cathode by Röntgen. (c) Shadows of objects placed in path of x-rays.

Production of x-rays. X-rays are produced when a target material is bombarded by a stream of electrons (cathode rays). The electrons strike the atoms of the target and part of the energy is transformed into x-radiation (2%) and part into heat (98%). X-rays are generated in x-ray tubes for which a typical circuit is shown in Fig. 1.3. The filament is heated by a low-voltage current and, as is characteristic of any hot metal, tends to emit electrons. The anode is positively charged to a high potential and accelerates the electrons from the vicinity of the filament to the target. To prevent the target from melting, cold water or oil is circulated through its mounting.

Energy of x-rays. When low-energy electrons strike an atom of target material, a broad band of x-radiation is emitted. If the accelerating voltage which drives the electrons to the target is increased, the energy of the electrons increases, and the distribution of intensity versus wavelength changes as shown in Fig. 1.4. Decreasing wavelengths indicate more penetrative radiation; increasing wavelengths indicate less penetrative radiation. The relative intensity of radiation is a function of the number of emis-

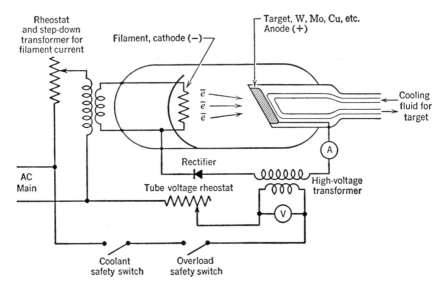

Fig. 1.3.   Schematic diagram of x-ray tube.

sions per unit time.   An analogy might be drawn between the
action of a drop forge (see section 16.14.) and the intensity-wave-
length relationship.   The number of blows of the hammer per unit
time would correspond to intensity, and the height of fall would
correspond to wavelength.   The total energy imparted by the drop
hammer would correspond to the number of blows multiplied by
the energy of each blow.   Likewise, the total energy of the spectrum for a particular curve shown in Fig. 1.4 is indicated by the
area under the curve.   Distributions of wavelengths corresponding
to the smooth curves of Fig. 1.4 are known as **continuous spectra**
which produce **white radiation.**

The **energy** E of the x-rays is given by $E = h\nu$, where $h =$
Planck's constant, 6.62×10^{-27} erg-second, and $\nu =$ frequency of the
radiation.   Electromagnetic radiation travels with a velocity c equal
to 3×10^{10} cm/sec.   Therefore, since $c = \lambda\nu$, where λ is the wavelength of the radiation, $E = hc/\lambda$.   If the charge e on the electron
is 4.8×10^{-10} esu and the electron is accelerated by a voltage V,
then the energy of the accelerated electron is eV.   When all the
energy of an accelerated electron is converted into x-rays, the most
energetic, penetrative, shortest wavelength rays are produced.
These minimal wavelengths, symbolized by $\lambda_{\min}$, would satisfy the
relationship

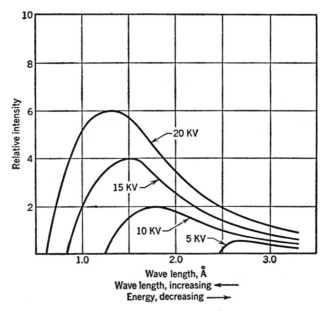

Fig. 1.4. Relative intensity versus wavelength for various tube voltages. Note that as the wavelength increases the radiation becomes less energetic.

$$E = hc/\lambda_{min}$$

and, since $eV = E$, then

$$eV = hc/\lambda_{min}$$

Solving for λ_{min}, and substituting the above values for h, c, and e,

$$\lambda_{min} = \frac{6.62 \times 10^{-27} \times 3 \times 10^{10}}{4.8 \times 10^{-10} \times V \times 3.33 \times 10^{-3}}$$

where 3.33×10^{-3} is a conversion factor to change volts to esu. Simplifying:

$$\lambda_{min} = 1.2430 \times 10^{-4}/V \text{ cm or } 12,430 \text{ Å}/V$$

where Å is an Ångstrom unit equal to 10^{-8} cm. This relationship between λ_{min} and V can be seen in the curves of Fig. 1.4. For these curves, the wavelength at peak intensity, $\lambda_{I_{max}}$, is about one and one-half times the minimum wavelength, i.e., $\lambda_{I_{max}} = 1.5 \lambda_{min}$. The area under the curves of Fig. 1.4 increases approximately as the square of the voltage; or, if the voltage is held constant, the area increases approximately in direct proportion to the atomic number of the target metal. The peak intensity increases approximately as the fourth or fifth power of the voltage.

Above a certain critical voltage, depending upon the target, the continuous spectrum develops sharp intensity peaks at definite wavelengths. The particular wavelengths at which the peaks are observed depend upon the target material. The occurrence of these peaks produces what is known as **characteristic radiation.** The characteristic spectrum for molybdenum is shown in Fig. 1.5. The characteristic lines are produced when the electrons strike the target atoms with sufficient energy to eject electrons from the inner shells of the atom. The characteristic lines are designated by letters K, L, and M, etc., corresponding to the shell from which an electron has been ejected. The K lines always refer to the shortest wavelengths, L to a somewhat longer wavelength, and so on. The K lines appear when electrons are ejected from the K-shell. This places the atom in a highly excited, unstable condition. If an electron from the L-shell falls into the K-shell to fill the vacancy, the atom returns to a less excited state and energy is given off having a wavelength called K_a. If an M-shell electron fills the K-shell vacancy, (a transition which is possible, but not as likely as transition from the L-shell to the K-shell), the energy liberated has a wavelength corresponding to K_β. If K_a radiation is produced, then L_a radiation also must appear. As can be seen from Fig. 1.5 (a), when the K-shell vacancy is filled by an L-shell electron, a vacancy temporarily exists in the L-shell. This in turn is filled by an electron from some more distant shell, such as the M-shell, and this produces L_a radiation. When the K_a line appears, the K_β, L, M, etc., lines also appear, because there is always the possibility of filling the K-shell not only from the L-shell to give K_a, but also from the M-shell to give K_β; further, if sufficient energy is available to remove a K electron, there is also enough energy to remove an L electron, etc., to give L, M, etc., lines.

The K_a line consists, actually, of two closely spaced lines known as K_{a_1} and K_{a_2}. Thus K_a is sometimes called an unresolved doublet, comprising K_{a_1} and K_{a_2}. The origins of K_{a_1} and K_{a_2} are shown in Fig. 1.5 (c) which shows the various ways in which L electrons can fill a vacancy in the K level. In x-ray diffraction work, usually only the three strongest lines are used. These are K_{a_1}, K_{a_2}, and K_{β_1}. The wavelengths and intensities of these lines relative to the

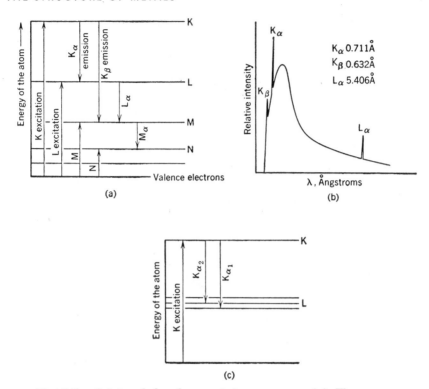

Fig. 1.5. Origin of the characteristic spectrum. (a) The energy required for excitation of electrons and liberated by filling of vacancies. (b) Some of the characteristic lines for a Mo target at 25 KV. The line for the Mα emission of part (a) is not shown. (c) The emissions corresponding to the $K\alpha_1$ and $K\alpha_2$ lines of the $K\alpha$ doublet.

intensity of K_{a_1} are shown for a molybdenum target in the table below:

Table 1.2

Line	Wavelength, Å	Intensity Relative to K_{a_1}
K_{a_1}	0.70926	1
K_{a_2}	0.71354	½
K_{β_1}	0.63225	⅕

It is customary to use the unresolved K_a doublet, since the K_{a_1} and K_{a_2} lines are so close together. Likewise, the subscript is usually dropped from K_{β_1}. It should be noted that an increase of the voltage on the tube does not change the wavelengths of the lines, though it does increase their intensity relative to the continuous spectrum.

Moseley's law.[2]   The square root of the frequency of radiation, v, is related to the atomic number, Z, of the target material according to the expression:

$$\sqrt{v} = c(Z - \sigma)$$

where c and σ are constants.   A plot of Z versus $\sqrt{v}$ gives a straight line as shown in Fig. 1.6.   The higher the atomic number of the target, the higher the frequency, the shorter the wavelength, and the more penetrative and energetic is the radiation from it.

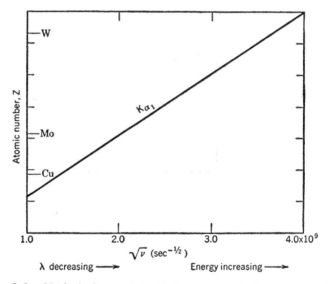

Fig. 1.6.   **Mosley's law.**   Note that wavelength decreases as frequency and energy of the radiation increase.

Absorption of x-rays.   When x-rays strike atoms, their energy is absorbed.   Consider a substance of thickness x, struck by x-rays having an initial intensity I_0, as shown in Fig. 1.7.   It has been observed that $(I_1 - I_2)/I_1 \propto -dx$, or $(I_1 - I_2)/I_1 = -\mu\, dx$ where μ is the linear absorption coefficient.   The value of μ depends upon the wavelength of the radiation (it is larger for long wavelengths than for short ones), the absorbing substance (it is larger, the higher the absorber's atomic number), and the density of the absorber (solid, liquid, or gas).   The expression can also be written

[2] H. G. Moseley.

$dI/I = -\mu \, dx$. Integration between the limits of I_0 and I_f, and 0 and x, gives

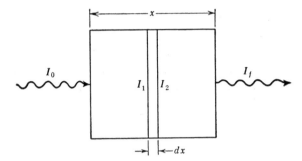

Fig. 1.7.   Absorption of x-rays.

$$\ln I_f - \ln I_0 = -\mu x$$
$$I_f = I_0 e^{-\mu x}$$

or as more commonly written,

$$I = I_0 e^{-\mu x}$$

Since the ability to absorb x-rays depends upon the density of the absorbing substance, a more general equation can be written if the mass absorption coefficient, μ/ϱ, is used in place of μ, where ϱ is the density of the absorbing substance:

$$I = I_0 e^{-\frac{\mu}{\varrho} \cdot \varrho x}$$

This expression is independent of the density of the absorber. For alloys, the value of μ/ϱ can be calculated from the weight percentage and values of μ/ϱ for the elements present:

$$(\mu/\varrho)_{\text{alloy}} = (w_A/100) \, (\mu/\varrho)_A + (w_B/100) \, (\mu/\varrho)_B + \dots$$

where w_A is the weight percentage of alloying element A, etc.

Effective absorption is actually the result both of true absorption, and of scattering. Scattering results when an x-ray strikes an atom, and secondary radiation emanates from the atom which acts as a point source. Only a negligible portion of this energy appears in the transmitted beam, because it radiates in all directions from the emanating atom. The effect is similar to the scattering of light by dust particles, fog, or smoke. The mass scattering coefficient of absorption is designated by σ/ϱ.

True absorption occurs when the incident quanta have sufficient energy to knock electrons from their orbits. As these vacancies are filled, secondary radiation is emitted from the excited atoms which act as point sources. The secondary radiation is always of longer wavelength than the incident radiation. Radiation absorbed in this fashion gives rise to the true mass absorption coefficient τ/ϱ. The mass absorption coefficient is the sum of the scattering and true absorption coefficients:

$$\mu/\varrho = \sigma/\varrho + \tau/\varrho$$

In metals having atomic numbers greater than iron ($Z = 26$), scattering is so slight relative to true absorption that it can be neglected. The true absorption coefficient is proportional to the fourth power of the atomic number, Z, and the third power of the wavelength, λ, thus:

$$\tau/\varrho = cZ^4\lambda^3$$

and

$$\mu/\varrho \cong cZ^4\lambda^3$$

where c is a constant. The value of c changes abruptly at certain wavelengths, known as absorption edges.

The **absorption edge** represents the wavelength of radiation with energy sufficient to knock an inner electron from its orbit. Fig. 1.8(a) shows the energy per quantum versus wavelength. As the wavelength decreases, the radiation becomes more energetic. Radiation of about 1.5 Å is just energetic enough to eject a K electron from a nickel atom. This is shown in Fig. 1.8(b). At a wavelength of about 2.5 Å, μ/ϱ is about 175. If the wavelength is decreased gradually, the amount of radiation absorbed also decreases, until the critical wavelength is reached at about 1.5 Å. The energy of the radiation at the criticial wavelength is sufficient to eject a K electron from the nickel atom and in so doing causes a large increase in the energy absorbed by the atom. This critical wavelength is known as the absorption edge. As the wavelength is further decreased beyond the absorption edge, decreasing amounts of radiation are absorbed. Ejection phenomena are responsible for the sharp increases in the value for c (in the expression $\mu/\varrho = cZ^4\lambda^3$) at the absorption edges. The absorption edges for platinum are shown in Fig. 1.8(c), which indicates the electron levels from which electrons are ejected.

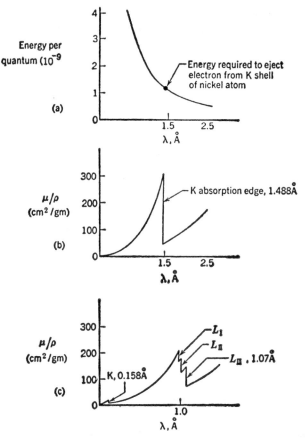

Fig. 1.8. The origin of absorption edges. (a) The energy per quantum of radiation of various wavelengths. The energy of radiation having a wavelength of about 1.5Å is sufficient to eject K-electrons from nickel atoms. (b) The K-absorption edge for nickel. (c) Some of the absorption edges for platinum.

Filters. In x-ray diffraction work, filters are used for producing monochromatic radiation. The filter is actually a carefully selected absorber. The filter material has an atomic number one less than the atomic number of the target. For a copper target, $(Z = 29)$, a nickel filter, $(Z = 28)$, is used. This places an absorption edge at a slightly shorter wavelength than the wavelength for K_a. Fig. 1.9 shows schematically the effect of a nickel filter on copper radiation. The filter absorbs almost all radiation except the very intense K_a doublets at a wavelength of 1.5418 Å. Monochromatic radiation is needed for x-ray diffraction for reasons which will be explained later.

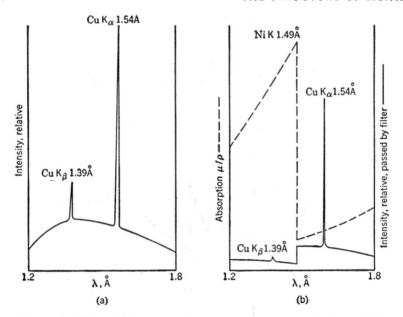

Fig. 1.9. Use of filters to produce monochromatic radiation. (a) Intensity versus wavelength for a copper target. (b) Absorption produced by nickel filter results in marked increase in intensity of Kα relative to other wavelengths present.

1.3. Crystallography of Metals

The atoms in crystalline solids are always arranged in a very regular, though not necessarily perfect, manner. This is true of both metallic and nonmetallic solids. Metallic crystal structures are easier to study than nonmetallic structures, because the arrangement of the atoms in metals and alloys is usually, though not always, relatively simple.

The arrangement of atoms in crystals can be described by use of a network of lines. Useful networks have a distinctive property: the points formed by the intersections of the lines have identical surroundings. Any such arrangement of points having identical surroundings is known as a **space lattice,** and the intersecting lines associated with the points form a line lattice. The line lattice can be produced by the intersections of the planes of a plane lattice. The positions of the points in the space lattice can be located by use of the lines which form a three-dimensional coordinate system.

Though fourteen space lattices are possible, only four of these are required to describe most metallic structures.   These are shown in Fig. 1.10.   The locations of the lattice points are indicated. Keep in mind that the arrangement of the lattice points is repeated to infinity in all directions.   Note that both body-centered cubic and face-centered cubic lattices can be described on the same sets of axes. When space lattices can be grouped together in such fashion, the group is said to fall within a particular crystal system.   There are seven crystal systems, but only three are commonly encountered in metallurgy : cubic, tetragonal, and hexagonal.

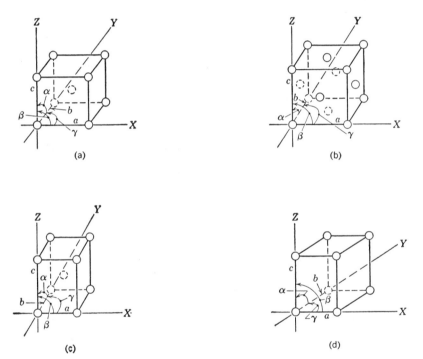

Fig. 1.10.   The four common metallic space lattices.   The letters a, b, and c refer to unit distances along the X, Y, and Z axes respectively.   The letters α, β, and γ refer to the angles opposite the X, Y, and Z axes respectively.   (a) Body-centered cubic, $a = b = c$, $\alpha = \beta = \gamma = 90°$.   Lattice points exist at the four corners and center of the cube.   (b) Face-centered cubic, $a = b = c$, $\alpha = \beta = \gamma = 90°$.   Lattice points exist at the four corners and in the center of each cube face.   (c) Body-centered tetragonal $a = b \neq c$, $\alpha = \beta = \gamma = 90°$.   Lattice points exist at each corner and in the center of the figure.   The top and bottom are squares, the sides are rectangles. (d) Simple hexagonal. $a = b \neq c$, $\alpha = \beta = 90°$, $\gamma = 60°$.   Lattice points exist at each corner of the figure.   The top and bottom are equilateral parallelograms, the sides are rectangles.

The characteristic arrangement of atoms in metallic crystals is known as the **crystal structure.** In the case of the body-centered cubic, face-centered cubic, and body-centered tetragonal structure, relationship between the structure and the corresponding space lattice is simple: there is an atom at each lattice point. In the case of the close-packed hexagonal structure, shown in Fig. 1.11, the relationship to the hexagonal lattice is a bit more complicated: there are two atoms associated with each lattice point.[3] One of these two atoms is at the corner of the structure and one is inside the structure. Table 1.3 shows the crystal structure and lattice constants of common metals.

Table 1.3

Metal	Structure	Lattice constants, Å	Closest approach, Å
α - Fe *	BCC	2.8664	2.481
Cr	BCC	2.8845	2.498
Mo	BCC	3.1466	2.725
V	BCC	3.039	2.632
W	BCC	3.1648	2.739
γ - Fe *	FCC	3.571	2.525
Al	FCC	4.0490	2.862
Ag	FCC	4.0856	2.888
Au	FCC	4.0783	2.884
Cu	FCC	3.6153	2.556
Ni	FCC	3.5238	2.491
Pt	FCC	3.9237	2.775
Be	CPH	a 2.2854	2.225
		c 3.5841	
Cd	CPH	a 2.9787	2.979
		c 5.617	
Mg	CPH	a 3.2092	3.196
		c 5.2103	
Ti	CPH	a 2.9504	2.89
		c 4.6833	
Zn	CPH	a 2.664	2.664
		c 4.945	
β - Sn	BCT	a 5.8311	3.022
		c 3.1817	

* Iron commonly exists in one of two crystalline structures: body-centered cubic (at ordinary atmospheric temperatures) or face-centered cubic (near 1700°F). The change from one structure to another with change in temperature is called an allotropic change, and any one such structure is known as the allotrope of the other. By permission from C. S. Barret, *Structure of Metals*, 2nd Ed., (New York: McGraw-Hill Book Co., Inc., 1952).

Crystals can be considered to be composed of **unit cells.** The unit cell is the smallest aggregate of atoms which, taken together, have all the properties (theoretically at least) of a crystal of the

[3] It is always true that at least one atom and often more than one atom is associated with every lattice point; but there is not necessarily a lattice point for each atom present.

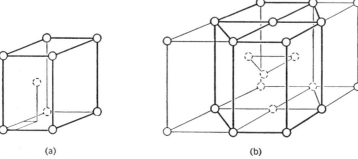

Fig. 1.11. The close-packed hexagonal crystal structure. (a) An interior atom exists at the coordinates $\frac{1}{3}a$, $\frac{1}{3}b$, and $\frac{1}{2}c$. (b) The hexagonal nature of the structure can be seen by considering two of the above units and halves of two additional units. The interior atoms form a layer which matches the hexagonal arrangement of the atoms in the top and bottom planes.

particular metal. Crystals always consist of many unit cells arranged like building blocks in a three-dimensional repeating pattern. All unit cells in a given crystal have the same orientation, i.e., their like faces are parallel.

In studying metal crystals it is frequently desirable to refer to particular planes and directions lying in these planes. For this purpose a system utilizing intercepts and indices has been devised. Fig. 1.12 shows the axes for the cubic crystal system and a few typical crystallographic planes. The **intercepts** of the planes are the number of unit distances from the origin at which the planes intersect the x, y, and z axes of the crystal system. For instance, plane A has intercepts of 1, 1, $\frac{1}{2}$, meaning that it intersects the x and the y axes at one unit distance on each and the z axis at one-half

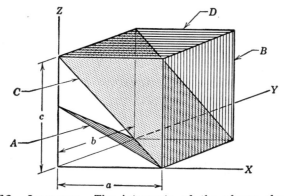

Fig. 1.12. Intercepts. The intercepts of the planes shown are

A 1, 1, $\frac{1}{2}$ B 1, ∞, ∞ C 1, ∞, 1 D ∞, ∞, 1

unit distance.   Planes parallel to a given axis are said to intercept that axis at infinity.   The origin of the axes is always selected so that none of the intercepts for any particular crystallographic plane are zero.

Miller indices are even more useful than the intercepts from which they are derived.   This is so because Miller indices are whole numbers and do not involve the use of the infinity symbol.   They are very convenient to use in x-ray diffraction analysis, as will be shown later.   Miller indices are found by taking the reciprocals of the intercepts and reducing these reciprocals to the smallest whole numbers having the same relative values as the reciprocals.   Thus, for plane A in Fig. 1.12, the intercepts are 1, 1, $\frac{1}{2}$.   The reciprocals are (112).   The Miller indices of planes are written without commas and enclosed in parentheses.   Some examples of Miller indices and the planes they identify are given in Fig. 1.13.   In the case of planes whose intercepts are negative, a negative sign is placed over the corresponding Miller index, as indicated for plane D of Fig. 1.13.

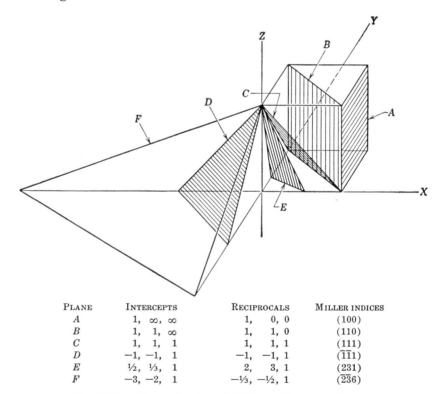

PLANE	INTERCEPTS	RECIPROCALS	MILLER INDICES
A	1, ∞, ∞	1, 0, 0	(100)
B	1, 1, ∞	1, 1, 0	(110)
C	1, 1, 1	1, 1, 1	(111)
D	-1, -1, 1	-1, -1, 1	($\bar{1}\bar{1}1$)
E	$\frac{1}{2}$, $\frac{1}{3}$, 1	2, 3, 1	(231)
F	-3, -2, 1	$-\frac{1}{3}$, $-\frac{1}{2}$, 1	($\bar{2}\bar{3}6$)

Fig. 1.13.   Determination of Miller indices for planes.

When the arrangement and density of atoms on planes of a crystal are the same, the planes are equivalent to one another. Equivalent planes which are also parallel form what are known as **sets of planes,** as shown in Fig. 1.14(a). Planes of the same set have the same absolute values of Miller indices, arranged in the same order. By shifting the origin of the reference axes, one can make even the signs of the indices identical. There always exist, in addition to parallel planes, a series of planes of various orientations having identical atom density and arrangement. An example of such a series is shown in Fig. 1.14(b-d). Such a series is known as a **family of planes.** The Miller indices for the planes of a given

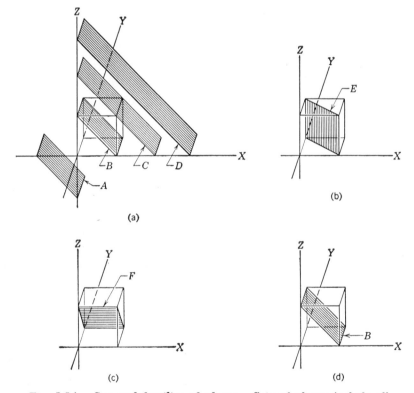

Fig. 1.14. Sets and families of planes. Sets of planes include all planes parallel to one another such as planes A, B, C, and D. Families of planes include all planes of identical density and arrangement of lattice points or atoms, regardless of orientation. The Miller indices of the above planes are:

A $(\bar{1}0\bar{1})$	C (101)	E (110)
B (101)	D (101)	F (011)

All planes shown are of the same family.

family always involve the same absolute numbers, though in different sequence. In fact, if a series of Miller indices has the same absolute numbers in a variety of sequences, the planes identified by this series are all of the same family. The Miller indices for a family of planes are enclosed in braces. Thus the family represented by (101), (110), (011), ($\bar{1}$01), ($\bar{1}$10), and (0$\bar{1}$1) is written {110}.

Directions as well as planes must also be identified for crystallographic work. Directions are always lines originating at the origin of the axes, as shown in Fig. 1.15. Directions having the same spacing of atoms along their lengths are equivalent directions and form a family of directions. Thus, in Fig. 1.15, OP_2, OP_3, and OP_4 are all of the same family. As in the case of families of planes, families of directions always have the same Miller indices, though the sequence of the numbers and their signs may vary. OP_2, OP_3, and OP_4 are all members of the <110> family of directions. Miller indices for individual directions are enclosed in square brackets; for families of directions they are enclosed in carets.

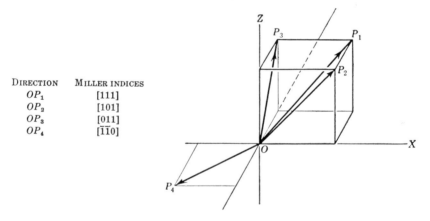

DIRECTION	MILLER INDICES
OP_1	[111]
OP_2	[101]
OP_3	[011]
OP_4	[$\bar{1}\bar{1}$0]

Fig. 1.15.   Miller indices for directions.

The planes and directions most densely populated with atoms are those of greatest importance in metal crystals. In general, the smaller the spacing between planes of a given set, the lower the density of these planes; conversely, the greater the spacing, the higher the atomic density. The Miller indices of the planes of high atomic density are low numbers. As the atomic density decreases, the Miller indices increase. Directions of high atomic density lie in the planes of high atomic density. The significance of close packing of atoms on planes and lines is further discussed in section 3.8 in connection with slip.

1.4. X-Ray Diffraction

When an x-ray strikes an atom, the atom acts as a point source of radiation having the same wavelength as the incident radiation. This fact is the basis for x-ray diffraction, by which radiation falling on the regularly spaced atoms of crystals is reinforced or cancelled in particular directions. This is shown in Fig. 1.16.

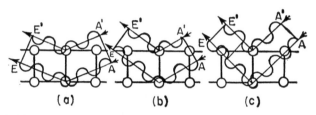

(a)   (b)   (c)

Fig. 1.16. Reinforcement and cancellation of scattered waves to produce diffracted beams. (a) First-order reflection, where $n = 1$. A difference of one wavelength exists between AE and $A'E'$. (b) Cancellation caused by a difference of one and one-half wavelengths between paths AE and $A'E'$. (c) Second-order reflection, where $n = 2$. A difference of two wavelengths exists between paths AE and $A'E'$.

Bragg's equation. Analysis of the patterns of diffracted radiation is usually based on Bragg's equation. In deriving Bragg's equation it is considered that planes of atoms within the crystal act as reflecting planes. Hence, an incident beam of monochromatic radiation is diffracted only in particular directions which depend upon the wavelength of the radiation and the spacing between the planes, as shown in Fig. 1.17.

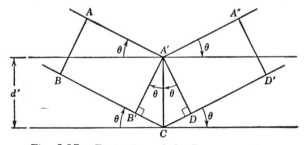

Fig. 1.17. Derivation of the Bragg equation.

In Fig. 1.17, *AB* represents a wave front of an advancing beam of monochromatic x-rays, having a wavelength of λ. When the wave front has advanced to *A′B′*, the portion striking the top plane immediately sends out secondary radiation of the same wavelength as the incident radiation. This radiation spreads in all directions. Meanwhile the wave front of the incident beam continues to advance from *B′* to *C*, and when it reaches *C* secondary radiation is again emitted in all directions. Consider secondary radiations from *A′* and *C* in directions *A′A″* and *CDD′*. If the distance *B′CD* is a whole number of wavelengths the crests of the scattered waves coincide and reinforcement occurs (see Fig. 1.16). If the distance *B′CD* is not a whole number of wavelengths the scattered waves are out of phase and cancellation occurs. For reinforcement,

$$B'CD = n\lambda$$

where *n* is a whole number representing the number of wavelengths difference between the rays scattered from the two planes in question. Since $B'C = CD = d' \sin \theta$, where *d′* is the distance between reflecting planes, then $B'CD = 2d' \sin \theta$, and

$$n\lambda = 2d' \sin \theta$$

If *d′/n* is set equal to *d*, then

$$\lambda = 2d \sin \theta$$

which is the usual form of Bragg's equation. This is the equivalent of saying (see Fig. 1.18) that the nth order diffraction from planes which are a distance *d′* apart is equivalent to the first order diffraction from planes which are a distance *d′/n* apart. For in-

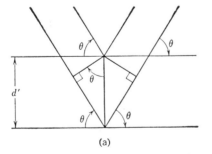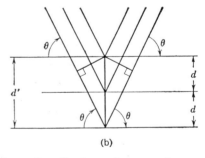

(a)   (b)

Fig. 1.18. Relations between spacing of reflecting planes and order of diffraction. (a) $n\lambda = 2d'\sin\theta$ for 2nd order from planes a distance *d′* apart. (b) $\lambda = 2d\sin\theta$ for 1st order from planes a distance $d = d'/2$ apart.

stance, the second order diffraction from the (100) planes is the same as the first order diffraction from the (200) planes. The form of the Bragg equation used henceforth is

$$\lambda = 2d \sin \theta \tag{1.4-1}$$

For various crystal structures, the spacing d between any two adjacent planes of a set having known Miller indices can be calculated, if the lattice constants are known. For instance, in a cubic crystal system having a lattice constant (i.e., length of the cube edge) equal to a, the distance d between adjacent planes having indices (hkl) is

$$d = \frac{a}{\sqrt{h^2 + k^2 + l^2}} \tag{1.4-2}$$

This equation can be combined with Bragg's equation:

$$\lambda = \frac{2a}{\sqrt{h^2 + k^2 + l^2}} \sin \theta$$

and

$$h^2 + k^2 + l^2 = \frac{4a^2 \sin^2 \theta}{\lambda^2}$$

setting $h^2 + k^2 + l^2 = Q^2$ and recalling that λ and a are constants, then

$$Q^2 C = \sin^2 \theta \tag{1.4-3}$$

This equation is useful in determining whether a structure is body- or face-centered cubic. Similar equations are available for the tetragonal and hexagonal systems.

Before using equation (1.4-3) it is necessary to discuss the case of missing reflections. Consider diffraction of a beam from the (001) plane of a simple cubic and a face-centered cubic structure, both structures having the same lattice constants, as shown in Fig. 1.19. The angle θ which satisfies Bragg's equation for diffraction in the simple cubic structure might be expected to produce a reflection from the face-centered cubic structure. However, the face-centered atoms produce an intermediate plane, (002). As can be seen from the figure, if the path ABC is a whole wavelength greater than GOH, then IEK is a half wavelength greater and cancellation occurs. Similar behavior is caused by the body-centered atoms in the body-centered cubic structure. Thus, for simple cubic structures, reflection can be expected from the {001} planes, but not from the same planes of the face-centered and body-centered structures.

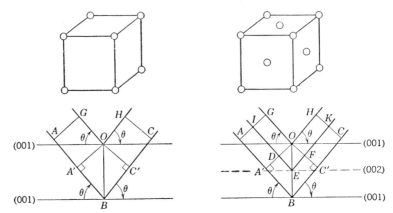

Fig. 1.19. Missing reflections. There is no reflection from {100} in the face-centered cubic system.

Similar reasoning, if extended to other planes and generalized, shows the following to hold:

1. reflections are obtained from planes in body-centered cubic structures only when the sum of $h + k + l$ is an even number;

Table 1.4

Indices of Crystal Planes (h, k, l)	Q^2 $(h^2 + k^2 + l^2)$	Reflections occurring ✓ Reflections not occurring X B.C.C.	F.C.C.
(100)	1	X	X
(110)	2	✓	X
(111)	3	X	✓
(200)	4	✓	✓
(210)	5	X	X
(211)	6	✓	X
(220)	8	✓	✓
(300) (221)	9	X	X
(310)	10	✓	X
(311)	11	X	✓
(222)	12	✓	✓
(320)	13	X	X
(321)	14	✓	X
(400)	16	✓	✓
(410) (322)	17	X	X
(411) (330)	18	✓	X
(331)	19	X	✓
(420)	20	✓	✓
(421)	21	X	X
(332)	22	✓	X

2. reflections are obtained from planes in face-centered cubic structures only when h, k, and l are all odd numbers, or all even numbers; i.e., when (h, k, l) are not mixed.

This information appears in Table 1.4.

Obtaining data for x-ray diffraction analysis. There are several methods for collecting x-ray diffraction data. One of the newest and most convenient methods is based on the use of a goniometer and Geiger counter, as illustrated in Fig. 1.20. The goniometer is a device by which accurate measurements of angles can be made.

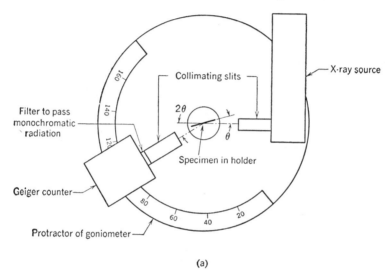

(a)

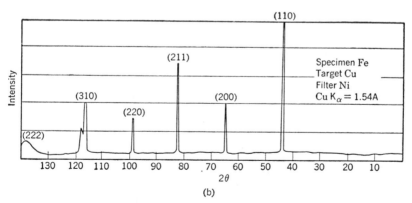

(b)

Fig. 1.20. Spectrogoniometer. (a) Diagram of instrument used for x-ray diffraction work. (b) An example of a record made by a recording instrument showing intensity versus 2θ values obtained on a spectrogoniometer.

The Geiger counter measures the intensity of diffracted radiation. As shown in the illustration, the specimen is mounted centrally on the goniometer. It rotates at half the angular velocity of the goniometer itself, which is power driven. When the specimen is in such position that the conditions of the Bragg equation are satisfied, a reflected beam is detected by the Geiger counter as an increase in intensity. This is recorded automatically on a strip recorder in which the paper movement is synchronized with the goniometer speed. Thus, the final record appears as shown in Fig. 1.20(b), in which angles are plotted horizontally and intensities, vertically. The angle indicated by the goniometer is actually twice the Bragg angle, as can be seen from study of Fig. 1.20(a). Therefore, in order to process the information, the angles must all be divided by two.

Other common methods for collecting data rely upon the use of photographic film held in specially constructed cameras. The film records the variations in intensity caused by diffraction. Knowing the geometry of the camera, the angular relationships needed for solution of the Bragg equation can be calculated.

In the method based on the use of a goniometer and Geiger counter, monochromatic radiation is used. This is obtained by the technique outlined in section 1.2 and illustrated by Fig. 1.9. The location of the filter just ahead of the Geiger counter is shown in Fig. 1.20(a). In other x-ray diffraction methods white radiation may be used.

Processing sample data. Monochromatic CuK_a radiation ($\lambda = 1.5418$ Å), was used, and diffraction peaks were observed at the following 2θ angles for a metallic specimen: 43.15°, 50.22°, 73.97°, 89.73°, 95.15°, 116.5°, 136.2°, and 145°. Was the specimen face-centered cubic or body-centered cubic? Find its lattice constant.

The data are most conveniently handled in tabular form:

2θ	θ	$Sin^2\theta$	If B.C.C.			If F.C.C.		
			(h, k, l)	Q^2	C	(h, k, l)	Q^2	c
43.15°	21°34.8′	0.13528	(110)	2	0.06764	(111)	3	0.04509
50.22°	25°6.6′	0.18010	(200)	4	0.04503	(200)	4	0.04503
73.97°	36°59.4′	0.36201	(211)	6	0.06037	(220)	8	0.04550
89.73°	44°52.2′	0.49774	(220)	8	0.06221	(311)	11	0.04525
95.15°	47°34.8′	0.54495	(310)	10	0.05450	(222)	12	0.04541
116.5°	58°15′	0.72310	(222)	12	0.06026	(400)	16	0.04509
136.2°	68°6′	0.86088	(321)	14	0.0615	(331)	19	0.04530
145.0°	72°30′	0.90958	(400)	16	0.0569	(420)	20	0.04548

From the above it can be seen that C in the expression $C = (\sin^2 \theta)/Q^2$ is not a constant for the reflecting planes of the body-centered cubic lattice. It is a constant for the reflecting planes of the face-centered cubic lattice. Hence, the specimen was face-centered cubic. It now remains to determine the length of the cube edge. This is approximated[4] by averaging the values of C, which gives 0.04527. Recalling that

$$\lambda = \frac{2a \sin \theta}{\sqrt{h^2 + k^2 + l^2}} = \frac{2a \sin \theta}{Q}$$

$$\therefore a = \frac{\lambda Q}{2 \sin \theta}$$

By Eq. (1.4-3),

$$\frac{Q}{\sin \theta} = \frac{1}{\sqrt{C}}$$

$$\therefore a = \frac{\lambda}{2 \sqrt{C}}$$

Substituting,

$$a = \frac{1.5418 \text{ Å}}{2 \sqrt{0.04527}} = 3.62 \text{ Å}$$

It can be verified from published data that the specimen was copper, which is face-centered cubic and in which the length of the cube edge is 3.6153 Å.

1.5. Other Evidence of Crystallinity

In addition to the diffraction of x-rays by crystals, there are other indications of regular atom arrangement in metals.

It is possible to make large single crystals of metals, and these have been found to exhibit *directional variations* in chemical activity, in mechanical properties such as stiffness, strength, and ductility, and in electrical properties. Different values are obtained for many properties, depending upon the direction of their measurement with respect to the crystal axes. The *directionality of properties is known as anisotropy*, and is an important characteristic of single crystals. Many ordinary pieces of metal are isotropic, that

[4] Actually the high-angle lines are more accurate than the low-angle lines, and hence should receive greater weight.

is, they do not possess directionality. The lack of directionality is due to the random orientation of crystals which make up isotropic metals. A structure of this kind gives rise to the commonly accepted mechanical properties of metals, which are actually the average directional properties of the many randomly oriented crystals. Single crystals, with their directional behavior, are rarely used in everyday applications, although they are extremely important in basic research.

The fact that most metals are made up of small crystals having different orientations can be demonstrated easily by *metallographic technique*. A piece of metal is highly polished and then etched with an active chemical reagent. Since the individual, differently oriented crystallites (more often called grains) of which the metal is composed are attacked at different rates, depending upon the direction of exposure to the etchant, we find that some grains etch more rapidly than others. Thus a surface is produced in which the grains may be darkened unevenly, depending upon the anisotropy of the grains and their orientation. This is shown in Fig. 1.21. In

Fig. 1.21. Polished and etched surface of annealed brass. Notice the different shadings of the various grains and the annealing twins, which appear as bands running across the grains. Etchant: $NH_4OH + H_2O_2$. Magnification: 500×. [Courtesy of the School of Engineering, Metals Laboratory, University of Massachusetts.]

addition to variations in the darkness of the individual grains, the regions separating the grains are more rapidly attacked than the grain centers, and appear as dark lines or grain boundaries.[5] Fig-

---

[5] The grain boundaries represent regions of crystal imperfection and high energy, and as such are attacked at a greater rate than the centers of the grains. See the paragraphs on the Beilby layer in section 1.6.

ure 1.23 is a two-dimensional sketch showing lattice orientation in adjoining grains of a polycrystalline metal.

When a polished piece of metal undergoes deformation, parallel lines or bands may appear in the grains of the surface. The regularity of the patterns formed by these lines is illustrated in Fig. 3.9, and is a further indication of the high degree of order which is characteristic of crystallinity. The nature of these lines is more fully discussed under the topics of slip lines and twins.

Sometimes when crystals of a metal form from a melt their structure develops without interference from either neighboring crystals or the walls of the container. Such isolated, freely formed crystals exhibit the typical sharp geometric faces often seen in mineral crystals. Again, we have evidence of the regularity of crystal structure and the ordered state associated with crystallinity.

The microscopic and macroscopic structure of metals. The microscopic structure of metals is a very broad field, and forms the basis of the branch of metallurgy known as metallography. The appearance of the microstructure is studied by polishing and then etching the polished surface with an appropriate chemical reagent. This makes visible the individual grains of polycrystalline metals, as described above. Sometimes polishing and etching are provided by the conditions of use, and if the grains in the metal are large enough, a microscope is not needed to distinguish them. Often weathered brass door handles show a coarse-grained structure of this type. The zinc on galvanized steel often shows large crystals similar to frost crystals on a windowpane. In addition to the grains and grain boundaries which are made visible by the polishing and etching technique, impurities and variations in chemical composition may become visible because different compositions are attacked at different rates and yield different products when they react with the etching reagent. If the structure can be identified by the naked eye, it is known as a macrostructure, while those requiring magnification are known as microstructures. The techniques for macro- and micro-examination differ mainly in details of preparation, the general approach being the same in both cases.

1.6. Submicroscopic Structure of Metals

X-ray diffraction makes it possible to determine the positions of atoms in crystal structures. Actually, the indicated positions are idealized; the true picture is a modified version of the idealized arrangement.

Bonding forces. The forces which hold metal atoms in place can be better understood by comparing them with the forces involved in nonmetallic solids.

Atoms in organic solids are usually bonded by forces brought about by a sharing of electrons. Carbon is an atom with four electrons in its outer shell of electrons. This shell of electrons assumes a more stable, lower energy condition if it contains eight electrons. Hydrogen is an atom having one electron in its one and only orbit of the K-shell. Addition of a second electron to the K-shell of hydrogen fills the shell and, as in the case of carbon, produces a more stable, lower energy arrangement. Therefore, if four hydrogen atoms can share their single electrons with the four electrons of a single carbon atom, a stable configuration is achieved as shown in Fig. 1.22(a). This is known as covalent bonding produced by a sharing of electrons.

Atoms in inorganic solids are bound by forces produced by a transfer of electrons, rather than by an actual sharing of electrons. Sodium chloride is an example of this, as illustrated in Fig. 1.22(b). Sodium in this case has one electron in its outer electron shell, and chlorine has seven. The arrangement of electrons in sodium is rendered more stable by loss of the extra electron so that a full outer electron shell remains. Likewise, when the outer shell of chlorine

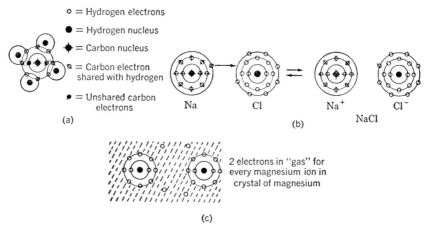

Fig. 1.22. **Types of solid binding.** (a) Covalent bonding by shared electrons. (b) Ionic binding by transferred electrons. (c) Metallic binding by mutual sharing of all valence electrons.

acquires an extra electron, it is filled and thus becomes more stable. This is known as ionic bonding produced by a transfer of electrons.

A third type of bonding is produced by weak electrostatic forces which arise from an unsymmetrical distribution of electrons about atoms or molecules, producing polarized particles whose regions of unlike charge attract one another. Forces of this type are of greatest importance in the liquefaction of gases. They are the familiar van der Waal's forces which account for deviations from the perfect gas law when gases are highly compressed. They exist also in some organic solids. Because van der Waal's forces are weak, they are easily overcome by the kinetic energy of heat, and solids relying on these forces have low melting points.

The fourth type of bonding is metallic crystal bonding. In metallic crystals, the valence electrons are mutually shared by all the atoms of the crystal. It should be remembered that there is an unlimited number of finite energy levels which can be assumed by electrons. The valence electrons fill large numbers of these orbits, each of which is continuous around each atom of the crystal. The energy of the mass is lowered by the filling of these orbits, and this tendency of the atoms to reach their lowest energy, most stable state produces the bonding forces. All the atoms of the crystal share a mutual attraction for the vast numbers of valence electrons which surround them. On the average, the forces of electrostatic repulsion keep the electrons uniformly distributed. Likewise, forces of electrostatic repulsion keep the positively charged atoms (which have lost their negatively charged electrons) from getting too close together. When the transition elements are stripped of their valence electrons, some of the inner electron shells, which are incomplete, are believed to share electrons as in covalent bonding, so that the transition elements are probably bonded by metallic and covalent bonding forces. The sharing of electrons on a grand scale in metallic bonding is in some respects similar to the sharing of electrons in covalent bonding. It also resembles the transfer of electrons which results in the formation of ions in ionic bonding.

Thermal effects. The positions of atoms, as indicated by x-ray diffraction analysis, are actually average positions of atom centers. As the temperature of a metal increases, the atoms oscillate more quickly and with greater amplitude about their average positions. When the melting point is reached, the bonding forces which hold the atoms in place are overcome, and the solid becomes a liquid.

The effective volume of the atom, and in turn the distance between atom centers, increases with increasing temperature. In the liquid state, *average* distance between atom centers is fixed for any given temperature, but the spacing of the atom centers is not regular as it is in solid metals. The thermal expansion of metals is accounted for by the increased amplitude and frequency of oscillation of the atoms with rise in temperature.

The temperature of a metal is a function of the average kinetic energy of the atoms comprising the metal. At any given instant there is a distribution of kinetic energies such that a few atoms are motionless or nearly so and a few others are moving at extremely high velocities. Most of the atoms, however, have velocities which are not so extreme. The atoms of extremely high velocity are capable of overcoming bonding forces. They thus can free themselves of their neighbors, creating a vacancy in the structure or flying off into space to create the vapor pressure of the solid. The energy required to produce the vacancy is transmitted by collision from one atom to the next, and so the vacancy can move through the solid. As the temperature of a metallic solid is raised, a higher proportion of the atoms attain energies sufficient to create vacancies. The number of vacancies is also believed to be higher in grain boundary regions (see next paragraph) and at the surface. These concepts are important in connection with diffusion, which is discussed later.

Grain boundary effects. Most solid metals are polycrystalline substances; i.e., they consist of many small crystals called crystallites or grains. Each grain consists of many thousands of unit cells, as described in section 1.3. Ideally speaking, within each grain every unit cell has the same orientation as every other unit cell. Distinction between adjoining grains is achieved only by differences in orientation of the unit cells of adjoining grains. Obviously, where adjoining grains meet, there must be a mismatching of unit cells having unlike orientations. This is represented in the two-dimensional sketch of Fig. 1.23. The regions where grains meet are known as grain boundaries. There the spacing between atom centers is irregular. The grain boundary region is usually less than 20 atoms in width. It therefore represents an extremely small fraction of the total mass of the polycrystalline structure. However, the properties of the grain boundary region profoundly affect the properties of the aggregate.

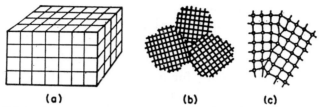

(a) **(b)** **(c)**

Fig 1.23. **Submicroscopic structure of metal.** (a) A single crystal, showing how the unit cells are arranged like building blocks. (b) A two-dimensional sketch, showing three grains meeting at a point. (c) The point of intersection, magnified to show distribution of the unit cells at the grain boundary.

Beilby layer. Atomic spacing is irregular at the surfaces of metals and alloys which have been rolled, machined, ground, or otherwise subjected to severe surface deformation in fabrication or service. Highly irregular spacing, known as the Beilby layer, persists to depths up to 10 or 15 atomic diameters. Below this layer there is irregularity in diminishing degree as the interior of the metal is approached.

The presence of the Beilby layer sometimes obscures metallographic results. It should always be removed before microscopic examination of the metal. It is most easily removed by etching, following "final" polishing. Next, the etching products are removed by a very brief and light second "final" polish, followed by a second etching. In this way the distorted surface is eliminated so that the true structure is observed.

Foreign atoms. If foreign atoms are introduced into the crystal structure, the atomic spacing is changed. For instance, if small amounts of aluminum are alloyed with copper, the *average* spacing of the atoms of the crystals so formed is found to increase. (This effect is later described in more detail in connection with solid solution hardening.) Sometimes, alloying results in atomic vacancies in the crystal structure: i.e., atoms are missing from the lattice points. This produces a *defect structure,* or *subtraction solid solution.* Vacancies created in the structure by alloying are not affected by temperature as are the vacancies described in connection with thermal effects.

Dislocations. First recognized in theory in 1934 and still being studied intensively, dislocations are useful in explaining some of the properties of metals and in predicting metallic behavior. The two principal types of dislocations are known as Taylor-Orowan or edge-type dislocations and Burgers or screw-type dislocations. The nature of these is indicated in Fig. 1.24. A few dislocations are believed to originate during formation of metal grains by solidification from a melt or by condensation of vapors. Thermal agitation of atoms may also account for a few dislocations. Most dislocations, however, are believed to originate when loads are applied to metals. The part played by dislocations in the mechanical properties of metals is set forth in a later chapter.

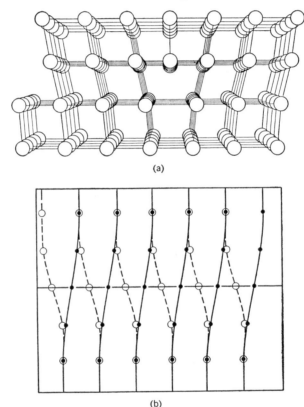

(a)

(b)

Fig. 1.24. **Common types of dislocations.** (a) Taylor-Orowan edge-type dislocation. (b) Burgers screw-type dislocation; the solid circles and open circles represent atoms in adjacent planes. [Reproduced by permission from J. E. Goldman, *The Science of Engineering Materials*, John Wiley and Sons, Inc., N. Y., 1957.]

Misalignment: submicroscopic and microscopic. Electron microscope studies have produced pictures [6] of submicroscopic blocks within grains. These blocks produce what is known as mo-

---

[6] The optical microscope is capable of about 2000 diameter enlargement. The electron microscope is capable of 100,000 diameter enlargement.

saic structure. X-ray diffraction patterns of such structures indicate a slight misalignment between such blocks. Mosaic structure
is observed in metals which have been subjected to combinations of
deformation and high temperature. The mosaic blocks are about
5000 Å on a side and are tilted from 10 to 15 minutes with respect
to one another.

Microscopic evidence of misalignment is often observed in cast
structures. Two arms of a dendritic or skeleton-like crystal may be
as much as 1° out of alignment with one another. This type of
crystal imperfection is known as lineage structure.

From the above discussion it should be apparent that metal
crystals are not absolutely perfect. That is to say, the atoms are
not always located exactly where the lattice points of the particular
lattice indicate they should be located. Metal crystals approach
ideal configurations very closely, but many of the minor deviations
from perfection are significantly related to metallic behavior. It
is for this reason that deviations from perfection have been mentioned here, and will be mentioned in subsequent chapters.

Questions

1.1. (a) Describe a simplified physical concept of the atom.

(b) How many electron orbits are associated with each atom? Can
an electron move gradually from one orbit to the next, or are there
forbidden gaps between orbits?

(c) Is a valence electron a higher energy electron than a K-shell
electron?

(d) When an electron from the M-shell fills a vacancy in the L-shell,
is energy liberated or absorbed by the atom?

(e) If an atom has a vacancy in the N-shell, is it in a higher or lower
energy state than when there are no vacancies present?

(f) Is a high energy or low energy condition more stable?

(g) What are isotopes? What is their significance in relation to
determination of atomic weights?

(h) Which electrons are responsible for chemical properties of
atoms?

1.2. (a) What are cathode rays? How do they differ from x-rays?

(b) How are x-rays produced?

(c) Distinguish between white radiation and the characteristic spectrum. What is the source of lines in the characteristic spectrum?

(d) What is the width of the lines of the characteristic spectrum?

(e) As wavelength increases does penetrative power increase or decrease? Does energy increase or decrease? Does the velocity of
the radiation increase or decrease?

(f) Distinguish between the intensity and energy of radiation.

(g) An x-ray tube with a tungsten target is producing white radiation with a peak intensity of 1.6 Å. At what voltage is the tube operating?

(h) Is K_β more energetic than K_a? Why? Is K_β more intense than K_a for a given voltage?

(i) If M lines appear on the characteristic spectrum, will K lines also necessarily appear? N lines?

(j) What is the effect of increasing the tube voltage on CuK_a?

(k) Using Fig. 1.6, approximate the value of c in Moseley's law. What is the value of σ? Will the line for K_β be above or below the line for K_{a_1}, in Fig. 1.6?

(l) What is the difference between the meaning of μ and μ/ϱ? What is the advantage of using μ/ϱ instead of μ?

(m) Does μ/ϱ depend more nearly upon σ/ϱ or τ/ϱ for elements having atomic numbers greater than 26?

(n) Is μ/ϱ greater for uranium (atomic number 92), or tungsten (atomic number 74)? If so, how much greater?

(o) What causes absorption edges?

(p) What is the function of filters used for x-ray diffraction work?

1.3. (a) What is a space lattice?

(b) Name and sketch the four space lattices commonly encountered in metallurgy.

(c) What is the relation between the arrangement of atoms in crystals and the space lattice points used to describe the crystals?

(d) What is a unit cell?

(e) How many atoms of a close-packed hexagonal crystal structure are associated with each lattice point of the hexagonal lattice?

(f) What are the Miller indices of the planes shown in the sketch below?

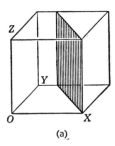
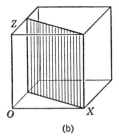
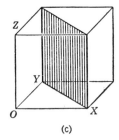

(a)   (b)   (c)

(g) On the XZ axes, draw a line representing the intersection of the (501) plane with the XZ plane.

(h) List the planes of the (210) family.

(i) What is the difference between a set of planes and a family of planes?

(j) Sketch the [420] direction.

1.4. Monochromatic CuK_a radiation ($\lambda = 1.5418$ Å) impinging on a metallic specimen yielded diffraction peaks at the following 2θ

angles: 44.2°, 51.5°, 76.05°, 92.62°, 98.25°, 121.65°, 144.45°, 155.2°. Is the specimen face-centered or body-centered cubic? What is the lattice constant? Identify the specimen from published data.

1.5. (a) Tensile strength was measured on specimens cut from single crystals of body-centered cubic iron. The axes of the tensile specimens corresponded to the directions *AB, AC, AD, FC, FE, DC,* and *DI* as shown in Fig. 3.5. Group the directions for which identical values were obtained.

(b) Explain briefly how a metallographic specimen is prepared. Why should specimens be repolished and re-etched after the first etching?

1.6. (a) Describe the nature of the metallic bond and compare it with ionic and covalent bonding.

(b) What is the effect of temperature on the positions of atoms in a crystal?

(c) Describe the nature of grain boundaries.

(d) What is the effect of foreign atoms on atomic spacing in crystals?

(e) How do thermal vacancies differ from vacancies created by alloying?

(f) Sketch and describe the two principle types of dislocations.

(g) What is mosaic structure? Lineage structure?

Bibliography

1.1. Barrett, C. S., *The Structure of Metals,* 2nd Ed. New York: McGraw-Hill Book Co., Inc., 1952.

1.2. Seitz, Frederick, *The Modern Theory of Solids.* New York: McGraw-Hill Book Co., Inc., 1940.

1.3. Kittel, Charles, *Introduction to Solid State Physics.* New York: John Wiley & Sons, Inc., 1953.

1.4. Symposium, *Imperfections in Nearly Perfect Crystals.* New York: John Wiley & Sons, Inc., 1952.

1.5. Smith, Morton C., *Principles of Physical Metallurgy.* New York: Harper and Brothers, 1956.

1.6. Goldman, J. E., *The Science of Engineering Materials.* New York: John Wiley & Sons, Inc., 1957.

1.7. Cullity, B. D., *Elements of X-Ray Diffraction.* Reading, Mass.: Addison-Wesley Publishing Co., Inc., 1956.

1.8. Clark, G. L., *Applied X-Rays,* 3rd Ed. New York: McGraw-Hill Book Co., Inc., 1940.

1.9. Richtmeyer, F. K., and E. H. Kennard, *Introduction to Modern Physics,* 4th Ed. New York: McGraw-Hill Book Co., Inc., 1947.

1.10. Dekker, A. J., *Solid State Physics.* Englewood Cliffs, N. J.: Prentice-Hall, Inc., 1957.

CHAPTER 2

The Solid State:
Freezing, Solutions, Diffusion

2.1. Liquid and Solid

Most metallurgical processes are concerned with the properties
and behavior of metals in either the solid or the liquid state. Some
methods for producing metals of great chemical activity or for
achieving very high purity also utilize the gaseous state, but this
state is not of general interest. A principal difference between
liquids and solids lies in the higher kinetic energy of atoms in a
liquid. In the liquid, the movement of the atoms is vigorous enough
to overcome the metallic crystal bonding forces which produce solid
metal. The lower kinetic energy of the atoms in solids makes possible the orderly atomic arrangement associated with crystals. In
molten metals, although the *average* atomic spacing is fixed for
any given temperature, order and regularity of spacing are largely
absent. As pointed out previously, the atoms of a metallic crystal
are not rigidly fixed at lattice points. Actually, in the solid state,
the atoms have enough kinetic energy to keep moving about the
lattice points, which are merely average postions. When the temperature is raised the amplitude and frequency of movement increase until, at the melting point, order is overcome by dis-
order.

2.2. Cooling Curves

A cooling curve for a freezing metal is shown in Fig. 2.1. This
is a plot of temperature, always abbreviated T in this text, versus
time abbreviated, t. Variations in the shape of cooling curves for
any particular metal or alloy are determined by the rate of heat

extraction from the metal. The rate of heat extraction in turn depends upon several variables:

1. The temperature difference between the metal and surroundings.
2. The specific heats of the metal and mold material.
3. The masses of metal and mold material.
4. The latent heat of fusion of the molten metal.
5. The thermal conductivity of the mold, the molten metal, and metal-mold interface.

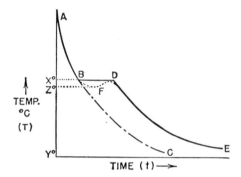

Fig. 2.1. Cooling curves. Curve ABC represents normal heat losses resulting from radiation, conduction, and convection in a mass of hot molten metal which has a freezing temperature below $Y°C$. The solid line, $ABDE$, is the curve for idealized freezing of a pure metal whose solidification temperature is $X°C$. $ABFE$ represents undercooling of the same metal which should freeze at $X°C$, but actually is cooled to $Z°C$ before freezing starts. $X°C - Z°C =$ the amount of undercooling.

If the mold is fairly thin, the properties of the mold surroundings must be considered. If the temperature gradient is high, the conductivity good, and there is a large difference in heat content, heat flows quickly from the metal in the mold, freezing is rapid, and the curve tends to drop sharply. For more and more rapid rates of freezing, the horizontal segment of the curve is shorter and there is likely to be more undercooling. The horizontal segment represents liberation of the latent heat of solidification, which is the difference in energy content between solid and liquid metal at the freezing temperature. The release of this energy in the form of heat prevents a drop in temperature, under equilibrium conditions, until all the metal is frozen.

2.3. Nucleation and Growth

The freezing of metals is a nucleation and growth process in which crystal nuclei first form, and then, by addition of more atoms, grow into grains or crystals.   Nuclei form when the kinetic energy of several atoms of melt reaches a low enough value to permit them to assume the lattice positions of the particular metal involved. Though the temperature remains constant, unless there is under-cooling, more and more heat is extracted and the nuclei continue to grow.   Finally growth is stopped by contact with neighboring crystals or by interference with container walls.   This is shown by Fig. 2.2.

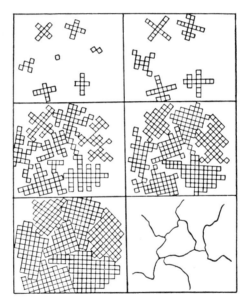

Fig. 2.2. **A schematic representation of crystallization.** [After W. Rosenhain, *An Introduction to the Study of Physical Metallurgy.* Constable and Company, Ltd. (London).]

It is believed that Burgers or screw-type dislocations are funda-mentally involved in the growth of crystals.   This type of disloca-tion results in a helical growth pattern which has been verified by microscopic examination.   It was formerly believed that crystals grew by successive additions of single layers of atoms, as shown in Fig. 2.3.   For a simple cubic structure, initiation of each additional layer of atoms requires the simultaneous addition of four atoms, which is similar to the nucleation process.   Calculated rates of growth based on this mechanism are much smaller than observed

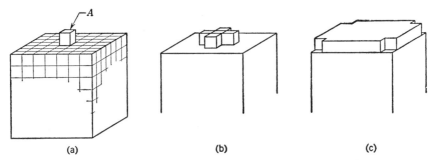

Fig. 2.3.   **Old concept of crystal growth.**   (a) Nucleation of new layer by addition of atoms at A.   (b) Additional atoms join surface until a new layer is formed, as in (c).   Then process repeats itself.

rates of growth.   On the other hand, if growth proceeds by addition of atoms along the edge of a screw dislocation, as shown in Fig. 2.4, the calculated and observed rates of growth are in good agreement.   This mechanism provides an ever-expanding open step to which atoms could be added continuously, without ever having to nucleate new layers.

2.4.   Factors Affecting the Size of Crystals Forming from a Melt

Crystal size is determined by the rate of growth relative to the rate of nucleation.   Any variable which affects the relative rate (known as the G/N ratio) in turn affects grain size.   Three of these variables are discussed below.

Temperature.   Although a metal should solidify at its freezing point, it is possible by undercooling to retain the liquid state at temperatures below the freezing point.   The freezing characteristics of some metals have been studied at various temperatures of solidification, measurements having been made of the rates of nucleation and growth at these temperatures.   The rate of growth relative to the rate of nucleation is greatest at or slightly below the freezing point.   When freezing occurs at appreciably lower temperatures, the value of G/N becomes smaller, and consequently grain size decreases.   A schematic representation of this is given in

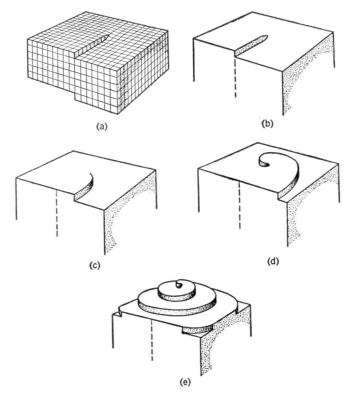

Fig. 2.4. Growth of a crystal. A screw dislocation produces spiral growth steps as indicated by the drawings (a) through (e). [Reproduced with permission from R. L. Fullman, "The Growth of Crystals," *Scientific American*, **192–3**, March, 1955.]

Fig. 2.5. It can be seen that undercooling produces fine-grained structures, and slow or equilibrium cooling yields coarse-grained structures.

Addition of insoluble materials to increase the rate of nucleation, N. The addition of alloying elements or compounds which form insoluble particles at the temperature of freezing serves to increase the rate of nucleation. Thus more grains form than if the insoluble particles had not been present. Aluminum, which is added to molten steel to deoxidize it, apparently forms very finely divided Al_2O_3 particles which act as nuclei and serve to reduce the grain size of the casting or ingot. The addition of titanium accomplishes the same result. If steel is cast by pouring over steel wool, the particles of steel wool remain undissolved (unless a very high pouring temperature is used) and increase the number of nuclei, thereby producing a fine-grained casting.

Agitation of the melt during freezing. Stirring a melt during freezing tends to produce a finer grain size, probably because the

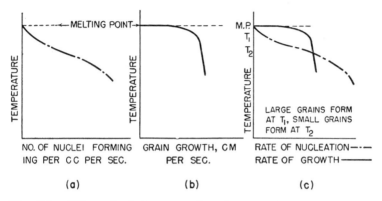

Fig. 2.5.   **Effect of relative rates of nucleation and growth on grain size.**   (a) Variation in rate of nucleation with temperature.   (b) Variation in rate of growth with temperature.   (c) A composite plot showing the variation in relative rates of nucleation and growth at different temperatures, and the effect on grain size.   If $G =$ rate of growth, and $N =$ rate of nucleation, then a large value of G relative to N, such as occurs at T_1, will produce coarse grains.   A small relative value of G/N, such as occurs at T_2, will produce small grains. Undercooling produces finer grain sizes than idealized cooling.

crystals are fragmented before they have an opportunity to grow very large.   The fragments may be considered to be nuclei, so that in effect the value of N has been increased.

2.5.   Conditions for Formation of Columnar Crystals

Crystal shape is largely dependent upon (1) the temperature gradient across the melt and (2) the directional growth properties of crystals.

If an *appreciable temperature gradient exists* between the internal surface of the mold and the center of the melt, the first freezing occurs at the mold-metal interface.   Freezing progresses inward as fast as heat can be withdrawn from the molten metal through the skin of already frozen metal and the mold walls. Nucleation occurs very slowly, if at all, in the central, hotter portions of the melt (see Fig. 2.5).   If, on the other hand, *little or no temperature gradient exists,* so that the entire melt and surroundings are at approximately the same temperature, nucleation occurs nearly as fast in the central portions of the molten metal as in the vicinity of the mold walls.   The growth of these nuclei is unhindered by the mold walls or by the presence of neighbors, because they are freely suspended (until the final stages of solidification).   If the *temperature gradient is very large,* the rate of heat extraction becomes so great that undercooling results.   The G/N ratio becomes very small, and as a result fine grains are formed.   Solidification is complete before there is an opportunity for columnar growth.

The tendency for directional growth of crystals is an example of anisotropy.   It involves merely a higher rate of growth in certain crystallographic directions than in others.   For instance, if the temperature gradient is sufficient, the first nuclei form at the mold walls, while at the same time the formation of nuclei is repressed in the center of the melt.   The nuclei which form at the mold walls have a random orientation.   Those grains whose orientation favors growth at right angles to the mold surface soon predominate, while the grains whose greatest growth tendencies are in directions parallel to the mold face (or approaching parallelism) soon run into one another, and their growth ceases.   Hence a columnar grain structure results, with grains at right angles to the mold surface.

2.6.   Crystal Size and Shape as Determined by Different Casting Methods

Let us now apply the preceding principles to a study of the effect of different casting methods on the size and shape of the grains in cast structures.   Reference is made to Fig. 2.6 for this discussion.

Consider first very slow or idealized freezing.   If we assume an infinitely slow cooling rate, there is no temperature gradient across the melt.   As the heat is slowly extracted, a few nuclei form with random orientations throughout the entire mass of molten metal. These swim freely in the liquid during the initial stages of freezing, and grow faster than new nuclei can form at the high temperatures involved (see Fig. 2.5).   The large value of G/N favors a structure consisting of a few large crystals whose equiaxed nature is assured by lack of a temperature gradient and the freedom of the crystals to orient themselves randomly. During the last stages of solidification the crystals become interlocked and freedom of movement is lost, but random orientation has already been achieved. This type of structure might be encountered in a well-insulated, preheated mold.

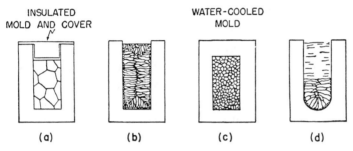

Fig. 2.6. **Size and shape of grains as a function of casting techniques.** (a) Large, equiaxed grains exist in slowly cooled castings produced in molds which slowly extract heat from the molten metal. Preheated molds used in precision casting may produce this structure. (b) If the casting solidifies at a rate intermediate between slow or idealized cooling and very rapid cooling, the casting may develop medium-sized grains of columnar shape. Metal ingot molds often provide conditions for this type of structure. (c) Water cooling of molds used in die casting causes undercooling which is rather severe. This yields a fine structure in which the grains are equiaxed. (d) Rounding the corners of a mold reduces the tendency for planes of weakness to form at the ends of columnar grains. [See part (b).]

If freezing occurs at an intermediate rate somewhere between conditions of idealized and very rapid freezing, the rate of heat extraction is such that there is an appreciable temperature gradient across the melt. This favors columnar growth of grains at right angles to the mold walls, as explained previously. Low-melting impurities are concentrated in the grain boundaries, producing hot shortness (weakness at elevated temperatures) and perhaps brittleness in the grain boundary region. Planes formed where the ends of the columnar grains meet are likely to be planes of weakness. For instance, a plane of weakness exists so as to bisect the right angle between two mold surfaces which meet at 90°. This should be avoided, where possible, by mold design which provides for rounded corners as shown in Fig. 2.6(*d*). The columnar structure sometimes is eliminated from ingots by proper working techniques such as forging or rolling.   In other instances a columnar structure can be replaced by a fine equiaxed grain structure if the melt is inoculated before casting, as in the case of titanium additions to steel.   Sand castings often exhibit a columnar structure.

Finally, suppose a very rapid freezing rate is encountered.   In this case the entire mass tends to become undercooled, producing a small value of G with respect to N.   This promotes the formation of many nuclei, none of which have time to grow to an appreciable size because of the speed of freezing.   Thus a fine-grained, equiaxed structure results.   This type of structure is found in permanent mold or die castings, especially in those cast shapes having thin sections.   In permanent mold casting, a metal mold is used in which the rate of heat extraction is high; in die casting, a metal die (i.e., mold) is also used and the rate of heat extraction is even greater as a result of water or oil cooling of the die.

2.7. Formation of Single Crystals

Large single crystals are of interest because they are used to study the directional mechanical, physical, and chemical properties of crystals.   The simplest method of producing single crystals involves very slowly cooling a well-insulated crucible containing the melt.   If properly controlled, only one nucleus and one crystal are allowed to form in the crucible.   In another method, a crucible which has a pointed bottom is slowly lowered from a furnace.   A nucleus forms in the tip of the crucible and grows upward at the same rate as the crucible is lowered, providing of course, that the rate of lowering is properly regulated.   It is also possible to produce single crystals by careful cold working and annealing.   The principles involved are discussed later in connection with annealing and recrystallization.   Single crystals have also been made by withdrawing a crystal fragment from a melt at a carefully controlled speed.   This method yields single crystals in the form of wire.

2.8. Formation of Crystals and Dendrites

Dendrites are crystals which resemble a pine tree in appearance. The growth of a crystal from its nucleus occurs in several directions, fixed by the anisotropic growth properties of the crystal. During solidification, a dendrite skeleton is formed. In the early stages of freezing there is enough molten metal to fill in the voids caused by solidification shrinkage. Toward the final stages of freezing, there is often insufficient molten metal to compensate for all the shrinkage, and the dendritic pattern sometimes may be seen here without polishing and etching. In a dendrite the first portion to form represents the highest melting composition, and this usually is the region of highest purity. The last portion to freeze represents the lowest melting composition and usually includes low-melting impurities. The rejection of impurities to the grain boundaries is known as dendritic segregation. Gravity segregation may become important, as in the bearing-metal alloys, where the first crystals to form may sink to the bottom of the melt unless steps are taken to prevent this. Crystals found in castings are not always dendritic, although dendrites are the usual form.

Crystals may also be formed by electrolysis of aqueous salt solutions or by electrolysis of molten salts at high temperatures. They may be formed by the condensation of metal vapors or by the decomposition at high temperatures of unstable metal compounds. New crystals may also form from old ones during annealing, or during changes of a metal from one crystal structure to another, as in the shift from gamma to alpha iron.

2.9. Solutions

Solutions in the liquid state are familiar to most people, but solutions in the solid state are somewhat less commonly understood and appreciated. Solid solutions differ from liquid solutions only in so far as differences exist between the solid and liquid states of matter. The fundamental concept of liquid solutions applies also to solid solutions; atoms or molecules of one kind are distributed throughout atoms or molecules of another kind to produce a mass which is homogeneous on a microscopic scale. When this condition is met a solution exists, regardless of whether it is in the gaseous, liquid, or solid state.

In many metal solid solutions, the ideal condition of microscopic homogeneity is not satisfied, because atom migration is restricted. Composition differences exist from point to point in such imperfect solid solutions. Under the proper conditions these solutions would achieve microscopic homogeneity. On a submicroscopic scale in a solution having microscopic homogeneity, the atoms generally are randomly distributed throughout one another, though not necessarily with a perfectly uniform distribution. In a few special cases there may be, as far as can be determined, a perfectly uniform and regular distribution.

Solid solutions are extremely important in metallurgical work, because alloying usually involves formation of solid solutions. As in liquid solutions, the metal which is dissolved is called the solute and the metal in which solution occurs is called the solvent. There are two major types of solid solutions, each of which is considered in the next several pages.

2.10. Substitutional Solid Solutions

When atoms of solute replace atoms of solvent at the lattice points, a substitutional solid solution is said to occur. As shown by Fig. 2.7, the solvent structure is distorted by the acceptance of a few solute atoms. Distortion is associated with hardening or strengthening of the solvent metal, discussed later in connection with the hardening of metals. Usually, but not always, the lattice

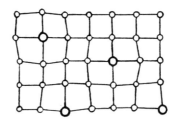

Fig. 2.7. **Substitutional solid solution.** Note the distortion of the lattice caused by the introduction of atoms of solute which are larger than those of the solvent.

constant of the solvent is increased by solute atoms which have larger radii than the solvent, and contracted by those having smaller radii.

Certain characteristics of different kinds of metal atoms are indicative of their capability of forming substitutional solid solutions. Substitutional solid solution is favored when:

1. The solvent and solute atoms are of similar sizes. If the atomic radii are within 15 percent of one another, unlimited solid solubility is possible, but not assured. For size differences larger than this, unlimited solid solubility is impossible.

2. The solvent and solute atoms are chemically similar. Chemical dissimilarity restricts substitutional solid solution. Chemical similarity is indicated by the nearness of the two atoms to one another in the periodic table.

3. The solvent and solute atoms are of the same crystal structure, i.e., both FCC or both BCC, etc.

4. Valence of the solvent is less than the valence of the solute. This can be stated as follows: if metal A has a lower valence than metal B, the solubility of B in A is greater than the solubility of A in B.

A special form of substitutional solid solution is the **superlattice.** This represents a very orderly distribution of solvent and solute atoms, as opposed to the usual random arrangement. Both ordinary substitutional solid solutions and superlattices produce microscopic homogeneity; the superlattice improves on this and produces homogeneity on a submicroscopic scale. The superlattice results from a process known as **ordering,** in which the solute atoms occupy specific lattice points in the structure. This is shown in Fig. 2.8 for an alloy of copper and gold, in which the ratio of copper atoms to gold atoms is 3 to 1. Before ordering,

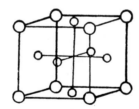

Fig. 2.8. **Superlattice formation of AuCu$_3$.** The small circles represent copper atoms; the large circles represent gold atoms. [After C. S. Barrett, *Structure of Metals.* McGraw-Hill Book Company, Inc., 1943.]

there is a random distribution of copper and gold atoms; after ordering, the copper atoms occupy the face-centered lattice points, and the gold atoms occupy the corners of the unit cells. The occurrence of ordering can be detected by x-ray diffraction. The FCC structure ordinarily does not reflect from the (100) and

certain other planes as explained by Fig. 1.19 and the accompanying text. This is true, before ordering, of the $AuCu_3$ alloy just
described. After ordering, the missing reflections from these
planes appear in the pattern. In order for the reflections from
the atoms in the (100) and (200) planes to cancel each other,
they must be of the same intensity. They can be of the same
intensity only if the atoms on both planes are identical or if there
is a random distribution of unlike atoms on these planes. The
intensity of secondary radiation emanating from atoms struck by
primary radiation of fixed intensity varies from element to element. Thus when ordering occurs, the secondary radiation from
the (100) and (200) is not of equal intensity and hence complete
cancellation does not occur.

Ordering and the formation of superlattices results in changes
in electric conductivity, specific heat, and some mechanical properties. When the ratios of atoms present in the alloy are small
simple whole numbers such as 1:1 or 3:1, and depending upon the
crystal structure, the electric conductivity may be improved by
a factor as high as 3. This is of practical significance. Hardness
and strength sometimes increase, but not to an extent that justifies
practical application of this behavior.

Although ordering and superlattice formation are associated
with small simple ratios of atoms, and although the ratios are
commonly designated by chemical formulae such as CuZn, AuCu,
$AuCu_3$, etc., superlattices should not be confused with intermetallic
compounds. Intermetallic compounds are characterized by sharp
melting points, great hardness, and extreme brittleness, and have
crystal structures not necessarily like those of either of their components. On the other hand, ordered alloys melt over a range of
temperatures, they are not necessarily very hard or very brittle, and
they have crystal structures like those of their components.

Order is achieved by slow cooling of alloys. It is destroyed
by raising the temperature, and disappears before melting occurs.
Order is partly achieved if the ratio of atoms is near the required
small simple ratio for the particular crystal structure involved.
The small excess numbers of solute or solvent atoms are then
randomly distributed throughout an otherwise orderly arrangement. Only if the ratios are exact can perfect order be achieved.

Another special form of the substitional solid solution is known
as a defect structure or **subtraction solid solution.** This has

already been mentioned in Section 1.6 in connection with the effects of foreign atoms on crystal structure. Defect structures occur when atoms of solute replace atoms of solvent and also cause disappearance of additional solvent atoms from their lattice points. For instance, when aluminum is alloyed with nickel, the addition of aluminum atoms removes some nickel atoms without replacing them. Defect structures are rare and are considered, in this book, as a special variation of the substitutional solid solution.

2.11. Interstitial Solid Solutions

When the atoms of solute dissolve in the spaces between the solvent atoms of the structure, an interstitial solid solution is formed. In order for this to occur, the solute atoms must be accommodated between closely neighboring solvent atoms. This is possible only when the atomic radius of the solute is less than 1 Å. The crystal structure is always distorted and hardened by the introduction of solute atoms, and an expansion of the unit cell always results. The interstitial solid solution of carbon in iron is indicated in Fig. 2.9. The void spaces (indicated by small circles in Fig. 2.9) which are likely to accommodate carbon atoms

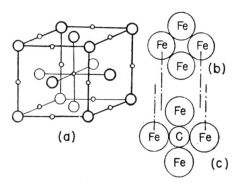

Fig. 2.9. **Interstitial solid solution.** (a) A unit cell of γ-iron. The small circles represent the locations of the largest void spaces. The voids tend to be filled by carbon atoms, thereby causing an enlargement and distortion of the lattice as shown in (b) and (c). [After C. S. Barrett, *Structure of Metals.* McGraw-Hill Book Company, Inc., 1943.]

are all crystallographically equivalent. This equivalence can be seen if the face-centered iron atoms are taken as the origin of the unit cell, rather than the corner atoms. Hydrogen, boron, and nitrogen, in addition to carbon, all form interstitial solid solutions. Atoms having an atomic radius larger than 1 Å can be made to occupy interstitial positions by bombardment with neutrons or fission fragments (see sections 3.33–3.36). Interstitial solid solutions are much less common than substitutional solid solutions.

2.12. Properties of Solid Solutions

Density, thermal expansion, and specific heat vary linearly, for all practical purposes, with the proportions of solute and solvent present. Electric and thermal conductivity, on the other hand, are always decreased when the solvent accepts solute atoms. Hardness and strength are always increased by solid solution formation. Ductility usually, but not always, decreases with increasing amounts of solute. The modulus of elasticity or stiffness of the solvent is not significantly changed by increasing quantities of solute.

2.13. Diffusion

From a metallurgical standpoint, diffusion in the solid state is an extremely important physical process. Solid-state diffusion is the means by which atoms migrate throughout the crystals of a metallic substance. When diffusion occurs in a solid solution, the net movement of solute atoms is away from regions where the solute atoms are most highly concentrated. An opposite movement of solvent atoms tends to occur simultaneously so that microscopic homogeneity eventually results. Diffusion also occurs in pure metals, in which the atoms randomly occupy different atom sites within the crystal over a period of time. The latter type of diffusion is known as self-diffusion. Diffusion enters into many metallurgical processes and phenomena, such as:

1. Annealing and recrystallization.
2. Homogenizing treatments of any kind.
3. The occurrence or absence of dendritic segregation.
4. The formation of bonds between metallic particles or pieces of metal as in powder metallurgy, brazing, soldering, welding, galvanizing.
5. Phase changes, such as the formation of alpha iron and iron carbide from gamma iron, and vice versa; and in precipitation or age hardening.

Most of the above processes are obscure at this point, but they are clarified in other portions of this book.

Mechanism of diffusion. Three possible ways by which diffusion occurs have been suggested. In interstitial solid solutions, the solute atoms probably migrate by travel through the interstices of the solute structure. In substitutional solid solution, it is probable that most diffusion depends upon the presence of vacancies in the crystal. A vacancy is filled by a solute or solvent atom, leaving a vacancy elsewhere. Thus the vacancy moves throughout the structure accommodating the diffusing atoms. This is shown schematically in Fig. 2.10. A third way by which diffusion might occur depends upon simultaneous interchange of two

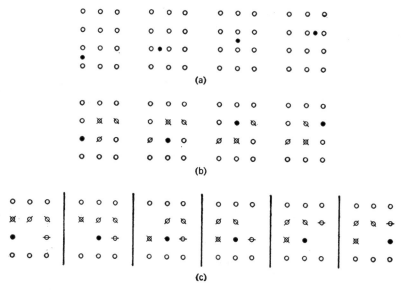

Fig. 2.10. Diffusion. (a) Diffusion through interstices (unlike atoms). (b) Diffusion by simultaneous interchange of two adjacent atoms (like or unlike atoms). (c) Diffusion through accommodation by lattice vacancies.

atoms located on nearby atom sites. This requires that both atoms be simultaneously highly energized, and, since this is not likely, the third mechanism is not believed to occur on a significant scale. Temperatures high enough to impart the energy necessary for two simultaneous atom jumps cause a sufficiently large increase in the numbers of vacancies that diffusion by the vacancy mechanism is thought to predominate. The vacancy mechanism probably also plays a significant role in interstitial solid solution diffusion.

Grain boundaries, with their high proportions of dislocations, have more vacancies than grain centers. Hence diffusion along grain boundaries occurs at a much greater rate than diffusion through the grains themselves. Diffusion of radioactive silver isotopes in silver occurs at the grain boundaries 10^4 times as fast as through the grains themselves, when the temperature is near the melting point. At room temperature, the rate of grain boundary diffusion is 10^{18} times as great as the rate of diffusion through the crystal. Diffusion also occurs along the surfaces of metallic crystals faster than through the grains, but there is not enough surface to produce appreciable diffusion in this manner. Diffusion occurs faster in polycrystalline metals than in single crystals, and faster in metals composed of fine grains as compared to those composed of coarse grains. Deformation of metals increases the number of crystal imperfections, and hence cold-working a metal increases the rate of diffusion. Raising the temperature increases the speed of diffusion because it increases the number of thermal vacancies and because it increases the energy of the atoms. For an atom to jump from a lattice point to a vacancy, it must possess some minimum amount of energy, sometimes called the **activation energy**. A certain activation energy is also required for atoms moving interstitially from one interstice to another.

Simplified diffusion equation. It has been experimentally observed that the diffusion of one metal throughout another in a solid solution depends upon the concentration gradient. The concentration gradient is the change in concentration of the diffusing metal, measured in the direction in which diffusion is occurring. The concentration gradient is a driving force similar to hydraulic head in fluid mechanics, or voltage in electricity. In addition to being directly proportional to concentration gradient, diffusion is also directly proportional to the area (normal to the direction of diffusion) through which diffusion is occurring. Thus:

$$R_{ix} \propto A \ (dc/dx)_i$$

where R is the rate of diffusion of substance i diffusing in the x direction (gm/sec), A is the area normal to the x direction through which diffusion is occurring (sq cm), and $(dc/dx)_i$ is the change in concentration of substance i measured in the x direction (gm/cc/cm). The proportionality sign can be replaced by an equals sign by introducing a diffusion constant D_i (cm²/sec). Then:

$$R_{ix} = D_i A (dc/dx)_i$$

The value of D_i depends upon the character of the metals involved, the temperature at which diffusion is occurring, the concentration of i, and the nature of the diffusion process (i.e. grain boundary, surface, transgranular, or some combination of these). The expression for D_i is

$$D_i = Ke^{-Q/RT}$$

where K is a constant depending upon the lattice constant and frequency of atom vibration (cm²/sec), e is the base of the natural logarithm, T is the absolute temperature, R is the universal gas constant (cal/mol deg), and Q is the activation energy mentioned above (cal/mol). The temperature dependence of the diffusion coefficient of gold in lead is shown in Fig. 2.11. Since the rate of

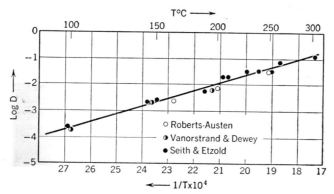

Fig. 2.11. **Temperature dependence of the diffusion coefficient of gold in lead.** [After Mehl; reproduced with permission from F. Seitz, *Modern Theory of Solids*, McGraw-Hill Book Co., Inc., 1940.]

diffusion is directly proportional to the diffusion coefficient, raising the temperature increases the rate of diffusion. This is indicated by the figure. An increase in temperature increases the value of D_i, because the number of atom vacancies and the number of atoms having the necessary energy of activation increase. From a practical standpoint, the value of D_i varies, depending upon whether diffusion is primarily grain boundary, surface, or transgranular.

The progress of diffusion in the solid state is shown schematically in Fig. 2.12. If a layer of copper is plated on a layer of brass, the zinc of the brass tends to diffuse into the copper, and

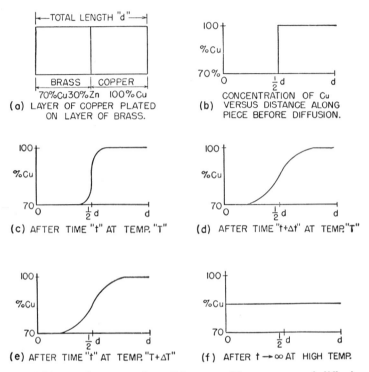

Fig. 2.12. **Diffusion in the solid state.** The progress of diffusion in the solid state is shown above. (a) The piece of metal in which diffusion is to be studied, consisting of portions of pure copper and brass. The plots in (b), (c), (d), (e), and (f) represent the composition of the bar at various points along its length after given times at certain temperatures. The slopes of these curves at different points represent concentration gradients.

the copper tends to diffuse into the zinc. The diffusion is speeded by a rise in temperature as shown by comparison of 2.12(c) and 2.12(e). Eventually the composition becomes uniform throughout the piece and diffusion ceases. The concentration gradient is indicated by the slope of the composition line. Initially, the concentration gradient is infinity at $\frac{1}{2}d$, and zero elsewhere. Therefore, movement of zinc and copper ions (except by self-diffusion) occurs only at the interface. As time goes on, the concentration gradient at $\frac{1}{2}d$ approaches zero, as it does elsewhere in the specimen, and eventually diffusion ceases.

Questions

2.1. Describe the solid state and point out the principle differences between the solid and liquid states.

2.2. Upon what factors does the rate of heat extraction from a melt depend?

2.3. (a) What is meant by nucleation and growth?
(b) What part is played by dislocations in the growth process?

2.4. (a) What important factors affect the size of crystals forming from a melt?
(b) With the aid of a schematic plot, explain how the temperature of solidification determines the grain size.

2.5. Upon what conditions does the formation of columnar crystals depend?

2.6. Explain the size and shape of crystals forming: (a) very slowly as in ideal cooling; (b) at intermediate freezing rates; (c) at very rapid freezing rates.

2.7. What is the importance of single crystals and how are they made?

2.8. Describe the formation of dendrites from a melt. In what other ways are crystals formed?

2.9. Give a broad definition of solution, applicable to the solid, liquid, and gaseous states.

2.10. (a) What is a substitutional solid solution?
(b) For which of the elements listed in Table 1.3 is unlimited substitutional solid solution possible?
(c) What factors favor substitutional solid solution?
(d) What is a superlattice?
(e) Distinguish between a superlattice and intermetallic compound.
(f) How can ordering be detected?
(g) What is a defect structure?

2.11. (a) What are the requirements relative to solute atoms for formation of interstitial solid solutions?
(b) What elements are likely to dissolve interstitially?

2.12. How does solid solution formation affect properties?

2.13. (a) Define diffusion. What is self-diffusion?
(b) Name some processes in which solid state diffusion is important.
(c) How is diffusion believed to occur in interstitial solid solutions? In substitutional solid solutions?
(d) Why is grain boundary diffusion faster than transgranular diffusion?
(e) Explain the effect of temperature on diffusion.
(f) State a simplified diffusion equation.

(g) What are the units of D_i? Show how you got your answer from the simplified diffusion equation.

(h) How does grain size affect the speed of diffusion? Why?

Bibliography

2.1. Barrett, C. S., *The Structure of Metals,* 2nd Ed. New York: Mc-Graw-Hill Book Co., Inc., 1952.

2.2. Seitz, Frederick, *The Modern Theory of Solids.* New York: Mc-Graw-Hill Book Co., Inc., 1940.

2.3. Kittel, Charles, *Introduction to Solid State Physics.* New York: John Wiley & Sons, Inc., 1953.

2.4. Symposium, *Imperfections in Nearly Perfect Crystals.* New York: John Wiley & Sons, Inc., 1952.

2.5. Smith, Morton C., *Principles of Physical Metallurgy.* New York: Harper and Brothers, 1956.

2.6. Chalmers, Bruce, *Progress in Metal Physics,* Vol. 1 and 2. New York: Interscience Publishers, Inc., 1949 and 1950.

2.7. Hume-Rothery, William, *Electrons, Atoms, Metals, and Alloys.* London: The Louis Cassier Co., Ltd., 1955.

2.8. Hoffmann, R. E., "Diffusion Short Circuits in Metals," *General Electric Review,* March 1956, pp. 28–31.

2.9. Cullity, B. D., "Diffusion in Metals," *Scientific American,* **196-5** (May 1957), pp. 103–108.

2.10. Chalmers, Bruce, "How Water Freezes," *Scientific American,* **200-2** (February 1959), pp. 114–122.

CHAPTER **3**

Mechanical Properties
and Metal Failure

MECHANICAL PROPERTIES

3.1. Strength

The strength properties of metals are probably their most important mechanical properties. Since metals behave differently under various load conditions, different tests have been devised to measure particular strength characteristics. The method of load application (tension, compression, or torsion), the rate of load application (impact, static, or cyclic), and the temperature of testing all may have an important bearing on the behavior of the metal. Therefore the term "strength" does not assume its full significance unless it is further qualified to indicate the conditions of its measurement.

In static tensile testing at room temperature, it has been found that most metals withstand certain loads without undergoing any permanent deformation. The maximum load which can be applied and later removed without leaving the metal permanently deformed is known as the elastic limit. Above the elastic limit for the particular metal considered, there is permanent deformation, and when this permanent deformation exceeds a certain arbitrarily specified amount, the yield strength of the metal is reached. The proportional limit is the point of loading at which the metal ceases to deform in direct proportion to stress, or in other words, ceases to follow Hooke's law. Mild steels often exhibit a very definite and sudden yielding at a constant load in the vicinity of the yield strength, and the value of the stress associated with this yielding is known as the yield point. The yield point in some ferrous metals is easier to detect during testing than is the yield strength in non-ferrous metals. The tensile strength or ultimate strength in tension is the maximum strength value observed under a tensile load, and is determined by dividing the original cross-sectional area into the maximum load sustained during the test. Figure 3.1 indicates the refinements which exist in the meanings of the above terms, as applied to typical stress-strain curves for metals in tension.

3.2. Stiffness

Stiffness is another very important property of metals. It is an indication of resistance to deformation below the elastic limit. It is sometimes confused with strength properties, but is atcually quite different. Graphically (see Fig. 3.1), stiffness is represented by the slope of the initial straight line portion of the stress-strain curve; the steeper the line, the greater the stiffness. Numerically, stiffness is computed by dividing the change in stress by the corresponding change in strain, below the elastic limit, thus

$$E = \Delta\sigma/\Delta\varepsilon$$

where E is Young's modulus, or modulus of stiffness, $\Delta\sigma$ is the change in stress required to produce a corresponding change in strain $\Delta\varepsilon$. It is significant to note that the stiffness of different kinds of steel is essentially the same regardless of carbon content, alloy content, or heat treatment, while the tensile strength and yield point show wide variations with these factors.

Metallic elastic resistance to loading is an interesting phenomenon. It can be explained on the basis of atomic distances, and binding forces. Consider the reactions between two atoms. When the atoms are far apart there are only negligible forces acting between them. As the atoms approach one another, their valence electrons fall into common orbits and the potential energy of the system is lowered. The common orbits which can be filled are nearer the nucleus and hence of lower energy the closer the atoms get to one another. Therefore the force of attraction from this source tends to increase as the distance between atoms decreases. On the other hand, as the atom centers approach one another, the filled electron shells (in orbits of lower energy than the common orbits containing the valence electrons) tend to overlap and create repulsive forces. In addition, the positively

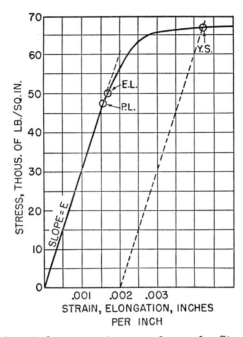

Fig. 3.1. A typical stress-strain curve for steel. Stress, abbreviated σ in this text, is measured in pounds per square inch, calculated on the basis of the original cross section of the piece. Strain, abbreviated ε, is measured as inches elongation per inch of the specimen, measured over a two-inch length of the specimen. The modulus of elasticity, E, is the slope of the initial straight portion of the curve, and can be found from $E = \Delta\sigma/\Delta\varepsilon$. The yield strength is usually the stress corresponding to the intersection of the stress-strain diagram with a line parallel to the straight portion of the curve, but intersecting the strain axis at 0.2 per cent elongation. The tensile strength or ultimate strength is the maximum stress, calculated on the basis of the original cross section, required to produce fracture. The proportional limit is the maximum stress at which stress and strain remain directly proportional to each other. The elastic limit is the maximum stress a piece can withstand without undergoing permanent deformation. The yield point is the first stress at which a marked increase in deformation of the material occurs without an increase in load. It is commonly observed in mild steels, but rarely encountered in other alloys. The proportional limit and elastic limit depend upon the ability to detect deviations from the initial straight portion of the curve. In most practical work, yield strength and yield point (if the latter exists) are used. The determination and use of proportional limit and elastic limit are mainly restricted to research laboratories. Unless fine instruments and care are used it is difficult to distinguish among elastic limit, proportional limit, yield strength, and yield point.

charged nuclei tend to repel one another. As one atom approaches another, both the forces of attraction and forces of repulsion increase, but not in the same ratios as distance decreases. This is represented schematically in Fig. 3.2. A net force exists

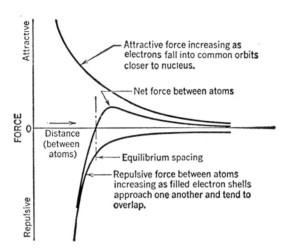

Fig. 3.2. Variation of attractive and repulsive forces between two atoms as the distance between them is varied.

between atoms which is the resultant of the attractive and repulsive forces. The spacing between atoms is stable when the resultant force is zero. This spacing is known as the equilibrium spacing. If an external force is applied which moves the atoms apart, the resultant force between atoms is attractive, so that when the external force is removed, the atoms move closer together and back to their equilibrium position. The reverse is true upon application and removal of an external force tending to push the atoms together. This greatly simplified image considers only two atoms and one dimension. In crystals there are many millions of atoms, each reacting with its nearest neighbors and subject to forces and movements in three dimensions. The equilibrium spacing between atoms is the distance between nearest neighbors, and the stiffness of a metallic substance is a function of the slope of the resultant force curve as it crosses the zero-force ordinate.

3.3. Ductility

The ability of metals to undergo deformation once the elastic limit has been exceeded is known as ductility. A metal with good ductility exhibits appreciable elongation under tension before fracture occurs. A metal which lacks ductility fractures without appreciable elongation, and is said to be brittle. Annealed low-carbon steel is very ductile, and a specimen 2.0 inches long may become 2.7 inches long before rupture, having undergone an elongation of 35 per cent. Some tool steels are very brittle and are capable of almost no elongation. Brittleness and ductility are opposites in sense. If a metal can be beaten into thin sheets it possesses a special form of ductility known as malleability. Gold is a malleable metal which can be hammered into thin sheets known as gold leaf.

3.4. Toughness

When a piece of metal combines a high elastic limit with good ductility, the metal is said to be tough. Toughness is graphically indicated by a large area under the stress-strain curve up to the point of rupture. (See Fig. 3.3.)

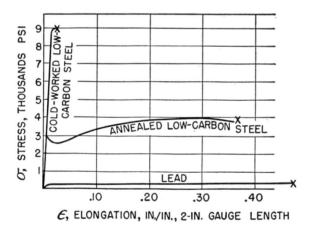

Fig. 3.3. **Toughness as shown by a stress-strain curve.** Toughness is a property of metals which indicates ability to absorb relatively large quantities of energy up to the point of rupture. It is found in metals which exhibit a high elastic limit and good ductility, so as to produce a large area under the stress-strain curve. The units of the area under the curve are pound-inches per cubic inch, i.e., kinetic energy which can be absorbed by a given volume of metal. The X's on the plots indicate the points of rupture. Lead, which has good ductility but a low yield strength, is not tough, nor is cold-worked steel, which has a high yield strength but almost no ductility. Annealed, low-carbon steel is tough, since it possesses both good ductility and a high yield point.

Information regarding toughness is usually obtained by conventional impact tests. Such tests usually involve striking of a small, notched specimen by means of a pendulum. The specimens are about two or three inches long and have a cross section almost one-half inch square. The blow of the pendulum tends to bend the specimen, but the notch is sufficiently deep to cause a fracture. Knowing the mass of the pendulum and its height of fall before impact and height of rise after impact, one can determine, by difference, the amount of energy absorbed by fracture of the specimen. This absorbed energy, measured in foot-pounds, indicates toughness. At the velocities of loading encountered in conventional impact testing, the behavior of the metal is substantially the same as if it were statically or very slowly loaded. Toughness values determined by impact test correlate well with values determined by ordinary tensile testing.

Impact testing is useful in determining the transition temperature range of alloys. This is particularly important in connection with steel. The transition temperature range is the range over which the ductility of an alloy falls off sharply. The loss of ductility is shown by a drop in impact toughness. For instance, typical alloy steels drop from about 40 ft lb to about 20 ft lb over the range from about 70°F to about −100°F.[1] Substantial loss of ductility of steel is generally considered to take place between 40°F and 0°F. The impact test is also useful in determining whether heat treatments have been successful in restoring ductility.

3.5. Hardness

Hardness is a very important property with a wide variety of meanings. Many different tests for hardness have been devised, and it is this multiplicity of tests which gives different meanings to the word. For our purposes, we will consider that hardness is resistance to indentation, and therefore involves and is closely associated with stiffness and the elastic limit of a metal. Hardness measurements such as Brinell, Rockwell, and Vickers can be considered to be relative indications of hardness, which must be interpreted in the light of the particular means by which they were obtained.

[1] These results are for a Charpy keyhole impact test on SAE-AISI 8630.

Some typical hardness readings are given in Table 3.1

Table 3.1. Hardness of Typical Alloys

Alloy	Rockwell		Brinell	Vickers
	R_B-scale	R_C-scale		
Wrought Iron	57	—	105	—
Low-carbon steel, annealed	55	—	100	—
Low-carbon steel, cold worked	80	—	148	155
Alloy steel, quenched and tempered	—	50	480	510
White cast iron	—	45	425	450
Gray cast iron	98	21	230	240
High-speed tool steel	—	65	740	830

3.6. Failure of Metals

Metals usually fail by one or more of the following mechanisms:

1. Failure by inelastic action at atmospheric temperatures.
2. Failure by creep or rupture at elevated temperatures.
3. Failure by fatigue.
4. Failure by corrosion.

Most of the remainder of this chapter is devoted to a discussion of the four principal mechanisms of metal failure. The very last sections of the chapter deal with the effects of radiation on metallic materials.

FAILURE BY INELASTIC ACTION AT ORDINARY TEMPERATURES

3.7. Failure by Deformation

When the elastic limit is exceeded, plastic deformation occurs, and if this deformation is serious enough to prevent the part from performing the functions for which it was designed, failure results. When a part is loaded a little beyond the elastic limit, it undergoes a small amount of permanent deformation. In so doing, the metal becomes stronger and harder, and this improvement in properties is called work hardening. (Work hardening is discussed again in Chapter 5.) The increase in strength eventually balances the load, and deformation ceases. If the load is increased slightly, additional permanent deformation and work hardening occur until the load is again balanced. This process goes on until rupture eventually occurs. The true stress-strain curve for any metal illustrates this behavior. The stress-strain curve shown in

Fig. 3.1 is the apparent stress-strain curve, i.e. stress is calculated by dividing the load by the *original* cross-section. For the true stress-strain curve, the load is divided by the actual cross-section existing at the time the load was applied. After the elastic limit has been reached the cross-section of the specimen becomes significantly smaller, and by the time the ultimate load has been applied, the cross-section has become much smaller than the original cross-section. This causes the true stress to rise above the apparent stress, and in fact accounts for continued strengthening of the metal until rupture occurs. Fig. 3.4 shows an apparent (i.e., conventional) stress-strain curve and a true stress-strain curve.

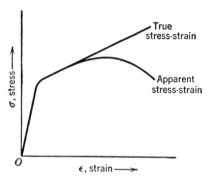

Fig. 3.4. **Stress-strain curves.** The relation between true stress-strain and apparent stress-strain is indicated.

So long as a metal part can continue in service, it has not failed, even though it has been permanently deformed. If the metal is a brittle material, fracture rather than deformation may be the cause of failure.

3.8. Mechanisms of Deformation

The most important mechanism of deformation is the process known as slip. A discussion of slip involves the concept of the atomic density of planes and lines, and therefore a brief explanation follows.

Atomic density of crystallographic planes and lines. Consider the body-centered cubic unit cell shown in Fig. 3.5. It is evident that certain planes passed through the unit cell have a greater atomic density than others. Within these planes there are certain directions along which atomic density is greatest. For example, one can calculate the atomic density of the unit cell itself. In the cell shown in Fig. 3.5 there are eight corner atoms, and one in the center of the cube. However, the unit cell does not contain 9 atoms. This is because the unit cell totally owns only one-eighth of each of the eight corner atoms shown. The remaining seven-eighths of each corner atom are owned variously by the seven other unit cells which meet at the corner of any given unit cell. Therefore, the unit cell totally possesses one-eighth of each of the eight corner atoms plus the one in its center, making a total of two atoms per unit cell.

Calculations of the atomic density of planes is based on similar reasoning. Consider BCHG, a portion of the (100) plane in Fig. 3.5. Keep in mind that for planes, two dimensions only are considered. This plane, if extended to infinity in all directions, would

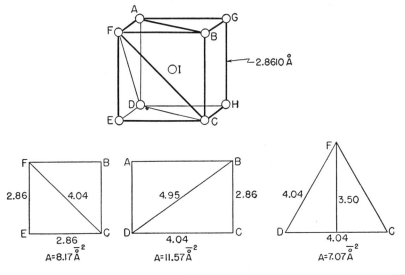

Plane or Line	Area of Length	Atoms Totally Possessed	Atomic Density
ABCD	11.57 square Å	2	0.173 atoms/sq. Å
FBEC	8.17 square Å	1	0.122 atoms/sq. Å
CDF	7.07 square Å	0.5	0.0707 atoms/sq. Å
BD	4.95 Å	2	0.403 atoms/Å
CF	4.04 Å	1	0.248 atoms/Å
CB	2.86 Å	1	0.350 atoms/Å

Fig. 3.5. Atomic density of crystallographic lines and planes. The unit cell above represents body-centered cubic iron. The atomic density of representative planes and lines is given in the table.

share each of its corner atoms with three areas similar to itself in shape and size. Thus, BCHG totally owns only one-fourth of each of four corner atoms. Hence its atomic population is one and its atomic density is one divided by the area of the plane. The atomic population of FDC which is a portion of the (111) plane, is one-sixth of each of three corner atoms, or one-half atom. One sixth is used because if FDC is extended to infinity six triangular areas of equivalent size and shape meet to share the atoms at the corners.

The atomic density is similarly calculated for lines or directions. For instance, consider the line FC which is equivalent to a segment of the <110> direction. This segment contains two atoms along its length, but actually shares each of the atoms at its ends with segments of equal length. Its total population is one atom, and its atomic density is one divided by the length of the segment.

Atomic density and plastic deformation. Slip is the process by which plastic deformation is most likely to occur. Slip involves the relative movement of layers of atoms in a crystal. Within any given layer, the relative positions of the atoms do not change. The plane midway between the boundary atoms of the two layers is known as the slip plane, as shown in Fig. 3.6. The direction of relative movement is known as the slip direction. Closer study of the drawing, plus a comparison with Fig. 3.5, show that slip has occurred in a direction of highest atomic density and in a plane of highest atomic density.

Critical resolved shear stress. In Fig. 3.7, there is a sketch of a single crystal consisting of several body-centered cubic unit cells. If an increasing load is applied to this crystal in the direction XY, slip will commence at some point in the process. For this particular structure slip is likely to occur along a plane of the {110} family, such as ABCD, and in a direction of the [111] family such as AC. The component of the applied load in the direction AC can be computed. The distribution of this component over the area ABCD is a shearing stress. The shearing stress which initiates slip in the plane ABCD in the direction AC is the critical resolved shear stress for that particular slip system. An understanding of the term is important in connection with later discussions on the hardening and strengthening of metals.

Slip systems. It has been observed that slip *always* occurs in the direction of highest atomic density. In face-centered cubic and

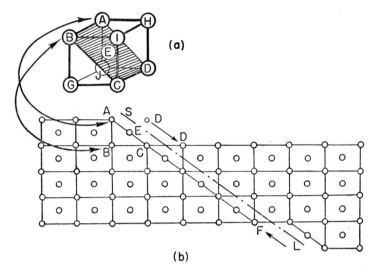

Fig. 3.6. Slip in a body-centered cubic structure. It is characteristic of slip that the orientation of unit cells on both sides of the slip plane remains the same as originally. It is also characteristic that all of the atoms in the two adjacent layers in which slip has occurred move the same relative amount, regardless of their distance from the slip plane. These characteristics of slip are shown above. (a) Body-centered cubic unit cell showing the plane represented in (b). In part (b) slip direction is *FA* and corresponds to *AEC* in (a). Note that *AF* is in plane *ABCD*. The actual slip plane is at right angles to the plane of the page and is parallel to plane *AICJ* in (a). *SL* is the intersection of the slip plane with the page.

close-packed hexagonal structures, slip always involves planes of highest atomic density. For face-centered cubic structures the most densely packed plane is the (111); for close-packed hexagonal it is the (001). In body-centered cubic structures slip always involves planes of very high atomic density, though not necessarily always a plane of highest atomic density (110). The other planes in the body-centered cubic structure in which slip has been observed to occur are the (112) and (123). Both of these have high atomic densities, though not quite as high as the (110). The close-packed hexagonal structures are most restricted in regard to possibilities for slip since only the basal (001) planes are involved. There are only three possible directions of highest density in the basal planes and hence only three slip systems. Similar reasoning shows that in the face-centered cubic structures there are 12 slip systems, and in the body-centered cubic structures 48 slip

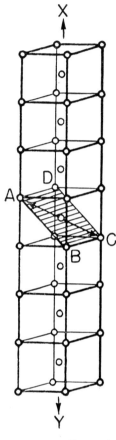

Fig. 3.7. **Critical resolved shear stress.** Consider a small single crystal made of seven body-centered cubic unit cells as shown to the left. When loaded beyond the elastic limit slip is likely to occur along direction AC in plane $ABCD$, or in a similar direction in the same or any other of the unit cells making up the crystal. Assume the unit cells are cubes whose sides are one inch long. If a load of P pounds is applied in the direction XY, sufficient to initiate or barely continue slip along AC, the shear stress produced by P is known as the *critical resolved shear stress.* The component of P along AC is $P/\sqrt{3}$ pounds, and when this is distributed over the area of shear, the shear stress is $P/\sqrt{6}$ pounds per square inch. It is this stress which is known as the critical resolved shear stress.

systems. Sometimes slip planes which are inactive at room temperature become active at elevated temperatures. Raising the temperature of some metals tends to increase the number of slip systems.

The fewer the number of slip systems, the less ductile the metal. Thus, the close-packed hexagonal metals are known for poor ductility. The face-centered cubic and body-centered cubic structures are known for good ductility. Consider an increasing tensile load applied to a single crystal of a close-packed hexagonal structure. If the (001) planes are either at right angles to or parallel to the line of action of the load, the shearing component of the load along these planes is zero. The shearing component increases to a maximum as the orientation of the basal planes approaches an angle of 45° relative to the direction of loading. Thus, when the basal planes are nearly at right angles to or parallel to the load, the rupture strength is reached before the shear stress is great enough to produce slip. Under these conditions brittle fracture results. When the basal planes make angles near 45° with the load, the critical resolved shear stress is reached before the rupture strength is exceeded and so slip and elongation occur. In the face-centered and body-centered cubic metals there are many possible slip systems of different orientations. It is therefore impossible, under simple axial loading, to orient the crystal relative to the load so that the rupture strength is exceeded prior to the occurrence of some slip.

Slip lines and slip bands. Microscopic evidence of slip is found in slip lines and slip bands. Slip occurs as an abrupt sliding of one layer of atoms over another. The relative movement of adjacent layers is about 2000 Å or 1000 atom distances. When relative motion this extensive has been achieved on one slip plane, motion ceases on that plane. Further slip occurs on a parallel plane at least 200 Å or 100 atom distances away from the previously active plane. Where a sufficient number of slip planes intersect the highly polished surface of a piece of metal, a dark line appears as shown in Fig. 3.9. These are known as slip lines. Their origin is indicated in Fig. 3.8, in which the top surface of

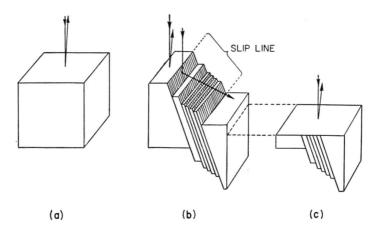

(a)   (b)   (c)

Fig. 3.8. Formation of slip lines. (a) Block of smoothly polished metal prior to deformation. (b) The same block after deformation, showing the intersection of individual slip planes with the polished surface to form slip lines. The intersection of a cluster of slip lines with the surface forms a slip band. (c) Repolishing removes all evidence of slip.

the blocklike crystal corresponds to the surface shown in the photo-micrograph of Fig. 3.9. If a large cluster of slip lines occurs, the formation is known as a slip band. If a surface having slip lines is polished, the slip lines disappear. Since the orientation of the unit cells in adjacent layers is essentially the same as the original orientation, etching does not show up the regions in which slip has occurred. This is significant for distinguishing between slip and twinning.

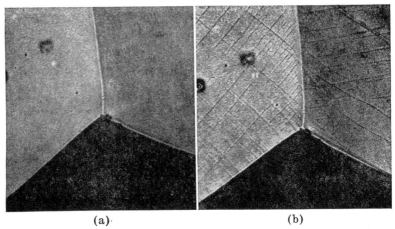

(a)   (b)

Fig. 3.9. **Slip lines.** The polished and etched surface of a piece of copper is shown (a) before deformation, and (b) after deformation. The small black spots are oxide inclusions. Slip lines are visible in (b). Electrolytic polish in 23 per cent H_3PO_4. Etchant: $NH_4OH + H_2O_2$. Magnification: 200×. [Courtesy of the School of Engineering, Metals Laboratory, University of Massachusetts.]

Deformation by twinning. Metals also deform by a process known as twinning. Less is known about twinning than about slip, but it is known that in twinning a section of the crystal takes a new orientation with respect to the parent orientation. The new orientation is such that the twin is the mirror image of the parent, and hence the use of the word "twin." The plane of reflection is known as the twinning plane. The twin may be *thought of* as being formed by a 180° rotation of a section of a crystal about the twinning axis, although *no actual rotation is involved.* This is illustrated in Fig. 3.10 for a body-centered cubic lattice. It is seen that the displacement of the atoms in the twin with respect to the atoms in the parent is directly proportional to the distance from the twinning planes. As pointed out in Fig. 3.6, a similar situation does not result from slip. In a few metals, twinning is the only mechanism by which deformation has been observed to occur. In many metals, however, it is of major interest because it occurs early in the process of deformation and in so doing brings slip systems into positions favorable for slip.

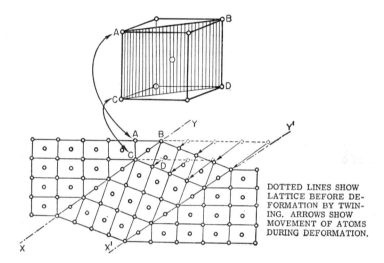

DOTTED LINES SHOW
LATTICE BEFORE DE-
FORMATION BY TWIN-
ING. ARROWS SHOW
MOVEMENT OF ATOMS
DURING DEFORMATION.

Fig. 3.10. **Twinning in a body-centered cubic structure.** The twinning planes intersect the plane of the page in *XY* and *X'Y'*. The region between *XY* and *X'Y'* is the twin. The regions to the left and right of the twinning planes have the orientation of the parent crystal. It is characteristic of twinning that the orientation of the twin is different from that of the parent. Subsequent polishing will not remove evidence of twinning as it will evidence of slip, and upon etching after polishing the twin will appear again. It is also characteristic of twinning that the greater the distance of an atom (in the twin) from the twinning planes, the greater its relative movement with respect to its original location. These characteristics are shown above.

Twins and twin bands. Microscopic examination of a polished and etched piece of metal in which twins have been produced may show a banded structure. The bands may appear as lines at low magnifications because in some instances they are very narrow, but at higher magnifications they can be resolved into twin bands. They are usually pointed at both ends, giving them a boat-shaped appearance. The fact that they are not slip lines is readily demonstrated by the fact that polishing and etching does not make them disappear as in the case of slip lines. Since the twin represents an actual difference in orientation of unit cells with respect to the parent orientation, it may have a different etching rate than the parent grain. Further, because of the fact that it runs down through considerable depth of the parent grain, repolishing and re-etching will not remove it. Twins are often observed in metals which have been annealed, possibly as a result of the growth of twin nuclei which were formed during the deformation of the metal. (See sections on annealing and recrystallization in Chapter 6.) Annealing twins are often broader bands than deformation twins, and they lack the characteristic pointed ends of deformation twins.

3.9. Dislocations and Slip

The theory of dislocations is useful because it explains the properties of metals better than earlier theories. In particular it explains slip behavior and strain hardening.

Assuming a perfect crystal, it would be necessary, in order for slip to occur, for bonds between all atoms on either side of the slip plane to break simultaneously. This is illustrated in Fig. 3.11(a). Calculations of the theoretical strength of metals based on this mechanism of deformation give results about 1000 times greater than observed strengths. If dislocations are considered, however, the observed properties of metals can be explained. Examination of Fig. 3.11(b–d) shows that if a dislocation is present, slip occurs through movement of the dislocation across the slip plane. In this process, only one atomic bond (in a two-dimensional picture) breaks at a time.

Actually there are believed to be many dislocations throughout metal crystals. The concentration of dislocations is stated in terms of the number of times dislocation lines intersect a unit area of a crystal. Estimates of the concentration run between $10^8/cm^2$ in good natural crystals and $10^{12}/cm^2$ in deformed crystals. Although these concentrations seem high, they actually represent only a very small proportion of the total crystal structure. At most, only about one atom per thousand is near the center of a dislocation line.

Each dislocation has associated with it a stress field. In the positive dislocation shown in Fig. 3.11(b), the atoms above the plane of dislocation are crowded because of the extra column of atoms. These atoms are in compression. Conversely, below the dislocation plane the atoms are in tension. The nature of the stress fields regulates the distribution and behavior of the dislocations.

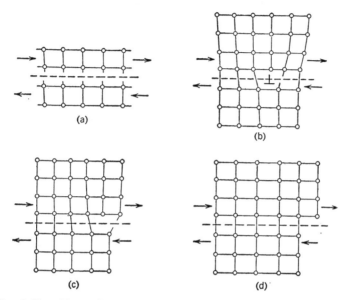

Fig. 3.11. **Slip.** (a) Shear requiring simultaneous breaking of many atomic bonds. (b–d) Shear requiring successive breaking of individual atomic bonds by movement of a positive dislocation.

Dislocations existing on the same slip plane, but having *opposite* signs, move in opposite directions upon loading, and if they meet, they annihilate one another. Thus dislocations of *opposite* sign on the same slip plane tend to disappear, disregistry is replaced by registry, and the metal tends to become stronger. Next consider dislocations of the *same* sign lying in the same slip plane. Upon loading, dislocations of the same sign tend to move in the same direction, as slip proceeds. However, the dislocations tend to repel one another, because crowding on one side and stretching on the other side of a slip plane are locally intensified by very close approach of two similar dislocations. Thus, if the lead dislocation in a group of dislocations having the same sign is blocked by an obstruction, the following dislocations pile up behind it in a somewhat uniformly spaced fashion.

Repulsion of dislocations of like sign and attraction of those of unlike sign occur not only when the dislocations are in the same plane, but also when dislocations lie in adjacent planes. Consider Fig. 3.12.   In this figure there are shown two adjacent planes, both containing a positive dislocation.   Above each line of dislocation, there is a compression field caused by the presence of an extra row of atoms.   Below each line of dislocation, there is a region in tension.   As these two dislocations approach each other, the compressed area of the lower dislocation tends to increase the expansion of the tensile region in the upper dislocation, and vice versa.

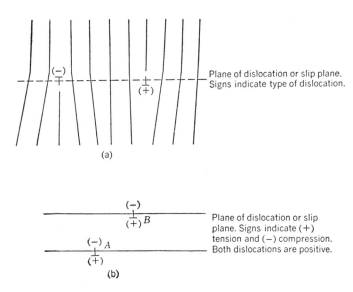

Plane of dislocation or slip plane. Signs indicate type of dislocation.

(a)

Plane of dislocation or slip plane. Signs indicate (+) tension and (−) compression. Both dislocations are positive.

(b)

Fig. 3.12.   Dislocation movement and distribution.   (a) Dislocations of opposite sign move toward each other and cancel out as slip progresses.   (b) Dislocations on adjacent planes repulse one another if of like sign.   Area A is in compression and would like to expand.   Area B is in tension and would like to contract.   Should the dislocations approach one another, A would increase the tension in B, and B would increase the compression in A.

Therefore, even though they are on different planes, dislocations of like sign repel one another.   If they are of unlike sign, the space between the two dislocations consists of one region in tension and another in compression.   As the two dislocations approach one another, there is relaxation in the area between them.   Hence, if of unlike sign, the dislocations attract one another even if they are not coplanar.

Thus, as slip proceeds in a single crystal, dislocations either (a) move to the free edge of the crystal and are dissipated, (b) move toward one another and if of unlike sign are cancelled, or (c) move toward one another, then repel each other if of like sign, and become locked in place, when they encounter an obstacle. The first two possibilities, (a) and (b), tend to cause disappearance of dislocations and hence increase reisistance to slip (i.e. increase strength). When (c) occurs, slip can continue only if sufficient additional energy is applied to overcome the repulsive forces, or cause the dislocations to move beyond the obstacle. Thus, all three possibilities result in increasing resistance to slip, as slip proceeds. (See Fig. 5.1.) Observed behavior of metals confirms this theory which explains also why slip proceeds on one plane and eventually ceases on that plane, to be followed by slip on a parallel plane, some distance away.

It might be deduced from the discussion above that the crystal structure becomes more perfect as dislocations are consumed by the process of slip. Actually, more dislocations seem to be generated than are consumed by straining. Work with single crystals of aluminum suggests that new dislocations are formed at the surface. But regardless of how many dislocations are formed, they are eventually consumed or locked in place, and the metal becomes stronger. Finally, a point is reached where the stress required to continue slip is greater than the stress required for rupture, and the metal breaks. In polycrystalline metallic materials, the movement of dislocations is stopped by the presence of grain boundaries. Since it is difficult to transfer slip across a boundary, such materials become stronger as slip proceeds.

3.10. Wear and Abrasion

Failure by inelastic action should also include wear and abrasion. A part which is subjected to continuous pounding by blows which exceed the elastic limit may eventually become so deformed that it can no longer perform its intended function. If a part is subjected to abrasive wear, minute surface layers are stressed not only beyond the elastic limit, but also beyond the point of rupture, so that very small particles of metal are actually torn away. Eventually the erosion may be so severe as to prevent the part from giving useful service, and failure occurs. Erosion may also reduce the cross-section which is carrying the load so that final failure occurs by plastic deformation.

Wear is frequently caused by *galling* or *seizing*. This occurs when two pieces of a similar metal or alloy are forced together under load. If the lubricating film between the parts is broken down by the load, a cold pressure-weld may join them. Upon separation of the members the weld is broken, and the stronger member carries with it particles of the weaker one, torn from its surface. To avoid this effect of pressure-welding, one may use dissimilar metal compositions for the two pieces involved, since dissimilar compositions do not readily weld together when cold. Cold welding occurs only between like crystals of adjacent surfaces, when similar orientations exist. Under sufficient pressure, the surface atoms assume the equilibrium spacing (see Fig. 3.2 and accompanying text), and a bond is formed across the interface.

3.11. Importance of Avoiding Abrupt Changes in Shape

It must be remembered that sharp changes in cross section or shape of a part always result in stress concentration. For instance, notches, holes, keyways, or sharp fillets produce areas of very high stresses. Ordinary formulas used for stress computation do not take into account the high stress concentrations in these portions of machine parts. Therefore a piece of metal may fail even though the computed stresses are below its known elastic limit. The stress at a local stress raiser, being above the calculated stress, may produce localized deformation which renders the part useless. This type of failure can be avoided by elimination of sharp changes in the shape of the piece, or if this is not possible, by allowing an extra factor of safety in the design of the part. Notched parts made of metals which are ordinarily ductile may behave in a brittle fashion. When strength and toughness are adversely affected by notching, the metal is said to be "notch sensitive." Some metals are much more notch sensitive than others.

FAILURE AT ELEVATED TEMPERATURES

3.12. Definition and Significance

Creep is the slow flow or plastic deformation of metals held for long periods of time at elevated temperatures and at stresses below the conventional room temperature values of yield strength, or at stresses which are sometimes even below the short-time yield strength or proportional limit measured at the elevated temperature in question. This is shown in Fig. 3.13. Creep failure has become increasingly significant as operating temperatures of equipment have been pushed upward in the search for greater efficiency.

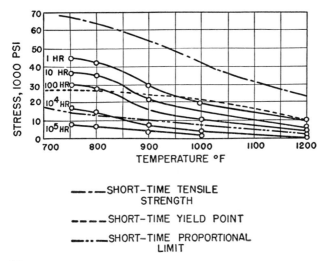

—··—SHORT—TIME TENSILE
STRENGTH

—— ——SHORT—TIME YIELD POINT

—··—SHORT—TIME PROPORTIONAL
LIMIT

Fig. 3.13. Creep occurring below proportional limit. Creep data for carbon steel, showing that creep can occur at stresses which are lower than the short-time, conventional proportional limit, yield point, or tensile strength. The solid lines represent 1 per cent creep in the time indicated, i.e., 1, 10, 100, 10,000, and 100,000 hours. The significance of the other curves is indicated by the key. Note that for higher stresses at a given temperature less time is required to produce a given amount of deformation. At higher temperatures a lower stress will produce an equivalent amount of creep in a shorter time. [Adapted from *Metals Handbook*, American Society for Metals, 1948.]

The higher the temperature of operation, the lower the stress required to produce a given deformation in a given time. Likewise, a given stress produces a greater deformation in the same time when the temperature is raised. Although inelastic deformation of metals at ordinary temperatures stops if sufficient strain hardening sets in to balance the load, in the case of creep, deformation continues until fracture ultimately occurs.

Very low stresses acting over long periods of time produce fracture without any appreciable prior deformation. This type of failure is studied by stress-rupture tests. Still another type of failure is caused by the thermal shock of rapid cooling and rapid heating.

3.13. Progress of Creep

Metals undergoing failure by creep have been observed to pass through three stages which are shown in Fig. 3.14. These can be detected by creep testing, in which specimens are subjected to constant stresses and temperatures. Strain (i.e., creep) and time are measured. A plot of creep versus time is made, and ideal data produce a plot similar to that of Fig. 3.14. When the load is applied, some deformation occurs at once. This deformation may consist of only elastic or both elastic and inelastic deformation, depending upon the conditions of loading. Following the instantaneous deformation, creep sets in and the metal slowly deforms at

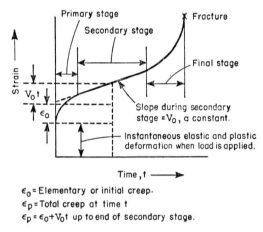

ϵ_0 = Elementary or initial creep.

ϵ_p = Total creep at time t

$\epsilon_p = \epsilon_0 + V_0 t$ up to end of secondary stage.

Fig. 3.14. Idealized creep curve.

a constantly diminishing rate. The stage of creep during which there occurs a decreasing rate of deformation is known as **primary creep.** Eventually the rate of deformation reaches a minimum value which remains constant for some interval of time. During this interval the specimen is undergoing **secondary creep. Final** or **tertiary creep** is reached when the specimen commences to deform at an increasing speed. During tertiary creep, tensile specimens elongate rapidly, and undergo a simultaneous reduction in cross-section. Under constant loads, reduction in cross-section eventually occurs, intensifying the stress and producing an increase in the strain rate. If the load is varied so as to produce a constant stress, the strain rate remains more nearly constant until fracture occurs.

Symbols used in plotting creep test results are ε_p, ε_0, t, and V_0, the meanings of which are illustrated in Fig. 3.14. At any time, t, after the initial application of load, the total creep, ε_p, will be given by:

$$\varepsilon_p = \varepsilon_0 + V_0 t$$

Thus it is possible to calculate the total amount of creep after intervals of time which are longer than the duration of the test. In order for these calculations to give correct results at least three important requirements must be met:

1. The duration of the test must give reliable values of V.

2. The time interval for which ε is calculated must be *less* than the time at which the final stage of creep would have been encountered had the test been run to completion.

3. The material must exhibit idealized creep behavior (i.e., must follow an ideal curve of the type shown in Fig. 3.14).

If these conditions are not met, calculated values of creep will be in error. The calculation is actually an algebraic substitute for a graphic extrapolation of the curve.

It is often necessary to study the creep behavior of a metal at different constant stresses and temperatures. Since each creep test requires many hours, the only practical way to obtain such information is to run a series of these tests simultaneously. By extrapolation or calculation, the results can be adapted to cover longer periods of time than the duration of the test. Such a family of curves is shown in Figs. 3.15(a) and 3.15(b). It is useful to replot the data in terms of stress versus creep, as shown in Fig. 3.15(c), where the curve represents a fixed time interval. From Fig. 3.15(b) the time required to produce a given amount of strain can be found for different stresses. For instance, 0.4 per cent creep will be produced at a stress of 14,000 psi in six years, or 16,000 psi in four years, or 22,500 psi in two years. In design work, if the life of the structure in which creep is to occur can be anticipated, then the maximum stress required to produce some limiting permissible amount of creep can be determined. For instance, assume the equipment is to be used for three years before replacement is necessary. If 0.50 per cent creep is permissible before failure occurs as a result of distortion, then the maximum stress should not exceed

25,000 psi. Another convenient way to represent the data is shown in Fig. 3.15 (d), which is a semi-log plot of stress versus time to produce a given amount of creep or rupture. Curves of the latter type are frequently extrapolated to predict long-time behavior on the

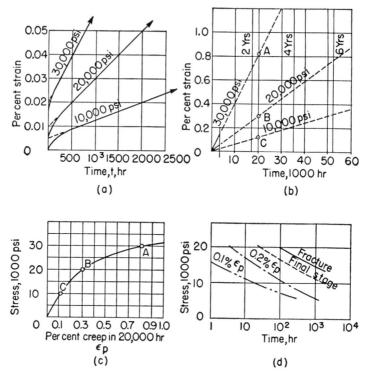

Fig. 3.15. **Creep and stress-rupture curves.** (a) Typical creep curves for three different stresses. Arrows indicate direction of extrapolations. (b) The same curves as in (a) except that extrapolations (broken lines) have been made to 60,000 hours. Note that the scale of plotting is different in (a) and (b). Part (c) shows stress versus per cent creep at the end of 20,000 hours as obtained from plot in (b). If a component can undergo 0.50 per cent elongation in a machine having a life of 20,000 hours, the component can withstand 25,000 psi. (d) Stress-rupture data for a different material (solid line). This plot also shows stress corresponding to the time required to produce 0.1 per cent and 0.2 per cent elongation, and the time required to initiate the third stage of creep.

basis of relatively short-time tests. This gives results of no greater certainty than previously mentioned extrapolations. Stress-rupture data are conveniently plotted on such coordinates, but an improvement over direct extrapolation of such short-time results has been devised. This method, evolved from the work of Holloman and Zener, is described in the following paragraphs.

3.14. Stress-rupture Data

The speed of a number of physical and physicochemical processes is dependent upon temperature according to the relationship:

$$E = Ae^{-Q/RT} \tag{1}$$

where E is the rate; A is a constant; Q is activation energy, or energy required by the process in order that it can continue. For a given stress, Q is constant. R is the gas constant; T is absolute temperature, °R (i.e., °F + 460); e is the base of natural logarithms.

The significance of these terms need not be understood for application of the method. (They are explained in any good text on thermodynamics or physical chemistry.) Since the rate is inversely proportional to time, the relation can be rewritten:

$$\frac{1}{t} = Ae^{-Q/RT} \tag{2}$$

where t is time in hours. Taking the natural logarithm of both sides:

$$\ln 1 - \ln t = \ln A - \frac{Q}{RT}$$

and converting to common logarithms, gives:

$$-\log t = \log A - \frac{Q}{2.3RT}$$

or

$$\log t + \log A = \frac{Q}{2.3RT}$$

Recalling that A is a constant, and multiplying through by T gives:

$$T(\log t + C) = \frac{Q}{2.3R} \tag{3}$$

Equation (3) can be rewritten as:

$$\log t = \frac{Q}{2.3RT} - C \tag{4}$$

which is an equation of the form:

$$y = kx - C$$

where $y = \log t$, $x = 1/T$, and k is a constant $= Q/2.3R$. A plot of y versus x or $\log t$ versus $1/T$ produces a straight line, with $-C$ the intercept on the y axis. That is to say, when T in equation (4) becomes very large, $Q/2.3RT \to 0$, and $\log t = -C$. Since Q is only a constant at a constant value of stress, there is a family of straight lines, one for each stress, in a plot of $\log t$ against $1/T$; this is shown in Fig. 3.16.

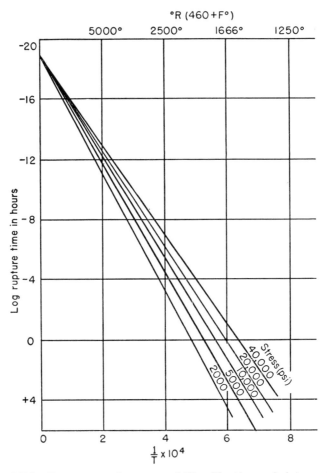

Fig. 3.16. Log rupture time versus 1/T. The time axis intercept is C for carbon molybdenum steel. [Reproduced with permission from J. Miller, "Aid for the High-Temperature Designer," *General Electric Review*, **55-6**, Nov., 1952.]

Refer again to equation (3), and recall that Q is a constant for a given value of stress, or $Q = f$ (σ), where σ is the stress. Thus, stress can be plotted against $T(C + \log t)$. It remains then to determine the value of C. This is done by running a series of high-temperature rupture tests at different stresses and temperatures for time intervals up to about one week. From these a family of curves similar to those shown in Fig. 3.16 is prepared. Extrapolating these to a value of $1/T = 0$ gives the value of $\log t = -C$. From these curves, values of t and T corresponding to a certain value of stress can be substituted in $T(C + \log t)$. A plot of stress versus $T(C + \log t)$ is then made. This process has been carried out for a number of different alloys and the results are shown in Fig. 3.17. From these, knowing the service temperatures, T, and the anticipated life of the equipment, t, the stress which can be tolerated is determined from the plot; e.g., consider an application in which S-590 alloy is to be used. Assume an operating temperature of 1500°F (1960°R) and a service life of 1 year (8760 hr). Substitute in $T(C + \log t)$:

$$1960(20 + 3.9) = 46.9 \times 10^3$$

From Fig. 3.17 this corresponds to a stress of about 10,000 psi. In other words, the maximum stress which can be withstood by S-590 alloy at 1500°F for a period of 1 year is 10,000 psi. (This does not include a safety factor and is an idealized stress figure.)

The method just described for determining stress-rupture data is said to be accurate within ±10 per cent. This is frequently better than obtained from extrapolations of stress-rupture curves. The chief advantage of the method is a saving in time. The time required for each determination is only about one week, as compared to the months or years needed for accumulation of data which is to be extrapolated. Not only does the procedure increase the effective capacity of testing equipment, but it makes possible prediction of stress-rupture behavior of new alloys very shortly after their development. Furthermore, designs based on extrapolations tend to be overly conservative. The new method therefore results in materials savings which are important where weight and critical alloys are concerned.

3.15. Mechanism of High Temperature Failures

Studies indicate that polycrystalline aggregates subjected to creep stresses at low temperatures tend to fail by mechanisms simi-

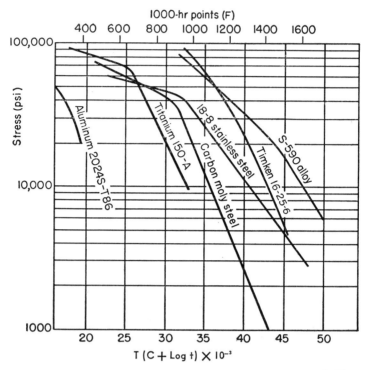

Fig. 3.17. Master rupture curves and values of C for several alloys.
Value of C in parameter $T(C + \log t)$ for several alloys: Aluminum
2024S-T86, 17; Titanium D9, 20; Low-carbon steel, 18; Carbon-
molybdenum steel 12Cr-3Mo-0.2V, 27; 18-8 Stainless, 19; 25-20
Stainless, 15; Timken 16-25-6, 20; S-590 Alloy, 20; S-816 Alloy, 18.
t, time in hours; T, temperature in °R; °R = °F + 460. [Repro-
duced from J. Miller, "Aid for the High-Temperature Designer,"
General Electric Review, **55-6**, Nov., 1952.]

lar to those encountered in short-time tensile tests at room temperature.   Slip occurs, as shown by the development of slip bands on
the polished surfaces of specimens, and final fracture is intracrystalline and is accompanied by necking.   Relatively high stresses
and high strain rates seem to promote this type of behavior.

At some higher temperature, depending upon the metal and
strain rate, polycrystalline aggregates exhibit much less tendency
to undergo slip.   The grains themselves seem to rotate and "swim"
in a "sea" consisting of the grain boundary network.   Final fracture occurs as a result of cracks opening at the grain boundaries.
The final fracture is intercrystalline rather than intracrystalline.

There is little necking and less elongation than at lower temperatures and higher strain rates. As the third stage of creep is approached the density of the specimen decreases, presumably as a result of growth of microfissures. The cracks which form undoubtedly behave as stress raisers and act in constraint of flow, producing a relatively brittle fracture. When fluctuating stresses are encountered, a fatigue crack may grow from one of the microfissures and hasten final fracture.

The tendency toward brittle, intercrystalline failures at higher temperatures and lower strain rates has given rise to the use of the term **equicohesive temperature.** Above the equicohesive temperature at a given strain rate, the failure is brittle and occurs at the grain boundaries, i.e., it is intercrystalline. Below the equicohesive temperature at a given strain rate, the failure is ductile, is accompanied by appreciable slip, and occurs across the grains, i.e., it is intracrystalline or transcrystalline. There are extreme values of temperature above which fracture is always of the brittle, intercrystalline type, or below which fracture is always of the ductile, intracrystalline type (excluding very high velocities of loading). The equicohesive temperature, like the recrystallization temperature, is not just one temperature which depends upon the metal. It is a temperature which is influenced by the strain rate and perhaps by other factors as yet unknown.

3.16. Factors Affecting Resistance to Long-time High-temperature Failure

Some of the factors which affect resistance to long-time high-temperature failure have been investigated (see References 3.14 and 3.15). Probably the most important effect on high-temperature behavior is exerted by the composition of the alloy involved. In a general way, the higher the melting range of the metal, the better the high-temperature properties. The melting range should not, however, be taken as a specific indication of high-temperature, long-time strength. For instance, two alloys of similar composition and melting temperatures can behave differently at high temperature for reasons to be given later. Nevertheless, the *general tendency* for improved high-temperature strength with increasing melting temperatures has been observed, and is shown in Table 3.2.

Table 3.2. Temperatures Above Which Creep Becomes of Practical Concern for Some Common Metals

Alloys	"Creep Temperature"	Approximate Melting Range
Lead, tin, zinc	Room temperature	350– 800°F (175– 420°C)
Aluminum	200–400°F (95–205°C)	900–1200°F (480– 650°C)
Brass and Bronze	300–400°F (150–205°C)	1500–1950°F (815–1065°C)
Carbon steels	650°F (345°C)	2400–2750°F (1315–1510°C)

Insofar as steels are concerned, the austenitic steels in which crystal structure is face-centered cubic perform much better at high temperatures than the body-centered cubic ferritic steels. This is caused by better creep and rupture strength of most austenitic alloys, and because of poorer scaling and oxidation resistance of most ferritic alloys. The effects of composition are discussed in greater detail in References 3.14 and 3.15. Fig. 3.18 compares the creep strength of some ferrous and nonferrous alloys.

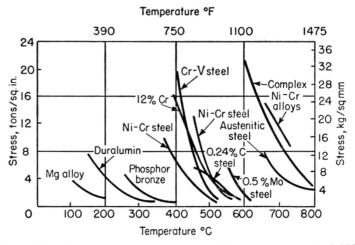

Fig. 3.18. Stress-temperature curves for 0.1 per cent creep in 1,000 hours. [After Tapsell; reproduced with permission from A. H. Sully, *Metallic Creep and Creep-Resistant Alloys*, Butterworth's Scientific Publications, 1949.]

Grain size. In view of the fact that at relatively high temperatures and low rates of strain, creep fracture occurs at the grain boundaries, it might be predicted that coarse-grained microstructures should perform better under conditions favorable to intercrystalline rupture. It might also be expected that a fine-grained composition should perform better at relatively low temperatures and high rates of strain. This behavior has been proved by test and experience. Thus, at very high temperatures, such as produced in jet engines, castings are frequently preferred over wrought parts. This is partly because grain size can be kept under better control in castings through the use of very slow solidification rates. (Castings are also preferred because of the difficulty of forging and machining many high-temperature alloys.)

Strain hardening. It has been found that for any specific material and temperature, the resistance to creep improves with increasing amounts of cold work (see Chapter 5), up to a certain point. Beyond this amount of cold work, creep resistance is impaired. The existence of optimum degrees of cold work for different temperatures is shown for an austenitic steel in Fig. 3.19. Perhaps this behavior is connected not only with the amount of cold work but also with the tendency for recrystallization. Recrystallization is accompanied by softening, which in turn should impair creep strength. Recrystallization (and presumably impairment of creep strength) can occur after smaller amounts of cold work at higher temperatures. This is indicated from the decrease in the optimum amount of cold work at higher creep temperatures, as shown in the curves of Fig. 3.19. It should be kept in mind that cold work tends to reduce the grain size of metals. Depending upon the amount of cold work, the grain size *after* recrystallization may be larger or smaller than the grain size prior to cold work or recrystallization. If the temperature of creep is high enough to produce recrystallization, grain size may be changed significantly. Such a change may be accompanied by variation of creep resistance, depending upon whether intercrystalline or transcrystalline failure is going to occur.

Heat treatment also exerts a considerable effect on creep resistance, as shown for a low-alloy steel in Fig. 3.20. Other alloys may show similar variations in behavior dependent upon heat treatment, but the complexities of the problem place it beyond the scope of this book.

3.17. Thermal Shock

The problem of *thermal shock* is receiving increasing attention. Thermal shock occurs as a result of rapid changes in temperature

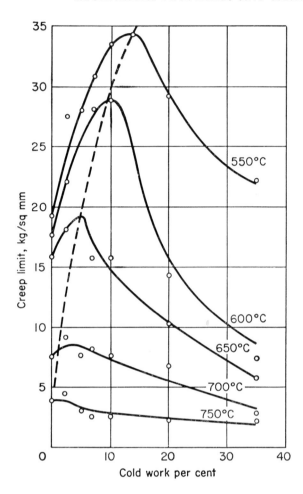

Fig. 3.19. Effect of cold work on creep at various temperatures.
These data are for steel containing 0.1 per cent carbon, 18 per cent
chromium, 9 per cent nickel, 1 per cent tungsten, and 0.7 per cent
titanium. [Reproduced by permission from H. R. Zschokke and
K. H. Niehus, *Journal, ISI,* **156,** 1947, Iron and Steel Institute.]

which cause changes in dimensions of metal parts. If all the portions of the part could change temperature simultaneously there
would be no difficulty. Unfortunately thin sections and corner
areas tend to assume the temperature of the surroundings faster
than heavy sections or flat areas. Metal near the surface heats and
cools faster than interior portions. Therefore, fluctuating stresses

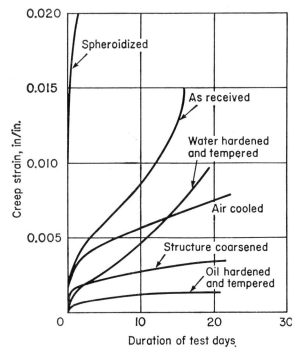

Fig. 3.20.   Effect of heat treatment on creep.   Creep curves for a steel containing 0.11 per cent carbon and 0.52 per cent molybdenum at a stress of 18,000 psi and temperature of 1022°F.   [Reproduced with permission from H. J. Tapsell and R. W. Ridley, *Proc. IME*, **153**, 1945, Institute of Mechanical Engineers.]

occur as a result of repeated nonuniform temperature changes. These stresses can produce a fatigue-like failure sometimes called *thermal fatigue.*   The tendency for thermal fatigue to occur depends upon the magnitude and frequency of the thermal changes, the shape of the part, and a number of measurable physical properties of the material from which the part is made.   Among these properties are thermal conductivity and tensile or fatigue strength, all of which should be high for good performance.   It is also desirable that thermal expansion and modulus of elasticity be low. Thermal expansion and modulus of elasticity do not vary radically with changes in composition and heat treatment of an alloy series. Thermal conductivity is unaffected by heat treatment and minor changes in composition.   Temperature fluctuations at a rate of almost 600°F (350°C) per second have been reported in aircraft turbines as a result of deceleration.   Thermal shock is frequently more of a problem in nonmetals than metals, because of poorer thermal conductivity and ductility of the nonmetals.

FAILURE BY FATIGUE

3.18.   Definition and Character of Fatigue Failure

Fatigue failure occurs as a brittle fracture produced by cyclic stresses which are usually below the elastic limit.   Since no appreciable deformation occurs prior to final fracture, there is no obvious warning that failure is impending.   The insidious nature of fatigue failure is emphasized by the low stresses involved, stresses which are much lower than the static stresses necessary to produce failure. Fatigue stresses may be axial, flexural, torsional, or a combination of these.   In some cases, they consist of a complete stress reversal between two equal and opposite stress limits, as shown in Fig. 3.21(a).   In other instances, they consist of an equal and opposite deviation on either side of a static stress.   Three possibilities are shown in Fig. 3.21(b).

There are numerous examples of machinery in which fatigue stresses are produced.   For instance, stress reversals are encoun-

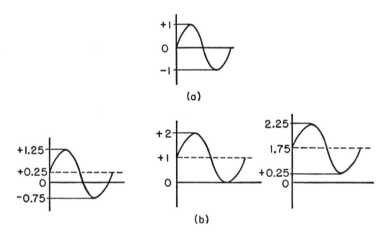

Fig. 3.21.   Nature of fatigue stress fluctuations.   Stress is plotted along vertical axis and time along horizontal axis of each drawing. (a) Fluctuations without static stresses vary from zero to some positive value equal to some negative value.   (b) Fluctuations may be superimposed on static stresses.   The dotted line indicates the magnitude of the static stress.

tered in the shaft of a power drive during alternate acceleration and deceleration. Axles also undergo a reversal of stress as they rotate. Operating machinery vibrates at critical speeds such that vibrations may produce fatigue stresses and failure.

Progress of fatigue failure. Fatigue failure starts as a slowly-spreading crack at a region of high stress concentration. The root of the crack is a region of extreme stress intensification and the crack is self-propagating. If the load on the member remains constant, the stress increases as the crack becomes larger, because there is less sound metal to carry the load. While the crack is growing, the adjoining faces rub against each other, producing smooth, polished surfaces. Eventually the remaining sound metal can no longer sustain the load and the member breaks. A brittle, cleavage-type fracture of granular appearance finally results because of the restraining action of the crack. Thus fatigue failures usually can be recognized from the two distinct zones of fracture present: the smooth polished area of the original crack, and a granular area of final fracture. The degree of polish depends upon the number of cycles of loading after formation of the crack and before complete failure occurs. The granularity of the region of final fracture depends upon the grain size of the metal. Fine-grained metals tend to be silky; coarse-grained metals are truly granular with large facets of individual grains visible in some cases.

Definitions. Universal agreement has not been reached on the use of the terms *fatigue strength, fatigue limit, endurance strength* and *endurance limit*. In this text fatigue strength and endurance strength are considered to be synonymous and mean *the stress, in pounds per square inch, at which failure is likely to occur after a definite number of cycles of stress.* On the other hand, endurance limit and fatigue limit are interpreted as the *maximum stress which can be applied repeatedly without causing failure.* In speaking of fatigue or endurance strength, the number of cycles of loading which produced failure must be specified. Thus, in Fig. 3.22(a), the fatigue strength is S_1, at N_1 cycles of loading. The *endurance limit* or *fatigue limit* is the limiting and maximum stress, S_m, which can be applied repeatedly (assumed as an infinite number of cycles N_∞) without producing failure, as shown in Fig. 3.22(b). Since most nonferrous metals do not have a limiting value of maximum stress,[2] the terms *fatigue* or *endurance strength* are usually used

[2] At least for cycles of loading below 100,000,000 cycles.

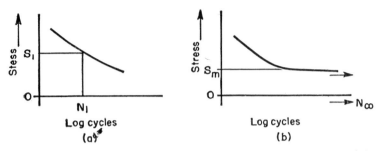

Fig. 3.22. Fatigue curves: stress versus log cycles to fracture. (a) Typical curve for nonferrous alloys. (b) Typical curve for ferrous alloys.

to describe their resistance to fatigue failure. The resistance of ferrous metals to fatigue is usually expressed in terms of fatigue or endurance limit. The usage described above is commonly, though not universally, accepted.

3.19. Fatigue Testing

The most common variety of fatigue test is the one in which a round specimen is subjected to completely reversed bending loads. Unless otherwise stated, it can be assumed that fatigue strength or endurance limit figures represent the result of such a test.

A typical specimen intended for use in an R. R. Moore type of rotating-beam fatigue-testing machine is shown in Fig. 3.23. About twenty polished specimens of the material are needed to determine each point on the curve. Each of the twenty specimens is placed in the machine and tested to fracture at a given load. Specimens from other groups are tested at different loads, corresponding to the points on the curve. The equipment is so designed that the specimen is loaded as a beam subjected to pure bending in its center section, as shown in Fig. 3.23(c). When the motor is turned on the beam rotates, alternately placing the outer fibers first in tension and then in compression. For each particular test, the machine runs until failure occurs, at which time the power is automatically shut off. A counter indicates the number of revolutions, and hence the number of cycles of loading. The results for each stress level are analyzed statistically to determine a central tendency or representative behavior. Typical data for some fatigue tests are shown in Fig. 3.24. Stress is plotted on a linear scale; the

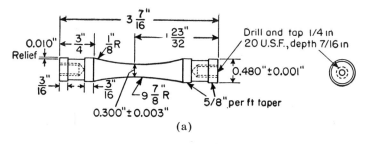

(a)

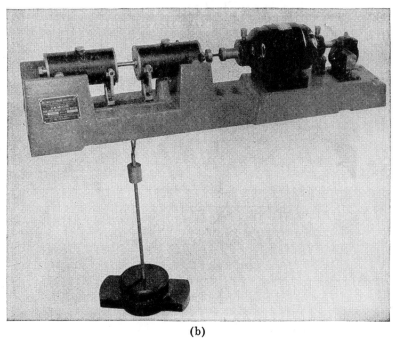

(b)

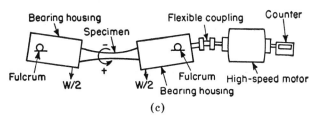

(c)

Fig. 3.23. Fatigue testing. (a) Specimen for R. R. Moore fatigue-testing apparatus. (b) The R. R. Moore fatigue-testing machine. (c) Schematic drawing of the R. R. Moore fatigue-testing machine, showing essential parts. [Photograph courtesy of Baldwin-Lima-Hamilton Corp., Philadelphia, Pa.]

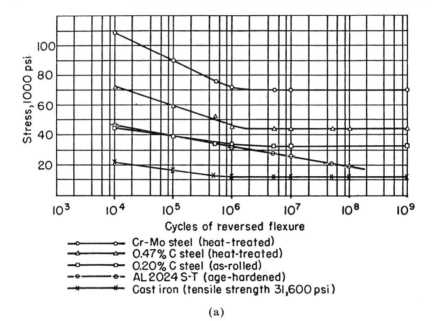

(a)

Number of Cycles of Stress	Endurance Limit, 1000 psi				
	Cr-Mo Steel (heat treated)	Carbon Steel (0.47% C) (heat treated)	Carbon Steel (0.20% C) (as rolled)	Aluminum Alloy 2024 S-T (age hardened)	Cast Iron, (tensile strength 31,600 psi)
10,000	108	71	45	45	21
100,000	90	58	39.5	39.5	16
500,000	76	52	34	34	13
1,000,000	73	44	33	31.5	12
5,000,000	70	44	32	27.5	12
10,000,000	70	44	32	25.5	12
50,000,000	..	44	..	21.5	12
100,000,000	..	44	..	20	12
Indefinitely large (a) .	70	44	32	..	12
(a) S-N curve horizontal					

(b)

Fig. 3.24. Fatigue curves: semi-log plot. (a) Curves for five common alloys. (b) Data from which curves in (a) were plotted. [Data from American Society for Metals, *Metals Handbook*, 1948.]

corresponding cycles to fracture on a logarithmic scale. Plots of this types are called *S-N* diagrams and show the stress versus the cycles required to cause fracture. The effect of plotting N on a logarithmic scale is to amplify the high-stress portion of the curve where a small change in stress produces a large change in cycles to fracture. This is useful in estimating behavior when members are subjected to a small number of overload cycles. At the same time, the use of a semi-log plot compresses the far reaches of the N-scale to a reasonable length.

In addition to flexural loading, machines are available for torsional and axial fatigue loading. Special tests in which the load is only partially reversed (see Fig. 3.21) are also conducted. The most generally used test, as has been pointed out, is one in which the stress reversal is complete and is produced by bending loads. Some new methods are being developed which give promise of predicting fatigue behavior based upon changes in magnetic characteristics, damping capacity, thermal expansion, natural frequency, and similar properties.

3.20. Effect of Variables on Fatigue Behavior of a Metal

A number of variables have been investigated for their effect on the fatigue resistance of metals. It would perhaps be expected that the **speed of testing** has an effect on fatigue behavior. An investigation of this factor at room temperature shows that with increasing speeds of loading there is a slight increase in fatigue limit, but the effect is almost negligible up to 10,000 cycles per minute. Even at 30,000 cycles per minute the fatigue limit increases less than 10 per cent over the value obtained at 1500 cycles per minute.

Temperature. Over the range of atmospheric temperatures encountered on the earth's surface, fatigue resistance increases slightly at low temperatures. For most structural metals fatigue resistance is impaired only after temperatures rise well in excess of atmospheric temperatures. The effects of high temperature are in some cases serious—for instance, in gas and steam turbines. When temperatures are as high as those required for turbine operation, the speed of loading should also receive attention.

Size effect. As the size of the member undergoing fatigue loading increases, there is a decrease in fatigue resistance. This has been confirmed by laboratory tests on specimens of different sizes. The size effect has also been confirmed by comparison of results obtained on relatively small laboratory specimens with service behavior of large machine components. On the average, small specimens (up to diameters of about 1 in.) show greater fatigue strength than large ones. The entire question of whether fatigue failure will occur at a certain number of cycles of stress requires use of the concepts of statistics. The size effect calls for the use of an appropriate safety factor when test results are applied to actual design problems.

Overstressing. When a metal is subjected to a sufficient number of cycles of stress above its original endurance limit the metal may be permanently damaged. If the damaged metal is then stressed at its endurance limit, fracture occurs prematurely. In Fig. 3.25 the *S-N* curve and the original endurance limit are indicated by the solid line. Three groups of virgin specimens are stressed for 50,000 cycles at stresses of 44,000, 40,000, and 37,500 psi. The groups of specimens are then subjected to cyclic stresses corresponding to the endurance limit (35,000 psi). Specimens from group number 1 fracture prematurely. On the other hand, specimens from groups 2 and 3 have not been sufficiently overstressed to cause damage and can be stressed indefinitely at 35,000 psi without fracture. The process is repeated with three more groups of specimens of virgin metal which are stressed for 200,000 cycles at three different stresses. These groups of specimens are then stressed at 35,000 psi. Groups 4 and 5 prematurely fracture, but specimens of group 6 do not. Thus, groups 4 and 5 were damaged by the overstressing. After considerable repetition of this sequence of testing, a damage line can be established, which separates the groups of specimens which were damaged from those which were not affected by stressing above the original endurance

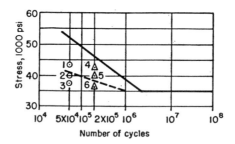

Fig. 3.25. Determination of damage line. The fatigue curve for virgin metal is shown by a solid line. The damage line is a broken line. Specimens stressed for a number of cycles so as to carry them above the damage line subsequently fracture prematurely if stressed at lower stresses. See text for detailed explanation.

limit. The area between the damage line and the original *S-N* curve is known as the *damage area*. Stress-cycle combinations which carry specimens into the damage area are likely to fail prematurely at stresses corresponding to the original endurance limit. Stress-cycle combinations below the damage area do not impair the fatigue resistance of the material.

The effects of overstressing are difficult to apply quantitatively in design problems. It should be kept in mind that if the stress is high enough a relatively small number of cycles of overloading produce damage which can cause premature failure. The general effect of overstressing can be visualized as a displacement of the original *S-N* diagram downward and to the left with respect to the original axes.

Understressing. The effects of understressing are essentially the opposite of overstressing. Understressing consists of loading a specimen for a large number of cycles below the endurance limit. The specimen can then be loaded at stresses as much as 25 per cent greater than the original endurance limit without causing fracture. The effects of understressing can be visualized as a displacement of the original *S-N* curve upward and to the right with respect to the original axes.

Effects of partial stress reversal. When the stress reversal is not complete, the maximum stress which can be withstood for any definite number of cycles increases with respect to the maximum stress for complete reversal. The amount of increase can be expressed by the general equation:

$$f_{\text{Max}} = f \frac{c+1}{c-r}$$

where f_{Max} is maximum cyclic stress for partial stress reversal, f is fatigue strength for complete stress reversal, and r is ratio of minimum (numerical) stress to maximum (numerical) stress. (The sign of r is negative when the stress reversal carries through zero. It is positive when both maximum and minimum stresses are in the same sense.) The term c is a constant which depends upon the metal and the kind of stress involved (i.e., shear, axial, or flexural).

For steel subjected to axial or flexural loading when r varies from -1.0 to $+0.25$, $c = 2.0$. As the degree of stress reversal diminishes, the value of f_{Max} becomes greater. When f_{Max} reaches the yield strength, the results given by the equation lose significance.

The effect of partial stress reversal can be considered equivalent to the effects of complete stress reversal combined with a static load (see Fig. 3.21). In actual practice this is analogous to an unchanging dead load upon which are superimposed fluctuating stresses caused by vibrations and variations in payload.

3.21. Sources of Fatigue Failure

Fatigue failure is believed to originate in the most highly stressed region in a structural member.   It should be recalled that under torsional or flexural loading, the maximum stresses in a beam or shaft occur in the outer fibers.   Fiber stress diminishes as the distance increases from the outer fibers.   Under flexural and torsional loads failure is likely to start at the surface of the member.   Stress raisers near the surface are likely to intensify this tendency.   If axial loading is encountered, the stress distribution is uniform over the cross-section of the member, and failure can be initiated just as easily by a defect far below the surface as by one near the surface. There are two major sources of stress raisers: (1) stress raisers resulting from design practices, and (2) stress raisers associated with processing techniques.

Stress raisers resulting from design practices.   The effects of notches and similar changes in shape have been mentioned before in connection with impact and static loading.   Abrupt changes in the shape of metal parts cause a concentration of stresses; the more sudden the change the greater the stress intensification.   The effect of abrupt changes in shape are shown in Fig. 3.26, which represents the fatigue behavior of shafts having differently shaped annular grooves.   An interesting application of tests of a series of samples like this is to use the results to calculate stress concentration factors.   For instance, in Fig. 3.26 the endurance limit of GI is about 49,000 psi and for AB it is about 19,000.   Assuming no stress concentration in GI, the stress concentration in AB is 49,000/19,000, or 2.58.   Keyways, splines, threads, shoulders, and holes are common examples of stress raisers which require special attention in the design of machine parts.   Some theoretical stress concentration factors are shown in Fig. 3.27.

Stress raisers resulting from processing techniques.   Each different method of fabrication produces its own peculiar defects. **Castings** may contain surface or subsurface discontinuities pro-

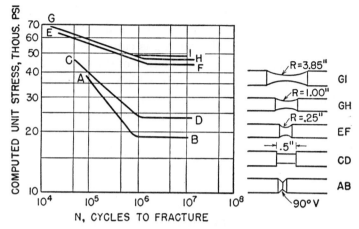

Fig. 3.26. The effect of abrupt changes in shape on fatigue strength. All samples in the illustration above were made from 0.49 per cent carbon steel, water quenched and tempered at 1200°F. The original diameter of all the bars was 0.40 inch, and the reduced diameter in all cases was 0.275 inch. The letters at the right of the sketches of the samples indicate the corresponding curves on the plot. [After D. Landau, *Fatigue of Metals*. The Nitralloy Corp., 1942.]

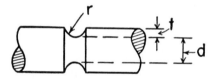

Fig. 3.27. Stress concentration. Theoretical stress-concentration factors are shown in the accompanying table which is based on mathematical analysis by Neuber. (After H. Neuber, Kerbspannungslehre. Berlin: Springer-Verlag, 1937.)

t/r	r/d									
	0.02	0.04	0.06	0.08	0.10	0.15	0.20	0.30	0.40	0.50
0.25	1.95	1.90	1.81	1.75	1.68	1.56	1.48	1.36	1.30	1.25
0.50	2.27	2.13	2.01	1.89	1.79	1.61	1.51	1.37	1.31	1.25
1.00	2.65	2.38	2.16	2.00	1.85	1.64	1.53	1.38	1.31	1.25
2.00	2.95	2.58	2.30	2.06	1.90	1.66	1.54	1.39	1.31	1.25
5.00	3.45	2.64	2.38	2.10	1.94	1.68	1.55	1.39	1.31	1.25

duced by entrapped oxidized metal, slag, and sand. Since these substances have no capacity to carry tensile loads they are stress raisers. When a molten metal solidifies and cools it undergoes shrinkage; this shrinkage may manifest itself in the form of voids and cracks. The solubility of gases in metal decreases sharply over the freezing range. If the liberated gas cannot escape, the casting may contain gas voids. In the production of die castings hot molten metal is forced into the mold at fairly high speed under pressure. Some of the air in the mold is usually trapped in the casting, and these voids are also stress raisers. **Weldments** exhibit defects which are similar to those found in castings. The metal deposited in the process of welding or metal melted during welding can be considered to have some of the properties of a small casting. Thus, the welds may contain oxides, slag (from the coating on the welding rod or flux used), shrinkage voids and gas voids. Welds may also suffer from undercutting and lack of penetration, both of which produce stress raisers. These are indicated in Fig. 3.28(a). **Mechanical working** can also produce stress raisers. Although mechanical working methods seem to be susceptible to better control, fatigue failure is still a consideration. Excessive cold working, caused by bending too sharply, produces cracks. Hot working such as rolling may produce surface defects such as seams, illustrated in Fig. 3.28(b). Excessive temperatures for hot working may cause the grain boundaries near the surface to oxidize. Temperatures which are too low for the severity of hot work produce cracks, often on the metal surface. Heating a metal too quickly for forging may result in the center remaining cold after the surface has gotten up to temperature. Forging in this condition causes internal cracks. **Machined parts** suffer mainly from rough surface finish. The effect of the fineness of surface is shown in Fig. 3.29. This illustration shows that the endurance limit suffers when the surface finish is poor. It also illustrates the effect of corrosive media on fatigue properties, a type of failure called *corrosion fatigue*, discussed later in connection with corrosion. **Electroplated and electroformed** parts which are produced by electrolytic deposition of a metal are not commonly used in applications where fatigue is a problem. Electrodeposited metal tends to contain microcracks, which run at right angles to the electroplated or electroformed surface. In electroplated parts one possible source of trouble is poor bonding between the plated metal and the basis metal. This is of concern in applications where plating is used to improve fatigue strength. **Powder metallurgy** is a process for manufacturing small metal parts by compressing metal powders, and later heating

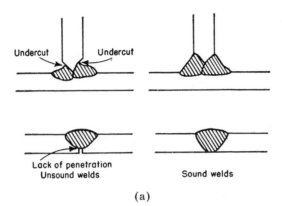

Undercut   Undercut

Lack of penetration
Unsound welds   Sound welds

(a)

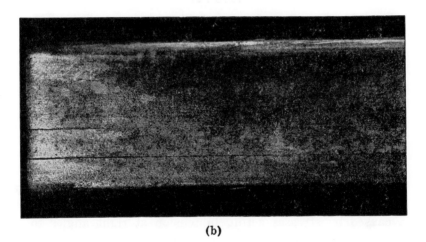

(b)

Fig. 3.28. Sources of fatigue failure. (a) Stress raisers in im-
properly made welds. (b) Seam in a hot-rolled steel billet. The
billet has a square cross-section, 2½ in. on a side, and has rounded
corners. After hot-rolling, the mill scale was removed to reveal
the actual metal surface and thereby show the defect. [Photograph
courtesy of Republic Steel Corp., Cleveland, Ohio.]

the pressed shape. During the compression cycle it is almost impossible to remove all the air entrapped between the fine particles
of metal. Some air is expelled during the heating, or *sintering*,
cycle, but enough voids remain to produce low fatigue resistance
in powder metal parts. Most of the remaining voids can be eliminated by coining or pressing a second time. However, this step increases the cost of the parts and should be avoided when possible.
Voids are also eliminated by impregnation with a low-melting alloy.

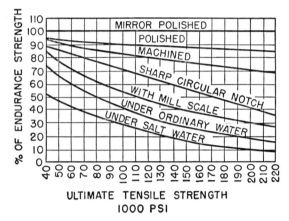

Fig. 3.29. The effect of surface finish on endurance limit. The endurance strength of a mirror polished bar is taken as 100 per cent and the endurance limits of other bars with different surface finishes are taken as percentages of the endurance limit of the mirror-finished bar. Note that the higher the ultimate strength of the material, the more harmful the effect of surface imperfections as regards fatigue strength. Ordinary water and salt water have damaged the surfaces of the bars used in two of the tests, so that fatigue failure is accelerated. This type of failure is known as *corrosion fatigue*. [After D. Landau, *Fatigue of Metals*. The Nitralloy Corp., 1942.]

Residual stresses should not be overlooked as sources of fatigue failure. The rupture associated with fatigue failure is a brittle one, caused by stresses acting in tension at right angles to the cleavage plane. Therefore, residual tensile surface stresses are undesirable, because they effectively decrease the stresses which produce failure. Residual tensile surface stresses may exist in castings as a result of restraint of dimensional change during cooling. They are similarly found in some pieces rapidly cooled from hot-working temperatures. Residual tensile surface stresses are also found in welded structures when thermal contraction is prevented by the rigidity of the structure. They are encountered in electro-deposited metals, perhaps as a result of evolution of hydrogen during formation of the deposit. Residual stresses are too complicated to permit a simplified statement as to their origins.

The **size effect** which is mentioned in Section 3.20 can be better understood in terms of defects and stress raisers. Assuming a random distribution of internal defects in the metal from which specimens or parts are made, it is likely that a large part will con-

tain a defect strategically located that will produce the stress intensification necessary to initiate failure. In parts made of perfect
metal, without internal stress raisers, failure is initiated at some
relatively deep surface scratch or finishing imperfection. The
larger the part, the greater the surface, and the greater is the probability that somewhere in the surface there will be the necessary
flaw. Thus, the greater the size of the member, the lower is its
fatigue strength. The determination of S-N curves emphasizes the
statistical spread of results. The larger the specimens, the more
generally they approach the low side of the S-N curve (which is
really a band of expected values). The smaller the specimen, the
greater is the spread of values and the higher the average results.
This also gives support to the explanation of size effect.

3.22. Improvement of Resistance to Fatigue Failure

There are a number of methods available for improving resistance to fatigue failure. Most of these are obvious from the nature
of the sources of fatigue failure; a few are not so obvious.

Improvement of design sometimes involves simply reducing the
severity of section changes; this can be achieved by using fillets and
more rounded contours. Profile keyways can be replaced by sled-
runner keyways in which there is a gradual approach from the
shaft diameter to the depth of the keyway channel. Rounded-bot-
tom keyways have proved very successful in reducing fatigue failures. Why liberal fillets are not more widely used is difficult to
understand, considering all the publicity given to their desirability.
Perhaps it is because it is easier for draftsmen, who are sometimes
responsible for design details, to draw a right angle cut than one
with a radius. Perhaps it is a matter of machine-shop custom.
For whatever reason, it is not difficult to find deep, sharp, right-
angle cuts in machine parts.

Another less obvious way to reduce stress concentration at
changes of section is to judiciously remove metal from parts, rather
than to add it, as in the case of fillets. Figure 3.30 shows some examples of improvement in stress distribution by careful redesign
and removal of metal.

Improvement and modification of processing methods offer possibilities for increasing resistance to fatigue failure. It may be
necessary to change from one method of manufacture to an entirely

different method, such as from a casting or weldment to a forged and machined part. In other cases, improvements in a given method may be sufficient, such as a modification of a mold design to eliminate shrinkage voids or stresses, or perhaps 100 per cent

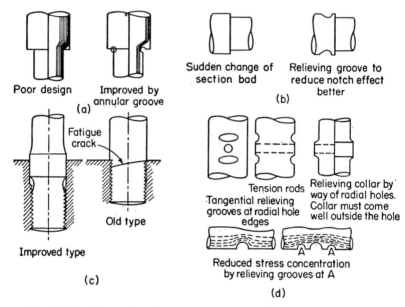

Fig. 3.30. Examples of stress mitigation by removal of metal. [Reproduced by permission from R. A. MacGregor, W. S. Burns, and F. Bacon, "Relation of Fatigue to Modern Engine Design," *Trans.*, **51**, 1935, Nort East Coast Institution of Engineers and Shipbuilders.]

x-ray inspection of castings or weldments for defects. When a machining operation is involved, specifications calling for a better surface finish may produce the desired results as shown by Fig. 3.29. Tool marks or scratches act as small notches and often initiate fatigue failures. As far as screw threads are concerned, rolled threads are generally conceded to have better fatigue properties than machined or ground threads.

Increasing the tensile strength of metal parts by through hardening or by use of a different metal is frequently used to improve fatigue behavior. This is successful because fatigue fractures are brittle fractures produced by tensile stresses acting at right angles to the cleavage planes of metal crystals. Good correlations exist between tensile strength and fatigue strength or endurance limit, as shown by Fig. 3.31.   An increase in tensile strength of a particular metal can be achieved by heat treatment in the case of steel, some cast irons, and a few nonferrous metals, notably the aluminum alloys.   Tensile strength can also be improved by cold working, but applications of this are more limited than of heat-treating methods.   It should be pointed out that some heat-treated alloy steels are particularly notch sensitive.   The use of high-strength (i.e., over 200,000 psi tensile strength) hardened alloy steel for threaded or severely notched parts may actually impair fatigue resistance of the part.

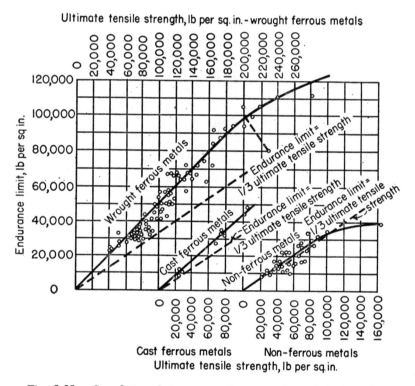

Fig. 3.31. **Correlation between tensile strength and fatigue behavior.** (Reproduced by permission from H. F. and M. B. Moore, *Textbook of Materials of Engineering*, 8th Ed., McGraw-Hill Book Co., Inc., 1953.)

The value of selecting a metal of higher tensile strength is obvious from consideration of Fig. 3.31.   As in the use of hardened alloy steel, notch sensitivity of the metals should be considered.   The ratio of endurance limit to tensile strength varies between one-third and one-half and is known as the **endurance ratio.**

Surface hardening is used to improve the fatigue behavior of steel and ferrous alloys. Surface hardening of steel can be accomplished by nitriding (putting nitrogen in the surface of the steel), by carburizing (putting carbon in the surface, combined with heat treating), and by flame hardening or by special forms of induction hardening (heat treatments in which the surface only is heated and quenched). Fig. 3.32 shows the effects of nitriding on fatigue strength.

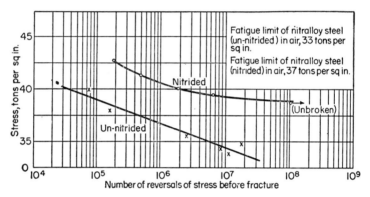

Fig. 3.32.   Effect of nitriding on fatigue strength.   [Reproduced by permission from D. Landau, *Fatigue of Metals*, The Nitralloy Corp., 1942.]

The surface of metal can also be hardened by cold working. Rolling of threads and shot peening are examples of this, although in these operations cold work alone is probably not entirely responsible for raising fatigue strength or endurance limit. The effect of cold rolling the surface layers is shown in Fig. 3.33.

Introduction of residual compressive stresses in the surface produces an increase in fatigue strength and endurance limit. This means is effective because of the fact that the stresses which produce fatigue fracture are surface tensile stresses, in most instances. If a residual surface compressive stress is present, this stress must be overcome by the action of the load before a tensile stress can be produced. Nitriding, carburizing, and some kinds of cold work are believed to achieve some of their effectiveness because they introduce residual compressive stresses in addition to strengthening the surface fibers of metal. Residual compressive stresses in the surface can also be produced by heat treating. Some hardened steel parts when quenched from the tempering temperature develop stresses of this kind. Simple metal shapes such as bars, cubes, and

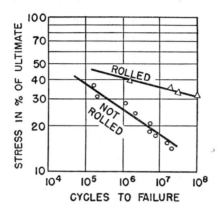

Fig. 3.33 Effect of cold work on fatigue strength. Cold rolling increases fatigue strength. Fatigue strength has been expressed in terms of percentage of ultimate strength. Note also that the above is a log-log plot. [Reproduced by permission from O. J. Horger and J. L. Maulbetsch, "Increasing the Fatigue Strength of Press-Fitted Axle Assemblies by Surface Rolling," *Trans. ASME*, **58**, 1936, American Society for Mechanical Engineers.]

spheres, if quenched from moderate temperatures, tend to develop residual compressive stresses near their surfaces.

3.23. Early Detection of Fatigue Failures

Even if the best material, design, and fabrication practice has been adopted for the manufacture of a certain part, there is still the possibility that fatigue failure may occur. From this standpoint, the early detection of fatigue is important. Visual inspection with a magnifying glass is the simplest method for detecting the start of fatigue. It is slow and tedious, and unless the crack is at the surface (as is usually the case) it is fruitless. Alternatively, the part may be coated with oil, the excess wiped off, and the part then struck a sharp blow. Oil oozes out of any surface cracks, and if whiting is now dusted over the part it adheres to the oil coming from the crack, thus making visual examination easier. Examination under fluorescent light with fluorescent oils is an improvement over the oil and whiting method. Magnetic detection of cracks is faster and more thorough than visual detection, but finds application only in metals and alloys which can be magnetized. Cracks are shown up by a leak in the magnetic field at the extremities of the crack. The leak attracts fine magnetic particles which have been dusted over the part. In order to be discovered, however, a crack must not be too far below the surface. The changes in the magnetic field caused by cracks can also be detected by electronic amplification methods. A third means of crack detection, which has the advantage of applicability to both magnetic and nonmagnetic parts, is the supersonic testing device. By this mechanism, a high-frequency sound beam which is shot into the part is reflected from the first surface it strikes. In the case of a sound piece of metal this is the far surface. In an unsound part any internal surface, caused by a discontinuity or crack, reflects the beam. The sound beam is converted to visual energy for greater convenience of observation. The supersonic method also shows up defects which are further below the surface than those discernible by magnetic means. However, the supersonic method is fairly slow and requires skillful manipulation so that trivialities are not mistaken for *bona fide* defects. If possible, it is desirable to test some finished parts before putting them into service in order to determine their fatigue characteristics. This is because the data upon which design is based are obtained by testing idealized samples whose selection, finish, smooth contours, and means of fabrication are a major consideration in their manufacture, whereas the actual part may not be as carefully made under conditions of actual production.

FAILURE BY CORROSION

3.24. Definition and Scope

Corrosion is a gradual chemical or electrochemical attack on a metal by its surroundings, such that the metal is converted into an oxide, salt, or some other compound. When the metal is changed to a compound it loses its strength, ductility, and the other desirable mechanical properties which metals possess. Corrosive attack manifests itself in many forms, frequently occurring in combination with other mechanisms of failure such as corrosion-fatigue, erosion-corrosion, and stress-corrosion. It may be brought about by an almost unlimited variety of corrosive media such as air, industrial atmospheres, soil, acids, bases, and salt solutions. It may also occur at elevated temperatures in media which are inert when near or below room temperature. This chapter points out the common features of the various kinds of corrosion, describes the basic mechanisms of corrosion, and explains some examples of specific types of corrosion. Methods for preventing and testing for corrosion are also presented.

3.25. Typical Chemical Reactions Involved in Corrosion

It is convenient to represent many common varieties of corrosion by one or more of five general chemical reactions. These reactions are:

1. Combinations of metals with nonmetals, in which water does not take part, such as:

$$Me + Nm \rightarrow MeNm \qquad (3.25\text{-}1)$$

where Me is a metallic element and Nm is a nonmetallic substance. A specific example of corrosion in which this kind of reaction occurs is the high-temperature oxidation of iron or steel in dry air:

$$2Fe + O_2 \rightarrow 2FeO \qquad (3.25\text{-}2)$$

It is also possible to form Fe_2O_3 as the corrosion product.

2. Combinations of metals with oxygen, in which water is necessary for the reaction to proceed, such as:

$$Me + \tfrac{1}{2}O_2 + H_2O \rightarrow Me(OH)_2 \qquad (3.25\text{-}3)$$

where Me is a suitable metallic element. Probably the most important specific example of this reaction is the rusting of steel under ordinary atmospheric conditions:

$$Fe + \tfrac{1}{2}O_2 + H_2O \rightarrow Fe(OH)_2 \qquad (3.25\text{-}4)$$

In dry air at room temperature iron and steel will not rust. In moist air the iron hydroxide which is formed [it may be $Fe(OH)_2$ or $Fe(OH)_3$] frequently decomposes to the appropriate oxide (FeO or Fe_2O_3), accompanied by loss of moisture:

$$Fe(OH)_2 \rightarrow FeO + H_2O \qquad (3.25\text{-}5)$$

so that the net reaction is:

$$Fe + \tfrac{1}{2}O_2 \xrightarrow{\text{H}_2\text{O}} FeO \qquad (3.25\text{-}6)$$

3. Displacement of hydrogen from acids or acid solutions:

$$Me + H_2SO_4 \rightarrow MeSO_4 + H_2 \qquad (3.25\text{-}7)$$

An example of corrosion involving this reaction is the attack of iron by sulfuric acid, or the tarnishing of silver by hydrogen sulfide in the presence of moisture:

$$Ag + H_2S \xrightarrow{\quad H_2O \quad} AgS + H_2 \qquad (3.25\text{-}8)$$

4. Displacement of hydrogen from water which usually contains small amounts of dissolved inorganic substances:

$$Me + 2H_2O \rightarrow Me(OH)_2 + H_2 \qquad (3.25\text{-}9)$$

Frequently oxygen dissolves in the water and combines with the liberated hydrogen:

$$H_2 + \tfrac{1}{2}O_2 \rightarrow H_2O \qquad (3.25\text{-}10)$$

The reaction can also be written:

$$Me \rightarrow Me^{++} + 2e \qquad (3.25\text{-}11)$$

$$2H_2O + 2e \rightarrow 2OH^- + H_2 \qquad (3.25\text{-}12)$$

The rusting of iron in water is a form of corrosion involving this reaction.

5. Displacement by one metal of the ions of another metal from a salt solution:

$$Me' + MeSO_4 \rightarrow Me'SO_4 + Me \qquad (3.25\text{-}13)$$

If iron is immersed in a solution of copper sulfate, copper will plate out on the iron and the iron will go into solution.

Although these reactions may not typify every kind of corrosion, they are involved in many common forms of it. An understanding of them will assist in understanding the nature of the problem and the steps taken to combat it.

3.26. Basic Mechanisms of Corrosion

Corrosion is the chemical means by which metals deteriorate and fail. Two basic mechanisms have been recognized: direct chemical attack and electrochemical attack. A number of distinct forms of electrochemical attack have also been identified. One or more of the chemical reactions described in Section 3.25 is usually involved, regardless of the basic mechanism by which attack proceeds.

Direct chemical attack includes all kinds of corrosion in which there is no appreciable flow of current through the metal over perceptible distances. This definition does not deny that electrochemical forces play a part in direct chemical attack, as they do in all chemical reactions. The significant feature is that there is no appreciable current flow on a macroscopic scale. Direct chemical attack usually results in fairly uniform attack over the surface of the metal. An example of direct chemical attack is the rusting of iron and steel in accordance with equations (3.25-4) and (3.25-9), or the high-temperature scaling of iron in accordance with equation (3.25-2). Another example of direct chemical attack is the corrosion of copper flashing in the atmosphere. The copper is attacked by the combined action of oxygen, moisture, and oxides of sulfur (from products of combustion) to form green basic copper sulfate. Fortunately, in most cases basic copper sulfate forms a tightly adherent film which provides protection and eventually stops corrosion. Equation (3.25-3) seems to govern this form of corrosion, accompanied by reaction of the $Cu(OH)_2$ formed with dissolved oxides of sulfur. The tarnishing of silverware is still another example of direct chemical attack [see equation (3.25-8)]. Observe that in the three examples cited, attack proceeds uniformly over the entire surface of the metal.

Electrochemical attack is the second major mechanism of corrosion. It is characterized by the establishment of anode and cathode areas, separated by finite distances in the metal, between which current flows. Either galvanic or concentration cells are set up, depending upon the circumstances of corrosion. Sometimes both kinds of cells exist simultaneously. Concentration cell corrosion is further subdivided into metal ion concentration cells and oxygen concentration cells. They are further described in Sections 3.28 and 3.29.

Table 3.3. The Electromotive Force Series

(From *Handbook of Chemistry*, 7th Ed., edited by N. A. Lange, Handbook Publishers, Inc., Sandusky, Ohio, 1949, pp. 1101–1106)

Metal	Ion	Single Electrode Potential
Lithium	Li+	+3.02
Potassium	K+	+2.92
Sodium	Na+	+2.71
Magnesium	Mg++	+2.34
Aluminum	Al+++	+1.67

Metal	Ion	Single Electrode Potential
Zinc	Zn++	+0.76
Chromium	Cr++	+0.71
Iron	Fe++	+0.44
Cadmium	Cd++	+0.40
Cobalt	Co++	+0.28
Nickel	Ni++	+0.25
Tin	Sn++	+0.14
Lead	Pb++	+0.13
Hydrogen	H+	0.00
Bismuth	Bi+++	−0.23
Copper	Cu++	−0.34
Mercury	Hg++	−0.80
Silver	Ag++	−0.80
Platinum	Pt++	ca −1.2
Gold	Au++	−1.7

3.27. Electrochemical Attack: the Electromotive Force Series

Before galvanic cell corrosion can be discussed, it is necessary to explain the significance of the electromotive force series. The series is an indication of the chemical activity of the metals, those high being more active than those low in the series. An abbreviated form of the series is given in Table 3.3. Active metals have a strong affinity for nonmetals such as oxygen, sulfur, and the halogens, and hence are usually found in the combined state. Less active metals, such as gold, silver, and platinum, have been found in the free condition at the earth's surface. If two clean pieces of dissimilar metals are electrically connected and placed in an electrolyte, the higher one in the series tends to dissolve and the one lower in the series tends to be protected from solution. Thus, the electromotive force series indicates the relative solution tendencies of the various metals. The series also indicates which metals tend to displace hydrogen from an acid in accordance with equation (3.25-7). Metals above hydrogen in the series displace it from an acid, but those below hydrogen do not. Metals which are higher in the series than metals in solution tend to displace the ions of the less active metal from solution, in accordance with equation (3.25-13). However, predictions of metallic behavior based on the electromotive force series assume that the reacting metals have clean, bright surfaces. If a metal surface is not clean to start with, or if it becomes coated with the products of reaction, predictions on the basis of the emf series are not reliable. The formation of corrosion-retarding films on metal surfaces is known as passivation which is discussed later in this chapter.

3.28. Electrochemical Attack: Galvanic Cells

When two dissimilar metals are electrically connected and immersed in an electrolyte solution, a *galvanic cell* is formed. A typical galvanic cell is shown in Fig. 3.34(a). The metal higher in the emf series tends to be attacked and becomes the anode. As the anode dissolves, an electrochemically equivalent amount of hydrogen or metallic element is deposited at the cathode. Thus, the anode is dissolved and the cathode is protected. When the metal at the anode goes into solution to form ions, electrons are liberated. The electrons flow through any electric connection, to arrive at the cathode. Here they neutralize the positive charges on the ions as

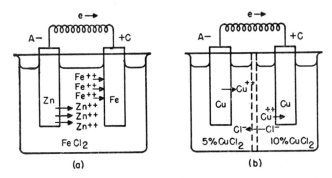

Fig. 3.34.   Examples of galvanic and concentration cells. (a) In a galvanic cell, two electrodes of different metals are immersed in an electrolyte. The more active metal becomes the anode A, which is negatively charged. The anode tends to be attacked. The less active metal becomes the cathode C, which is positively charged. The cathode tends to be protected. Electrons flow along the wire from the anode to the cathode. (b) In a concentration cell, two electrodes of the same metal are immersed in two different concentrations of the same electrolyte, separated by a porous plate which retards mixing of the solutions. The anode, labeled A, is attacked, Cu going into solution from it. The cathode, labeled C, is protected, Cu^{++} ions plating on it as metallic copper. Cl^- ions pass through the porous plate from right to left, and electrons flow around the wire as shown. The region of low ion concentration in the electrolyte is anodic, and the region of high concentration is cathodic.

the ions come out of solution. Galvanic corrosion occurs on the unprotected steel of ships' hulls. The steel is anodic to the brass of the screws and therefore the hull is selectively attacked.

The rate of galvanic attack depends upon the relative areas of cathodic and anodic metal. The rate of attack varies directly with the ratio of cathode to anode, i.e., a relatively small anode area will be attacked faster than a relatively large one. In the case of the ship's hull, the anode area is fairly large; although attack does occur it is not as rapid as it would be if the hull were made of brass and the screws were made of steel. Area effects also explain the very rapid rate of attack of steel rivets when they are used for copper members. In this case, the steel undergoes rapid attack, whereas attack of steel members is negligible if copper rivets are used.

3.29. Electrochemical Attack: Concentration Cells

Where two pieces of the same metal are immersed in two different concentrations of an oxygen solution or of an electrolyte, a concentration cell is produced. Attack occurs at the electrode in the solution of lower ion or oxygen concentration. Electrons flow from anode to cathode through the electric connection. The anode goes into solution and the cathode is protected. Thus, concentration cells are of two kinds: (1) metal-ion cells and (2) oxygen cells.

In a metal-ion concentration cell the solution potential or tendency for the metal to go into solution varies inversely as the ion concentration of that particular metal. Thus, in Fig. 3.34(b) the copper in the five per cent solution of $CuCl_2$ will be anodic to the copper in the ten per cent solution.

An example of a metal-ion concentration cell is shown in Fig. 3.35(a), which represents a section through a submerged riveted lap joint. The space between the lapped plates in Fig. 3.35(a) becomes progressively smaller as the rivet is approached. The ion concentration in the liquid between the plates increases as the distance from the rivet decreases. The ion concentration is lower at the extremities of the joint (marked A in the figure) because fresh solution of low ion concentration continually replaces solution in which there has been ion build-up. Thus A becomes anodic with respect to C and attack occurs as shown.

In **oxygen concentration cells,** differences in the concentration of dissolved oxygen rather than differences in metal-ion concentration cause the cell to become operative. In these cells, the area of *low* oxygen-concentration becomes *anodic,* while the area of *high* concentration becomes *cathodic.*

An example of an oxygen concentration cell is shown in Fig. 3.35(*b*). In this illustration, the oxygen is depleted down inside the crevice, and there is little opportunity to replace it. At the extremities of the joint, a flow of fresh solution of higher oxygen concentration continually replaces any oxygen which tends to be consumed here. Thus, the anodic area *A* is, in this case, deep within the crevice, and the cathodic area *C* is at some distance from the rivet. Compared to the metal-ion concentration cell, the location of anode and cathode areas is now reversed.

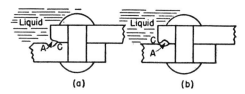

Fig. 3.35. **Concentration cell corrosion.** (a) and (b) illustrate two mechanisms by which concentration cell corrosion can cause attack near a submerged riveted joint. In part (a), *A* is anodic, of low metal-ion concentration in a moving solution, which prevents build-up; *C* is cathodic, of high ion concentration, where stagnant region allows for build-up. In part (b), *A* is anodic, of low oxygen concentration because oxygen cannot be replaced from the liquid as it is used up during corrosion; *C* is cathodic, of high oxygen concentration because oxygen supply is continually replaced by fresh moving solution. [Reproduced by permission of International Nickel Co., Inc.]

Oxygen-concentration cell corrosion can be demonstrated by hanging vertically a piece of thin steel sheet in a beaker of water. After a period of time, note that corrosion has proceeded more rapidly around the bottom of the sheet than around the top. This occurs because oxygen dissolves from the air at the surface of the water and diffuses downward. Therefore, at the top of the sheet of steel, the oxygen concentration is higher and attack is less rapid. At greater distances from the surface, the oxygen concentration diminishes and attack occurs faster. Electrons flow in the piece of steel from anode to cathode areas.

The nature of concentration cells and galvanic cells is summarized below:

Cathode Areas (+)	Anode Areas (−)
Concentrated electrolyte	Dilute electrolyte
Stagnant solution (metal-ion concentration cells)	Moving solution (metal-ion concentration cells)
Aerated solution (oxygen-concentration cells)	De-aerated solution (oxygen-concentration cells)
Metals low in emf series	Metals high in emf series
Electrons flow from cathode to ions in solution	Electrons flow from ions going into solution from the anode
Protection	Attack

3.30. Passivation

It has been pointed out that the surface condition of a piece of metal has an important bearing on its tendency to corrode.   If the corroding medium reacts with the metal to form an adherent protective coating which inhibits further deterioration of the metal, **passivation** is said to have occurred.   Passivation alters the position of the metal in the electromotive force series by changing the chemical activity of the metal.

A good example of passivation is provided by aluminum and its alloys.   Although aluminum stands high in the electromotive force series and is a fairly active metal, it does not corrode as readily in the atmosphere as does iron, a much less active metal.   This behavior of aluminum is explained by the formation of a dense, adherent film of aluminum oxide which affords protection to the metal below the surface.   In the case of corroding iron and carbon steels, the oxide film (rust) is not dense and adherent and does not provide lasting protection.   Stainless steel is another example of an alloy which resists corrosion because of the formation of a passive layer (probably an oxide).   Although oxide films account for a number of examples of passivation, they are not the only kinds of passive layers encountered.

Practical galvanic series differ from the electromotive force series in that they take into account the formation of passive films by reaction of metal and environment.   A practical series has been determined for salt water immersion of the common structural metals.   It is shown in Table 3.4.   This series has been found useful in connection with many electrolytes other than sea water.   In practice, the list is used to predict galvanic corrosion tendencies produced by placing dissimilar metals in contact with each other. If two metals fairly close to each other in this series are used in an application, corrosive tendencies are mild. The farther the metals are from one another in the series, the greater the corrosive tendencies. The metal higher in the series is selectively attacked.

Table 3.4. Galvanic Series in Sea Water *

CORRODED END (ANODIC)	(Continuation)
Magnesium	Tin
Magnesium alloys	Muntz metal
Zinc	Manganese bronze
Galvanized steel or galvanized wrought iron	Naval brass
Aluminum (5052SH, 3004S, 3003S, 1100S, 6053S-T in this order)	Nickel (active)
	Inconel (active)
	Yellow brass
Alclad	Admiralty brass
Cadmium	Aluminum bronze
Aluminum (2017S-T, 2024S-T in this order)	Red brass
	Copper
Mild steel	Silicon bronze
Wrought iron	Ambrac
Cast iron	70-30 Copper-nickel
Ni-resist	Composition G-bronze
13% Chromium stainless steel, type 410 (active)	Composition M-bronze
	Nickel (passive)
50-50 Lead-tin solder	Inconel (passive)
18-8 Stainless steel, type 304 (active)	Monel (passive)
	18-8 Stainless steel, type 304 (passive)
18-8-3 Stainless steel, type 316 (active)	18-8-3 Stainless steel, type 316 (passive)
Lead	PROTECTED END (CATHODIC)
(Cont'd. next column)	

* From *The Technical Editor Speaks,* The International Nickel Co., Inc., New York, 1949, p. 25.

3.31. Specific Forms of Corrosion

A number of specific forms of corrosion are so common that they should be dealt with in some detail.

Pitting results in the formation of small holes which may penetrate thin stock. It has been observed in aluminum alloys, copper alloys, stainless steel, and some high-nickel alloys. Pitting is an electrochemical form of attack in which either galvanic or concentration cells cause the attack.

Galvanic cells originate from local composition differences existing at the surface of the metal. In commercially pure metals, small impurities having a different solution potential produce corrosion.

A localized impurity of greater activity (that is, more anodic) than the "pure" metal is much more serious than an impurity of lesser activity than the "pure" metal because of the relative size of anode to cathode area, as explained in section 3.28. Galvanic cells also originate on the surface of a piece of metal of uniform composition when a passive layer is broken away by mechanical means. The exposed region is anodic, and because of its relatively small area it corrodes rapidly. The presence of dirt or foreign matter adhering to the surface of metal may exclude oxygen and prevent formation of a continuous passive film. When the dirt is removed or falls away from the surface an active area is exposed, and attack proceeds rapidly.

Concentration cells also cause pitting. These cells may be created by scratches and other surface defects. There is a tendency for the oxygen concentration to be lower at the bottoms of surface imperfections; this may produce concentration cell attack. The lack of oxygen tends to prevent formation of a passive layer, which might eventually stop attack, and the pit gets deeper and larger. In some instances metal-ion concentration increases enough at the bottom of the imperfection to set up another cell which opposes the oxygen concentration cell. If the opposing metal-ion concentration effect is great enough, the growth of the pit may cease. Oxygen concentration cells may also result from the presence of dirt adhering loosely to the surface, or from crevices associated with lap joints, spot welds, or improper design and fabrication techniques. See Fig. 3.36.

Intergranular attack occurs when the grain boundaries of metal are selectively corroded. It is probably caused by galvanic action, resulting from composition differences existing between the grain boundary and grain center of the metal being attacked. It has been observed in some kinds of chromium-nickel stainless steels, particularly following improper welding or heat-treating practices. It has also been observed in some copper-base alloys such as the brasses. The growth of intergranular cracks is favored by establishment of oxygen concentration cells and the relatively small anode area. See Fig. 3.37.

Dezincification is a form of corrosion which is peculiar to copper-zinc alloys (i.e., brasses). As the name implies, dezincification results in a loss of zinc from brass leaving behind a spongy mass of copper. There is no agreement on exactly how this occurs, but it is

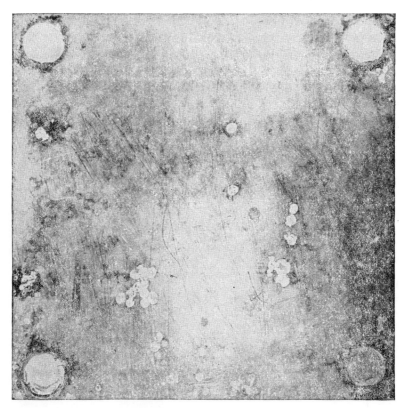

Fig. 3.36. Concentration-cell corrosion (at the bolt holes) and corrosion associated with barnacles.

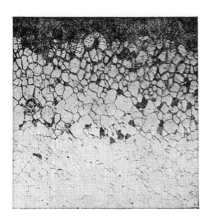

Fig. 3.37. A form of galvanic electrochemical attack known as intergranular corrosion. The alloy composition at the grain boundaries has a higher solution potential than the composition of the grain centers. After attack has proceeded to some depth below the surface, concentration-cell effects can be noticed.

probably associated with microscopic galvanic cells. These could be caused by microdifferences in composition and attendant variations in solution potential. Dezincification occurs in two forms: (1) plug-type or (2) uniform attack. Plug-type dezincification probably is brought on by local removal of passive films. Attack starts over a small portion on the surface and proceeds into the metal. Uniform attack is an over-all, as compared to localized, corrosive attack. See Fig. 3.38.

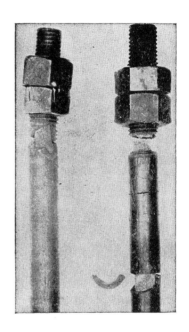

Fig. 3.38. A form of galvanic electrochemical attack known as dezincification. Layers of zinc-rich alloy have selectively dissolved from the copper-zinc-alloy bolts shown.

High-temperature corrosion frequently involves resistance to oxidation or reaction with the products of combustion of fuels. Corrosion under these conditions often proceeds as direct chemical attack. Chromium when present in iron or steel as an alloying element provides resistance to oxidation. The more severe the conditions, the higher is the percentage of chromium needed. Beyond 30 per cent, little additional benefit results from the use of chromium. The protection afforded by chromium is probably the result of formation of a passive film of chromium oxide. Water vapor, carbon dioxide, and sulfur dioxide, all of which are common combustion products, increase the tendency of steel to corrode in air at high temperatures. Some low-grade petroleum fuels form V_2O_5 when they are burned. This compound impairs the corrosion resistance of the straight chromium-iron alloys. To combat the effects of V_2O_5 nickel is used in almost equal proportions with iron and lesser amounts of chromium.[3] This combination resists oxidation, and also attack by sulfur compounds in the products of combustion. Nickel and nickel-rich alloys, although they resist oxidation, tend to form an intergranular network of weak NiS when sulfur compounds are present at high temperatures under reducing conditions. This latter difficulty is overcome by using sufficient chromium and iron with the nickel, and operating with an excess of oxygen. Silicon and aluminum in addition to chromium, are used as alloy additions to improve resistance to high-temperature oxidation.

High-temperature corrosion is accelerated by alternate heating and cooling, because passive scale formations expand and contract at different rates than the metals they tend to protect. Thus spalling or flaking occurs, and additional bright metal is exposed to further attack. See Fig. 3.39.

Fig. 3.39. **High-temperature scaling,** a form of direct chemical attack, caused by 1677 hours, exposure at temperatures between 1500° and 1700°F. The samples shown are about 5 in. long. Description of samples from left to right: Type 1 Ni-Resist, Type 1 Ni-Resist plus 3 per cent chromium, Type 3 Ni-Resist, Type 4 Ni-Resist, Unalloyed iron, Grate-bar iron, Stove iron, FB-A Inoculated iron, Type 2 Ni-Resist, Type 2 Ni-Resist plus 3 per cent chromium, Type 309 stainless steel.

Erosion-corrosion is a combination of one of the basic mechanisms of corrosion with mechanical erosion. Frequently metals which resist corrosion because of the formation of passive layers

[3] 37 per cent nickel, 18 per cent chromium, and 45 per cent iron.

lose their stability when the passive film is mechanically eroded away. Erosion is caused by turbulent flow of fluids. Turbulence in turn is produced by high velocities of flow, by changes in pipe diameter, by elbows, and by fittings. Closely associated with turbulent flow is the effect of cavitation. Cavitation is the formation of cavities in metal by liquid rapidly moving over the metal surface. It is believed the cavities are produced by the formation and sudden collapse of vapor bubbles at the surface. The pressure in the bubbles is very low and the bubbles themselves are unstable. Sudden collapse occurs and exerts a pounding action which tends to wear away metal or protective films. If cavitation is combined with corrosion, the two mechanisms supplement each other. Cavitation removes passive layers, and the exposed bright metal is corroded away. This roughens the surface and promotes more cavitation, so that a stable passive film never gets an opportunity to form. This particular form of erosion-corrosion is known as cavitation corrosion. See Fig. 3.40. Erosion is also produced by solids suspended in fluids. Examples are grit and dirt or salts which precipitate from cooling saturated solutions. Pump impellers made of

Fig. 3.40. Cavitation erosion of a wet cylinder liner of a diesel engine after six months of service. Bore 20½ in.

metals which resist corrosion indefinitely in stagnant solutions sometimes are corroded away in a matter of weeks by the same solutions when the impeller is put in service.

Stress corrosion is likely to occur when static surface tensile stresses act in combination with a corrosive medium. See Fig. 3.41. The stresses can be residual stresses resulting from previous steps in the fabrication or use of the metal. The stresses can also be the result of applied loads, but they must in both cases be at the surface and tensile in nature. Failure is believed to start by corrosion at anodic areas in the surface of the metal, and surface tensile stresses are intensified at the bottom of minute corrosion notches. These stresses cause continual breakdown of any passive film which might tend to form, and so corrosion proceeds at the root of the fissure. As the crack grows deeper, stresses from applied loads are intensified at accelerating speeds and corrosion proceeds faster. It is possible that oxygen-concentration cells also enter the picture. When applied loads are present final fracture may occur with sudden violence.

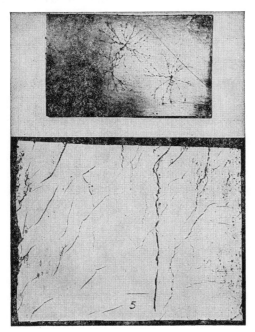

Fig. 3.41. A complex mechanism of corrosion known as stress corrosion cracking.

Examples of stress corrosion failures are the *season cracking* of brass and the *caustic embrittlement* of boilers. Formerly, as a result of the manufacture of brass cartridge cases, residual tensile stresses were left in the metal. Coupled with the effects of a corrosive atmosphere, notably moisture, salt air, and nitrogen compounds, the cartridge cases frequently developed season cracks. Since the cartridge case prevents the escape of propellent gases in a gun by providing a gas-tight seal, the presence of cracks is undesirable. Cracks in cartridge cases also permit escape of volatile materials from powder during storage; causing a change in the ballistic properties of the cartridge. The tendency toward season cracking of brass has been largely eliminated by modification of manufacturing techniques so as to remove residual stresses.

Caustic embrittlement occurs in riveted boilers, at locations where escaping steam from the boiler causes a concentration of dissolved solids such as Na_2SO_4, NaCl, and NaOH. Such concentrated solutions are corrosive and, when combined with residual stresses produced by riveting, may cause a form of stress-corrosion. The pressure of the steam inside the boiler also contributes to the tensile stress pattern. Final fracture is frequently brittle and sudden as a result of the notch effects of the cracks formed.

Corrosion fatigue is caused by the action of a corrosive medium combined with variable stresses. In this type of failure a corrosive medium attacks the surface of the metal, producing stress raisers which nucleate a fatigue failure. Although the portions of the fracture caused by corrosion are frequently intergranular, the final fracture is transcrystalline. Corrosion fatigue has been experienced in the heat-exchanger tubes of chemical equipment. Apparently, in this case, restraint of thermal expansion and contraction is the source of variable stresses. Another example of corrosion fatigue is the failure of sucker rods used in oil wells. See Fig. 3.42.

3.32. Anticorrosion Methods

As a result of accumulated experience and study of the mechanisms by which corrosion proceeds, a number of successful methods for preventing or inhibiting corrosion have been developed. These are discussed below.

Selection of metal. One of the most obvious ways of improving corrosion resistance is to use a more corrosion resistant metal. Although initial costs may be increased by such a procedure, the savings resulting from lower maintenance and replacement charges should not be overlooked. Predictions as to how a specific metal

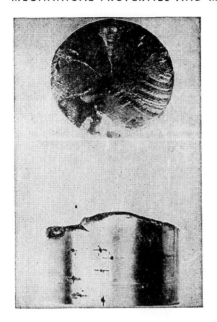

Fig. 3.42. Corrosion fatigue cracking, a complex mechanism of corrosion, which has caused fracture of a marine propeller shaft. (Photographs for Figs. 3.36–3.42 courtesy of International Nickel Co., New York.)

composition is going to respond to a given set of corrosive conditions are risky. Fortunately there are a number of references (*3.19*), (*3.21*), and (*3.22*) which report the results of many investigations of corrosion behavior. Consulting these may provide the specific information required or at least a general indication of what to expect.

Organic coatings are commonly used to improve resistance to corrosion. The expression *organic coatings* includes organic films such as paints, resins and varnish. Other organic materials are tar, grease, asphalt compounds, adhesive plastic tapes, etc. Although some of these, such as paints, often contain inorganic substances, the effective ingredients are organic materials. The quality of the covering is perhaps improved or the cost lowered by the use of inorganic fillers. Protection is afforded through exclusion of moisture, air, and other corrosive media. Since the coatings are organic they are subject to deterioration at high temperatures, and are recommended only for use at or below the boiling point of water.

Inorganic coatings include ceramic materials, such as fired enamelware. Examples of this are enameled cooking utensils, bathtubs, and washbasins. These coatings resist elevated temperatures and are usually hard, wear-resistant, and brittle.

Metallic coatings are used either to protect against structural damage or to preserve appearance. Metallic coatings are applied by electroplating, dipping, and spraying with atomized molten metal. Protection is afforded in some cases because the metal coating is resistant to attack whereas the basis metal is not. In other applications the coating is anodic to the basis metal. The coating is sacrificed, thus preventing attack until appreciable portions of the metal coating are removed. Galvanized sheet steel and fence wire are examples of cathodic protection. Until most of the zinc has corroded away, the steel beneath it is protected. On the other hand, tin cans resist corrosion only while the thin coating of tin remains continuous. If a pinhole develops, galvanic action causes accelerated corrosion of the steel beneath the tin, steel being anodic to tin in most media. Tin is passive to many chemicals encountered in food processing. Resin coatings (organic materials) are now used as a substitute for tin in some applications.

Inhibitors are chemicals which when added to the corrosive medium render it inert, or which when applied to the surface of the metal react to produce passivity. A rather detailed discussion of inhibitors and passivators is presented in reference (*3.19*). If the inhibitor does not provide complete protection to all surfaces of a system, pitting and local intensive attack may result in more serious damage than if the inhibitor had not been used. This difficulty often can be overcome by adjustment of the concentration of inhibitor used. Examples are the addition of soluble oils to the water of automobile cooling systems, and the addition of sodium phosphate or sodium nitrate to boiler water.

Mechanical treatments are aimed at the prevention of stress corrosion. Nitriding or cold-working operations, such as shot peening or cold rolling, are often used. These produce **residual compressive** surface stresses which must be overcome by applied tensile stresses before stress corrosion can occur. The topic of residual stresses is briefly discussed in Sections 3.21 and 3.22.

Cathodic protection is achieved when a metal structure which would normally be attacked is made cathodic by impressing a reversed flow of current. The current can originate from any d-c source such as a generator, rectifier, or galvanic cell. The principles of cathodic protection are applied to underground structures such as pipe lines, sheathing on cables, and storage tanks. Different methods of current distribution are shown in Fig. 3.43.   Instead of using rectifiers or generators, buried anodes of zinc, aluminum or magnesium are used successfully.   Cathodic protection is used for the protection of *inside* surfaces of such structures as water storage tanks and condensers.   Many domestic hot-water heaters

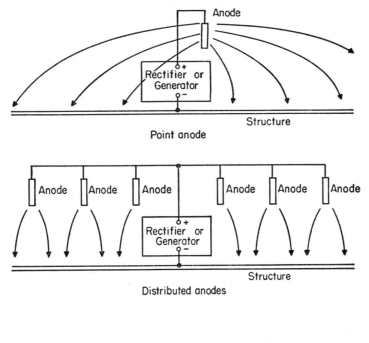

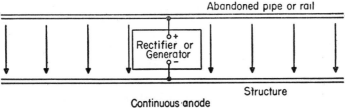

Fig. 3.43.   **Types of forced drainage anodes for protection of underground structures.** [Reproduced with permission from H. H. Uhlig, *Corrosion Handbook*, John Wiley and Sons, Inc., 1948.]

are equipped with expendable magnesium or zinc rods suspended in the tank.   These selectively dissolve, affording protection to any exposed steel.   Prevention of corrosion of ships' hulls, rudders, propeller struts, and shafting is accomplished by attaching zinc or magnesium anodes to the hull in the vicinity of the screws. Ordinarily, steel portions of the ship are anodic to the brass screws. After attachment of zinc or magnesium blocks the steel becomes cathodic, while the zinc or magnesium become anodic. A schematic illustration of cathodic protection of ships' hulls and domestic water tanks is shown in Fig. 3.44. Studies of the use of current from rectifiers and generators for protection of ships' hulls are being carried out by the U. S. Navy.

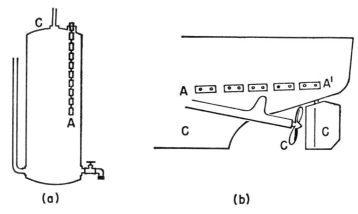

(a)   (b)

Fig. 3.44. **Cathodic protection.** (a) Zinc or magnesium is suspended in water tanks to prevent corrosion of the tank. The zinc or magnesium becomes the anode A, and the tank becomes the cathode C. Electrons flow from A to C within the metal structure as the anode selectively dissolves. (b) A line of zinc or magnesium anode bars, AA', attached to the hull of a ship makes the hull and rudder cathodic. Without anode bars, the hull and rudder are anodic with respect to the screws and would be corroded. Anodes are sacrificed deliberately to protect vital parts of the structure and periodic replacement is necessary.

Air and water conditioning are both used to reduce corrosion. Air conditioning became popular as a means of protecting "mothballed" ships following World War II. This particular phase of preservation involves sealing of spaces containing equipment to be protected, followed by removal of most of the moisture from the air. The method is successful because *dry* air at atmospheric temperatures does not cause corrosion of common structural metals. Water conditioning consists of removing dissolved gases, usually oxygen of the air, from water. This process is useful for preventing or reducing corrosion in steel pipe lines.

EFFECTS OF RADIATION ON METALLIC MATERIALS

3.33. Types of Radiation

The types of radiation encountered in the production of atomic energy are sometimes subdivided into two broad classes: light particles and heavy particles. The **light particles** include beta rays and gamma rays. Beta rays are electrons and are thus the same as the cathode rays discussed in section 1.2. Gamma rays are electromagnetic radiations similar to x-rays, but having shorter wave lengths. The wave lengths of gamma rays vary from 0.0001 Å to about 0.1 Å, whereas x-rays vary from about .04 Å to 1 Å. Gamma rays are thus much more energetic than x-rays. However, neither the beta rays nor the gamma rays encountered in reactors have a significant effect on the properties of metals and alloys. They do produce important changes in the properties of some nonmetallic materials.

The **heavy particles** include alpha particles, neutrons, and fission fragments. Alpha particles are helium nuclei consisting of two protons and two neutrons, and hence carry a positive charge of 2. The helium nuclei have a mass more than 7000 times as great as the electron, and 4 times as great as the mass of a hydrogen atom.

Neutrons, which were mentioned in section 1.1, have a mass of 1, and carry no charge. The neutrons are further classified as thermal neutrons and epithermal neutrons. Thermal neutrons have energies of about 1/40 ev; epithermal neutrons have energies as high as 2 mev (million electron volts). Thermal neutrons are also called slow neutrons, and epithermal neutrons are called fast neutrons.

Fission fragments are formed as a result of larger atoms split into smaller ones. This occurs when uranium atoms undergo fission, and also by reaction between neutrons and atoms such as the boron isotope having an atomic weight of 10:

$$_0n^1 + {}_5B^{10} \rightarrow {}_2He^4 + {}_3Li^7 \qquad (3.33\text{-}1)$$

(The superscripts indicate the masses of the particles, and the subscripts indicate the atomic numbers.) Alpha particles are actually fission fragments.

3.34. Effects of Radiation

The light particles are capable of displacing electrons in the electron cloud or of ejecting planetary electrons, as is described in connection with x-rays (see section 1.2). This results in a merely temporary disturbance producing no permanent change in the properties of the metal.

The heavy particles, particularly the fast neutrons, have notable effects on properties of metallic substances. Neutrons, being electrically neutral, do not interact except by direct collision with the nucleus. Since the radius of the nucleus is only 1/10000 of the radius of the atom, a neutron travels, on the average, many thousands of atomic distances before contacting a nucleus. Neutrons change from fast neutrons to slow neutrons by transfer of their kinetic energy to the nuclei with which they collide. In the case of collisions with hydrogen nuclei, about two-dozen collisions are required for such conversion. Thus, the effects of fast neutrons extend deeply into metals. On the other hand, fission fragments and alpha particles are initially highly charged and react with the electric fields of atoms they approach. Hence, loss of energy from fission fragments and alpha particles occurs within a few microns of the surface and damage is highly localized.

Four effects of heavy particle radiation are recognized. These are: (a) the creation of vacancies in the crystal, (b) the relocation of atoms to interstitial or irregular positions in the crystals, (c) the creation of impurity atoms, and (d) the creation of very small areas of very high temperatures (sometimes called *thermal spikes*).

3.35. Radiation and Fuel Assemblies

Alpha particles and other fission fragments do most of their damage to fuel elements, fuel element cladding, and the control rods. Neutrons also do damage to these components, but neutrons are so much more penetrative that their effect is felt in structural members at greater distances from the fuel assembly.

Damage to the fuel element is not considered of direct importance, since its strength requirements are low. However, dimensional changes occur as a result of the creation of new atoms. Thus, the cladding tends to separate from the fuel.   This is troublesome since uranium is a very reactive metal which is readily corroded by air or water.

Control rods frequently contain boron which captures slow neutrons and undergoes the reaction shown in equation (3.33-1).   The extra atoms formed by this reaction must be accommodated by the crystal structure, and this introduces embrittling strains.   (See Chapter 5.)

3.36. Radiation and Structural Metals

Most structural metals become harder, stronger, and less ductile when irradiated at ordinary temperatures.   At high temperatures, creep strength and stress-rupture strength are likely to be affected. Further high-temperature study is required prior to drawing general conclusions.

The creation of new atoms tends to cause hardening and loss of ductility by alloying.   (See Chapter 5.)   The relocation of atoms to irregular or interstitial positions is similar to the effect of cold work and distortion of crystal structure, causing loss of ductility and increased strength.   Large atoms (with atomic radii greater than 1 Å) in interstitial positions are difficult to visualize, since such a distribution is created only by irradiation.

The very small areas of extremely high temperature which are created by heavy particle bombardment cool quickly as a result of the quenching effect of surrounding metal.   In steel this is likely to cause localized hardening and embrittlement.   (See Chapter 7.) As bombardment proceeds, the localized effects accumulate over larger areas, but to date, at least, the effect is not considered to present a serious hazard.

The transition temperature, or temperature at which steel suffers a large loss in ductility, is raised by irradiation.   Ordinary carbon steel tends to lose ductility around 0–20°F, but after irradiating this temperature may be raised to 20–40°F.

The creation of vacancies has been observed to increase the speed of diffusion.   This shows up in connection with age and precipitation hardening.   (See Chapter 5.)

Questions

3.1. How is the reported strength of a metal affected by the manner in which strength values are determined?

3.2. With the aid of a properly labeled stress-strain diagram, define: (a) proportional limit; (b) elastic limit; (c) yield strength; (d) yield point; (e) ultimate strength; (f) stiffness.

3.3. What relationship exists between ductility, strength, and toughness? How does stiffness differ from strength?

3.4. With the aid of a diagram, describe the variations in the forces of attraction and repulsion between two atoms as they approach one another. Describe the variation in net force.

3.5. What property is indicated by the results of impact testing? In what units is the property measured? Describe two useful applications of impact testing. Does ordinary impact testing reveal information regarding the effects of velocity of loading?

3.6. Would a steel having a R_C hardness of 50 be harder than a steel whose hardness is $R_B 80$?

3.7. Is work hardening illustrated better by a true or apparent stress-strain curve?

3.8. (a) What is the most important mechanism of deformation?
(b) What is the atomic density of (112) for body-centered cubic iron? How does the density of this compare with planes listed in Fig. 3.5?
(c) Why is the atomic density of planes and lines important?
(d) Define critical resolved shear stress.
(e) Under what conditions of loading is a single crystal of magnesium likely to fail without deformation? Why?
(f) What is a slip line? A slip band?
(g) How can slip lines be distinguished from twins?
(h) Describe the differences between slip and twinning.
(i) Refer to Fig. 3.7. A load of L pounds acting in the XY direction is applied to the crystal shown. What shear stress is produced in the plane $ABCD$ along the direction AB?
(j) Refer to question 3.8 (i). What shear stress is produced along the direction BC?
(k) Refer to questions 3.8 (i) and (j) and Fig. 3.7. Why doesn't slip occur along AB, in which direction the shear stress is greatest?

3.9. (a) Why is the theory of dislocations useful?
(b) Describe how dislocations make slip easier.
(c) Why do dislocations of like sign tend to repel one another? What happens when dislocations of opposite sign meet?
(d) What happens to dislocations as slip proceeds?

(e) Why does resistance to slip increase as slip proceeds?

(f) As slip proceeds does the number of dislocations increase or decrease?

3.10. What is galling?

3.11. What is the effect on stress distribution of abrupt changes in shape?

3.12. Define creep. What are the four variables with which creep is commonly concerned? How does creep failure differ from stress-rupture failure? How do *time to fracture* and *ductility at fracture* vary with decreasing creep stresses?

3.13. (a) Name the three stages of creep and describe their characteristics. Are three distinct stages of creep always clearly recognizable?

(b) What is the practical aim of creep testing?

(c) Refer to Fig. 3.15. What stress will produce 0.3 per cent creep in five years?

(d) Refer to Fig. 3.15. Suppose the anticipated life of the part undergoing creep is six years, and the permissible creep is 0.6 per cent. What is the maximum stress the part can stand under idealized conditions?

(e) The data in the table below were collected for some steel intended for use at elevated temperatures. The part in which the steel is to be used can elongate 0.8 per cent and still perform its intended design function. Design service life is 50,000 hr at 900°F. What is the maximum stress to which the part can be subjected? If your answer is to be reasonable, what important assumptions must be made?

Per cent Elongation at 1000°F for Various Stresses and Times Indicated

Time	Stress (psi)			
(hours)	**4,500**	**4,000**	**3,500**	**2,000**
20,000	1.0	0.625	0.300	0.050
15,000	0.875	.550	.225	
10,000	.675	.475	.225	.038
7,500	.625	.400	.175	
5,000	.550	.350	.150	
2,500	.425	.270	.125	.025
1,500	.325	.213	.100	

Per cent Elongation at 900°F for Various Stresses and Times Indicated

Time	Stress (psi)		
(hours)	**4,500**	**4,000**	**3,500**
20,000	0.825	0.425	0.125
15,000	.700	.360	.100
10,000	.560	.313	.082
7,500	.535	.280	.075
5,000	.460	.250	.060
2,500	.325	.200	.050

3.14. (a) Consider Fig. 3.17. Timken 16-25-6 can withstand a certain stress for 100 hours at 1300°F. How many hours at the same stress can be withstood at 1100°F?

(b) What is the stress of question 3.14 (a)?

(c) What are the advantages of the method for predicting long-time rupture strengths from brief high-temperature tests?

3.15. (a) Describe the mechanism of high-temperature failures.

(b) What is the equicohesive temperature? Why can a single temperature not be stated as the equicohesive temperature for a given composition?

3.16. (a) Discuss the effect of composition on resistance to high-temperature failure.

(b) What is the effect of grain size on resistance to high-temperature failure?

(c) What is the effect of cold work on resistance to high-temperature failure?

3.17. (a) Under what conditions does thermal shock occur?

(b) What kind of failure results from thermal shock?

(c) Low values of which properties favor thermal fatigue? High values of which properties favor thermal fatigue?

3.18. (a) Under what conditions does fatigue failure occur?

(b) State some examples of cases where fatigue failure is likely to occur.

(c) Describe the progress of a fatigue failure. Account for the appearance of the fracture.

(d) What usage is applied to the terms *fatigue strength, fatigue limit, endurance strength,* and *endurance limit*?

3.19. (a) How is a fatigue test conducted?

(b) Why are fatigue results usually plotted on semi-log paper?

(c) Unless otherwise stated, what kind of stress is used in determinations of fatigue strength?

3.20. (a) What is the effect of varying the speed of loading on fatigue behavior?

(b) What is the effect of very low temperatures as compared with room temperature, on fatigue resistance?

(c) Describe the effect of size of the member on its fatigue strength.

(d) Describe how the effects of overstressing are studied.

(e) What is the effect of understressing?

(f) What is the effect of varying the range of stress reversal on fatigue behavior?

(g) Which three of the factors considered in Questions 3.20(a) through 3.20(f) are the most important considerations?

3.21. (a) What are the two major sources of stress raisers?

(b) Calculate the stress concentration in *CD* and *EF* assuming there is uniform stress distribution in *GI* of Fig. 3.26.

(c) Describe the kinds of stress raisers resulting from casting, welding and machining.

(d) Why are residual surface tensile stresses believed to act as sources of fatigue failure?

(e) On the basis of your knowledge of stress raisers, explain the size effect.

3.22. (a) Describe examples of how improvements in design can result in better fatigue resistance.

(b) State an example of improvement in fatigue strength resulting from a better processing method.

(c) List three ways of improving resistance to fatigue failure in addition to the two mentioned in Questions 3.22(a) and 3.22((b).

(d) Why is surface hardening a useful way of improving resistance to fatigue failure?

(e) List the different ways of accomplishing surface hardening.

3.23. The fatigue strength for a particular aluminum alloy tested at 500×10^6 cycles of completely reversed stress is 16,500 psi. For partial stress reversal, $f_{Max} = 21,000$ psi, find the minimum stress if $c = 1.20$. If f_{Max} is axial and tensile, will f_{Min} be compressive or tensile?

3.24. What methods are used for early detection of fatigue failure?

3.25. (a) Define corrosion.

(b) Name some mechanisms of corrosion in which corrosion is combined with mechanical actions.

(c) State some examples of corrosive media.

3.26. (a) Write equations which represent five basic reactions involved in corrosion.

(b) Give an example of corrosion involving direct combination of metal and nonmetal.

(c) Give an example of corrosion produced by the combined action of moisture and oxygen.

(d) Give an example in which corrosion results in displacement of hydrogen from an acid.

(e) Give an example of reaction of a metal with water and dissolved oxygen.

(f) Give an example of corrosion involving a displacement reaction.

3.27. (a) Name and distinguish between the two basic mechanisms of corrosive attack.

(b) Give some examples of direct chemical attack.

3.28. (a) What is the significance of the electromotive force series?

(b) How is the electromotive force series determined (refer to a general chemistry or physical chemistry text)?

(c) What limits the use of the emf series in predicting actual corrosive behavior?

(d) List the following metals in order of decreasing solution potential: copper, lead, iron, magnesium.

3.29. (a) Sketch a typical galvanic cell, and label its parts. Indicate the direction of electron flow.

(b) Give an example of galvanic corrosion.

3.30. (a) What distinguishes the two kinds of concentration cells?

(b) Sketch a typical concentration cell and label its parts. Indicate the direction of electron flow.

(c) What determines whether a riveted lap joint corrodes at the extremities of the joint or deep within the joint?

(d) Summarize the nature of concentration and galvanic cells.

3.31. (a) What is passivation?

(b) How do practical galvanic series differ from the emf series?

(c) In the practical series listed in Table 3.4 which metals are listed in both passive and active states?

(d) Which of the following pairs of metals would you expect to corrode by galvanic action in salt water: (1) red brass and bronze? (2) Monel and Inconel (both passive)? (3) magnesium and mild steel? (4) zinc and galvanized steel?

3.32. (a) Describe the nature of pitting.

(b) What is *intergranular attack?*

(c) To alloys of what metals is dezincification common?

(d) Describe the effects of chromium and nickel on the high-temperature corrosion of ferrous alloys?

(e) What is erosion-corrosion? How is it related to cavitation?

(f) Define the nature of the stresses involved in stress corrosion.

(g) Give some examples of stress corrosion.

(h) Describe the progress of corrosion fatigue. What is the nature of the stresses involved?

(i) How could corrosion fatigue be distinguished from intergranular attack?

(j) Which of the forms of corrosion described in the text involve only direct chemical attack?

3.33. (a) List the common anticorrosion methods.

(b) The name of which anticorrosion method fits the plating of hardware and home appliances?

(c) Does the protection afforded by electroplating of domestic hardware originate with galvanic action or the production of a passive metal surface?

(d) List sources of information regarding corrosive behavior of specific metals to specific environments.

(e) What limitation is encountered in the use of organic coatings for prevention of corrosion?

(f) What is one disadvantage of inorganic coatings for prevention of corrosion?

(g) What precaution should be observed regarding the use of inhibitors for corrosion prevention?

(h) How do mechanical treatments improve corrosion resistance?

(i) Describe two different ways of achieving cathodic protection.

(j) State some practical applications of cathodic protection.

(k) Explain how air and water conditioning achieve protection against corrosion.

3.34. (a) Differentiate between light particle and heavy particle radiation.

(b) Why are the effects of light particle radiation on metals not considered serious?

(c) Why does neutron damage extend more deeply into metal than damage by alpha particles?

(d) What are the four recognized effects of heavy particle radiation?

(e) Describe the effects of radiation on fuel assemblies.

(f) Describe the effects of radiation on structural metals.

Bibliography

3.1.   Williams, S. R., *Hardness and Hardness Measurements*. Cleveland: American Society for Metals, 1942.

3.2.   Lysaght, V. E., *Indentation Hardness Testing*. New York: Reinhold Publishing Corp., 1949.

3.3.   Holloman, John H., *The Problem of Fracture*. New York: American Welding Society, 1946.

3.4.   *The Technical Editor Speaks*. New York: The International Nickel Co., Inc., 1949.

3.5.   Davis, H. E., G. E. Troxell, and C. T. Wiskocil, *The Testing and Inspection of Engineering Materials*, 2nd Ed. New York: McGraw-Hill Book Co., Inc., 1955.

3.6.   Keyser, Carl A., *Materials of Engineering*. Englewood Cliffs, N. J.: Prentice-Hall, Inc., 1956.

3.7.   Lightner, M. W., and R. W. Vanderbeck, *Factors Involved in Brittle Fracture*. U. S. Steel Corporation, 1957.

3.8.   Moore, H. F., and M. Moore, *Textbook of Materials of Engineering*, 8th Ed. New York: McGraw-Hill Book Co., Inc., 1953.

3.9.   Gillett, H. W., *The Behavior of Engineering Metals*. New York: John Wiley & Sons, Inc., 1951.

3.10. *Mechanical Wear*. Cleveland: American Society for Metals, 1950.

3.11. *Cold Working of Metals*. Cleveland: American Society for Metals, 1949.

3.12. Cazaud, R., *Fatigue of Metals*. London: Chapman and Hall, Ltd., 1953.

3.13. Symposium, *Fatigue and Fracture of Metals*, ed. W. M. Murray, published jointly by The Technology Press, M.I.T., Cambridge, Mass., and John Wiley & Sons, Inc., New York, 1950.

3.14. Smith, G. V., *Properties of Metals at Elevated Temperatures*. New York: McGraw-Hill Book Co., Inc., 1950.

3.15. Sully, A. H., *Metallic Creep and Creep Resistant Alloys*. New York: Interscience Publishers, Inc., 1949.

3.16. Pfeil, L. B., "How to Evaluate High-temperature Performance of Materials," *Materials and Methods*, **37-3** (March 1953), pp. 79–84.

3.17. Clark, F. H., *Metals at High Temperature*. New York: Reinhold Publishing Corp., 1950.

3.18. *High Temperature Properties of Metals*, a series of lectures. Cleveland: American Society for Metals, 1951.

3.19. Uhlig, H. K., *The Corrosion Handbook*. New York: John Wiley & Sons, Inc., 1948.

3.20. *Corrosion of Metals*. Cleveland: American Society for Metals, 1946.

3.21. Rabald, E., *Corrosion Guide*. New York: Elsevier Publishing Co., Inc., 1951.

3.22. Speller, Frank W., *Corrosion, Causes and Prevention*, 3rd Ed. New York: McGraw-Hill Book Co., Inc., 1951.

3.23. Special Report, "How Radiation Affects Materials," *Nucleonics*, **14-9** (September 1956), pp. 53–88.

3.24. Leeser, D. O., "How Nuclear Radiation Affects Engineering Materials," *Materials and Methods*, **40-2** (August 1954), pp. 109–120.

3.25. Leeser, D. O., "Engineering Materials in Nuclear-Fueled Power Plants," *Materials and Methods*, **41-5** (May 1955), pp. 98–103.

3.26. Murray, Raymond L., *Introduction to Nuclear Engineering*, Englewood Cliffs, N. J.: Prentice-Hall, Inc., 1955.

3.27. Warde, J. M., "Materials for Nuclear Power Reactors," *Materials and Methods*, **44-2** (August 1956), pp. 121–143.

CHAPTER 4

Equilibrium Diagrams

4.1. Equilibrium or Phase Diagrams

These diagrams are used to represent some of the changes which metals undergo when they are slowly heated or cooled. This may involve melting, freezing, and some types of heat treating. As a preliminary to the topic of equilibrium diagrams, some definitions are given below.

State, or state of matter. The three possible states of matter are solid, liquid, and gas. Metals are usually considered in the solid or liquid state. They may also exist as vapors, but this is not significant in the handling of most ordinary metals. Equilibrium diagrams, from the standpoint of metallurgy, are concerned, in part, with changes in the state of metals.

System. A system is here considered a body of matter completely isolated from its surroundings. Of course this isolation is not a practical possibility, but from a theoretical viewpoint is a valuable concept. A system is the body of matter under consideration without regard for its surroundings.

The word *system* is also used to denote a series of alloys containing the same components. For instance, the *copper-zinc system* refers to all possible alloys of copper and zinc. Which of the two meanings is intended is made clear by the way in which the term is used.

Phase. A phase is a homogeneous body of matter. It may be a physically distinct portion of a system, or may encompass the entire system, in which case the system is homogeneous. On the other hand, the system may be heterogeneous and contain several different phases. Different states of matter, such as ice and water, are different phases. Different crystal forms of the same material represent different phases, such as ferrite and austenite, both of

141

which are forms of iron. Two immiscible solutions in a system, such as oil and water, also represent two phases. With regard to metals, immiscible solid solutions as well as immiscible liquid solutions may comprise the phases of a system. More than two phases can exist at one time in certain systems.[1] Equilibrium diagrams are concerned with phase changes as well as with changes of state.

Component. The components of a system are the pure elements or compounds which make up the system. A system may have only one component or it may have an infinite number. Equilibrium diagrams for metals are commonly concerned with two-component systems, such as the iron-iron carbide diagram, or the copper-aluminum diagram. They may also involve three components, such as the copper-tin-zinc diagram.

Equilibrium. A condition of no net change is a condition in which equilibrium exists. The total amounts of the various phases remain constant.

Equilibrium diagram. As applied to physical metallurgy, equilibrium diagrams are plots of temperature versus composition, showing the compositions and amounts of the various phases which exist at various temperatures under conditions of equilibrium.

Constituent. Any portion of an alloy system which can be identified microscopically is a constituent. A constituent may consist of only one phase (e.g., ferrite in steel) or several phases (e.g., pearlite, which is found in steel and is composed of ferrite and cementite).

4.2. Isomorphous Systems

One of the simplest forms of metal equilibrium diagram is that of an isomorphous alloy system. In isomorphous systems there is complete solubility of the components in both the solid and the liquid states. Copper and nickel are the alloying components of an isomorphous alloy diagram which is shown in Fig. 4.1. Note that temperature is plotted along the vertical axis, while composition is plotted along the horizontal axis. For composition, the weight percentage of only one component (copper in this case), is plotted, the balance of the composition being nickel. The liquidus and

[1] The phase rule of Willard Gibbs defines the conditions under which phases can exist. It is found discussed in most advanced physical metallurgy books and in texts on physical chemistry.

solidus lines, as indicated in the figure, divide the diagram into three areas. In the area above the liquidus all compositions exist as liquids, and in the area below the solidus all compositions are solid. In the space between the liquidus and solidus lines, a system is made up of both solid and liquid phases, i.e., a crystalline solid solution plus a liquid solution.

The equilibrium melting and freezing of pure metals or metallic compounds occurs at a constant temperature. Thus if we apply heat at a constant rate to a ladle of pure solid copper, the temperature of the copper rises steadily until melting begins. At the melting point, even though the rate of heat input is steady, the temperature cannot rise until all the copper has melted. On the other hand, during cooling of molten copper, the temperature cannot drop below the freezing point until all the copper has solidified. The freezing points of the two pure components are shown on the diagram. Copper solidifies at 1981°F, while nickel freezes at 2646°F. Impure solids do not usually melt or freeze at constant temperatures (although there are numerous exceptions pointed out later). For instance, when a solid alloy containing 50 per cent copper and 50 per cent nickel is heated, no melting occurs until a temperature of about 2275°F is reached. At this point, some liquid forms, and as the temperature rises higher and higher, more and more alloy melts until finally at 2400°F the entire mass is liquid. The reverse occurs upon cooling the 50 per cent copper alloy from 2500°F. At 2400°F the first solidification occurs, and as the temperature drops, more solid forms from the melt, until at 2275°F solidification is complete. These figures can be obtained for any alloy by reading the temperature on the diagram at which the composition of the alloy (in the case just cited, 50 per cent copper) intersects the liquidus and solidus lines.

Now consider what the diagram states about cooling a system containing 30 per cent copper from a temperature of 2600°F. The first step in making use of the diagram always consists of finding the intersection made by the abscissa (i.e., composition) and the ordinate (i.e., temperature). For our particular system containing 30 per cent copper at a temperature of 2600°F this occurs at point *A*. The system is in the liquid state, because *A* falls above the liquidus line in the area marked "liquid solution." Upon cooling, no changes occur in the system until a temperature of 2520°F is reached. The intersection of the temperature line with the 30 per

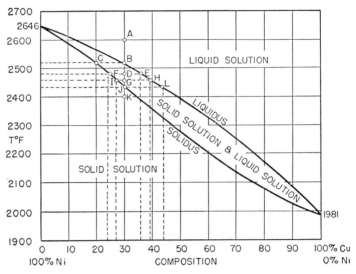

Fig. 4.1. An isomorphous system. An interpretation of the copper-nickel isomorphous system, for an alloy containing 30 per cent copper is given below.

Temperature	Location of System on Plot	Phases Present	Compositions of Phases	Per cent of Total Weight Represented by Phases
2600	A	liquid	30% Cu	100% liquid (L)
2520	B	liquid	$>30\%$ Cu	Essentially 100% L
		solid	20% Cu	Negligible solid (S)
2475	D	liquid	36% Cu	50% L, from: $$\frac{FD(100)}{FE} = \frac{(30-24)(100)}{36-24} = 50\% \ L$$
		solid	24% Cu	50% S, from: $$\frac{DE(100)}{FE} = \frac{(36-30)(100)}{36-24} = 50\% \ S$$
2460	G	liquid	39% Cu	25% L, from: $$\frac{IG(100)}{IH} = \frac{(30-27)(100)}{39-27} = 25\% \ L$$
		solid	27% Cu	75% S, from: $$\frac{GH(100)}{IH} = \frac{(39-30)(100)}{39-27} = 75\% \ S$$
2435	J	liquid	43% Cu	Negligible L
		solid	$<30\%$ Cu	Essentially 100% S
2400	K	solid	30% Cu	100% S

144

cent copper composition line falls on the liquidus at B, indicating that we are now entering a two-phase region and therefore some solid can be expected to commence forming.

The diagram not only indicates that the 30 per cent copper alloy first commences to freeze at B, but it also provides the information that the composition of the first solid to form consists of 20 per cent copper and 80 per cent nickel. This fact is determined by extending the temperature line from B over to the other boundary (solidus) line of the two-phase region and dropping a perpendicular from this intersection (point C) to the composition axis. At a temperature of 2520°F, the two phases which must be in equilibrium have the compositions given by B and C. In fact, within the two-phase region at any particular temperature, the compositions of the two phases which are always in equilibrium at that temperature can be found by dropping perpendiculars from the intersections made by the temperature line with the solidus and liquidus lines. The horizontal segment of an isotherm connecting two phases which are in equilibrium in a two-phase region is known as a "tie" line. CB, FE, IH, and JL are tie lines in Fig. 4.1.

If a solid containing 20 per cent copper crystallizes from a liquid containing 30 per cent copper, obviously, the liquid remaining must have a composition higher in copper content than the original liquid. The slope of the liquidus line indicates that the temperature at which the remaining liquid freezes must be below 2520°F, and therefore if freezing is to continue the temperature must drop.

When a temperature of 2475°F is reached, the intersection of the line of total composition and the isotherm places us at point D, well within the two-phase region. The only two phases which can exist in equilibrium with one another at this temperature have the compositions corresponding to F and E. These compositions are determined, as always, by perpendiculars dropped from the intersection of the tie line with the boundaries of the two-phase region. F corresponds to a solid solution composition of 24 per cent copper and E to a liquid solution of 36 per cent copper. Since nothing has been added to or taken away from the system, the amounts of solid and liquid phases must obviously be such that they produce the same total composition as before, namely 30 per cent copper and 70 per cent nickel. This occurs if equal amounts of solid and liquid phases are present, that is, one-half or 50 per cent of the weight of the system is made up of a solid containing 24 per cent copper and one-half is made up of a liquid containing 36 per cent copper. If originally there had been 100 pounds of molten copper-nickel alloy, there would have been 30 pounds of copper and 70 pounds of nickel in the ladle. Then at 2475°F we would have:

$$50 \times 0.24 = 12 = \text{weight of copper in solid phase}$$
$$50 \times 0.36 = 18 = \text{weight of copper in liquid phase}$$
$$\overline{30 = \text{total weight of copper}}$$

Notice that the lengths of the segments FD and DE are equal. This has significance and indicates that there are equal amounts of solid phase and liquid phase at the particular temperature and total composition under consideration. As the temperature drops, both the solid and liquid compositions grow richer in copper. For instance, at 2520°F the solid contained 20 per cent copper, while at 2475°F the solid composition has shifted to 24 per cent copper, and the liquid, which initially contained 30 per cent copper now contains 36 per cent copper.

At 2460°F the intersection of the total composition abscissa (30 per cent copper) and the temperature ordinate occurs at G. This is in a two-phase area, and the compositions of the two phases can be found by dropping perpendiculars from the intersections of the tie line with the boundaries of the two-phase region. The solid is found to contain 27 per cent copper, while the liquid contains 39 per cent copper. Knowing this, the relative amounts of solid and liquid can be found:

Let x = fraction of solid; then $1.00 - x$ = fraction of liquid.

$$0.27x + (1.00 - x)(0.39) = 0.30$$

(where the system contains 30 per cent copper).

$$0.12x = 0.09; \quad x = 0.75$$

That is, 75 per cent of the system is in the solid state, and 25 per cent is in the liquid state.

At 2435°F, the intersection of composition and temperature occurs at point J on the solidus. At this temperature the last remaining liquid (containing 43 per cent copper) freezes. The solid now contains 30 per cent copper, which is the same as the composition of the original liquid. Below this temperature no further changes occur.

Thus for any given temperature and composition it is always possible to determine the phase or phases in equilibrium, the compositions of the phases, and the amount of each phase present.

Consider the heating rather than the cooling of an isomorphous alloy. For simplicity, refer to the same copper-nickel system. At 2400°F the alloy containing 30 per cent copper is completely solid. Upon heating this solid the first liquid forms at 2435°F and contains 43 per cent copper. This leaves the remaining solid richer in nickel than it was originally, and hence melting can continue only if the temperature rises. At 2460°F the liquid in equilibrium with the solid contains 39 per cent copper, and the solid contains 27 per cent copper. Thus as melting proceeds both liquid and solid become richer in the higher melting component. Finally at 2520°F the remaining small amount of solid containing 20 per cent copper melts, producing a liquid whose composition is 30 per cent copper. This is the same composition as the starting solid. The relative amounts of the various phases can be found in the manner previously described.

4.3. The Lever Principle

It is usually more convenient to determine the amounts of the phases present by graphical rather than mathematical means. The graphic method is an application of what is known as the lever principle. Consider a system whose total composition is 30 per cent copper and 70 per cent nickel. At 2460°F the relative amounts of the two phases present are given by the relative lengths of the two segments of the tie line, IG and GH on Fig. 4.1. Thus:

$$\text{Per cent solid solution} = \frac{GH}{IH} \times 100$$

$$\text{Per cent liquid solution} = \frac{IG}{IH} \times 100$$

Measurement of the actual lengths of these segments shows that 75 per cent of the system is solid, while 25 per cent is liquid. Since, in the diagram, equal percentages are represented by equal distances, the lengths can be computed in terms of percentages. Actual measurements of length are unnecessary. The amount of solid solution is

$$\frac{39 - 30}{39 - 27} \times 100 = 75 \text{ per cent of the system}$$

The amount of liquid solution is

$$\frac{30 - 27}{39 - 27} \times 100 = 25 \text{ per cent of the system}$$

The name "lever principle" comes from the fact that the tie line may be considered to be a lever whose fulcrum is placed at the total composition (30 per cent copper in the illustration above) and whose arms carry weights (i.e., relative amounts of the phases) inversely proportional to their lengths.

4.4. Coring

The preceding discussion of the isomorphous system was based on the assumption that cooling occurred very slowly and that equilibrium conditions existed during freezing. In ordinary practice, cooling and solidification occur so quickly that appreciable deviations from true equilibrium are produced. This may result in segregation of low- and high-melting compositions, known as coring. Sometimes coring is called dendritic segregation. While coring is particularly significant in isomorphous systems, it can also occur in eutectic and peritectic systems, as is discussed later.

Equilibrium is not maintained between solid and liquid phases during the freezing of metals under ordinary conditions. This can be attributed to lack of time for adequate diffusion in the solid phase, and results in coring. The origin of a cored structure is shown in Fig. 4.2(a), which shows a portion of an isomorphous system. When a liquid, whose total composition is represented by X, is cooled to T_1, freezing commences [1] by formation of crystals of α_1. By the time the temperature has dropped to T_2, the liquid composition has changed to L_2, and crystals of α_2 are forming from it. However, the α_1 solid has not had a chance to change to composition α_2 because there has been insufficient time for diffusion to establish equilibrium. Therefore the average composition of the solid phase

---

[1] Actually, because of undercooling, freezing starts at some temperature below T_1. The exact temperature depends on the amount of undercooling and is therefore not a definitely fixed value. Hence, T_1 is convenient to use as the temperature at which freezing commences.

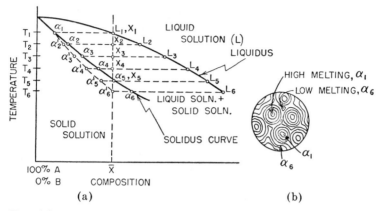

Fig. 4.2. Coring. (a) A portion of a phase diagram to illustrate the origin of coring during nonequilibrium cooling of molten metal. (b) A schematic sketch of the microstructure resulting from coring of the total composition $\overline{X}$ shown in the phase diagram above.

exists somewhere between α_1 and α_2, say at α'_2. The percentages of liquid and solid phases are:

$$\text{Per cent solid} = \frac{X_2 L_2}{\alpha'_2 L_2} \times 100; \quad \text{Per cent liquid} = \frac{\alpha'_2 X_2}{\alpha'_2 L_2} \times 100$$

Application of the lever principle shows that when freezing occurs quickly there is more liquid and less solid present at any given temperature than when freezing occurs slowly.

As freezing progresses, the average composition of the solid phase follows the broken line. In the diagram shown it is always at the left of the equilibrium solidus curve. At T_5 under equilibrium freezing the system would be completely solid. In the actual case, it can be seen that some liquid is still present:

$$\text{Per cent liquid} = \frac{\alpha'_5 X_5}{\alpha'_5 L_5} \times 100$$

Not until T_6 is reached is the composition of the solid phase the same as the starting composition of the liquid. At this temperature freezing is completed.

The process of freezing results in what is known as a cored structure, as shown in Fig. 4.2(b). This sketch represents a section through several dendrite arms. It should be noted that the high-melting compositions are at the centers of the arms while the low-melting compositions are concentrated between the arms. Distinct layers having a finite thickness are not actually observed, since the change in composition is a continuous one which more often appears as a gradual change.   The presence of cored structures makes possible the observance of dendrites in solid solution alloys.

The reverse of coring is known as liquation.   It occurs on heating of an alloy, and results in segregation, because diffusion does not have time to equalize the solid solution compositions as more and more of the metal melts.   As a result of the segregation arising from coring and liquation, it may be found that, upon heating an alloy, melting occurs at temperatures below those indicated by the equilibrium diagram for the particular composition involved.   This is due to the concentration of low-melting compositions at the grain boundaries or spaces between the dendrite arms.   In some alloys poor hot strength may be attributed to liquation.

4.5.   Eutectic Systems

Let us now consider a second common type of equilibrium diagram known as the eutectic.   The eutectic diagram applies to alloys in which there is always one composition of liquid which solidifies at a temperature below the freezing points of either of the pure components, and upon freezing forms two solid solutions.   The copper-silver diagram, an example of a eutectic system, is shown in Fig. 4.3.   The areas and lines of this diagram have been labeled.

Above the liquidus lines, the system is always liquid.   Along the left-hand vertical axis there is a single-phase region called α, which consists of a solid solution of copper in silver.   On the right-hand side there is another single-phase region, in this case designated β, which is a solid solution of silver in copper.   In phase diagrams the single-phase regions are always separated by a two-phase region made up of both the single phases which the two-phase region separates.   Thus, we have between the α and β phase regions an area made up of α plus β, between the α and liquid regions an α plus liquid area, and between the β and liquid a β plus liquid region. The eutectic reaction isotherm is a line of constant temperature, and therefore it is parallel to the composition axis.   It is the freezing temperature of the eutectic liquid, and for the silver-copper system this is 1434°F.   The solidus lines show when solidification is complete in the single-phase regions.   The solvus lines, for which there are no analogies in isomorphous systems, are really solubility curves.   For the α-solid solution, the solvus line indicates that at 1434°F silver can retain up to 8.8 per cent copper in solid solution, but at 600°F, the silver can dissolve only 1 per cent copper.   The other solvus curve represents the solubility of silver in copper, which varies from 8 per cent at 1434°F down to less than 1 per cent at 600°F.

Consider the equilibrium cooling of several different compositions of silver-copper alloys, as examples of how to use the diagram. For the first illustration assume an alloy containing 7 per cent copper, 93 per cent silver, at a temperature of 1750°F. The intersection of abscissa and ordinate occurs at point A and places the system in the liquid region. When this metal is cooled slowly, the first solid forms at 1680°F, containing about 2.5 per cent copper and 97.5 per cent silver. This is α-solid solution in which silver is the solvent and copper the solute. At about 1650°F approximately equal amounts of solid solution and liquid are present. The solid solution at this temperature contains about 5 per cent copper, while the liquid in equilibrium with it contains about 9 per cent copper. The relative amounts of solid and liquid are found by application of the lever principle:

$$\alpha = \frac{EF}{DF} \times 100 = 50 \text{ per cent}$$

$$L = \frac{DE}{DF} \times 100 = 50 \text{ per cent}$$

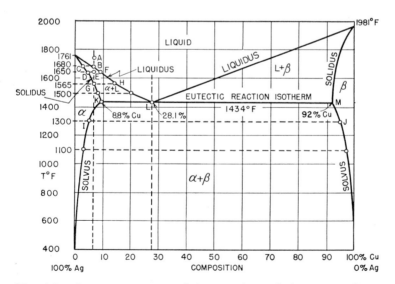

Fig. 4.3. A eutectic system. Interpretations of the copper-silver eutectic system for the cases of alloys containing (a) 7 per cent copper, (b) 28.1 per cent copper, and (c) 20 per cent copper are given in the accompanying table.

(a) For an Alloy Containing 7 per cent Copper

Tempera-ture	Phases Present	Composi-tions of Phases	Per Cent of Total Weight Represented by Phases	Microstructure
1750	liquid	7% Cu	100% L	homogeneous melt
1680	liquid	7+% Cu	essentially 100% L	α-SOLID SOLUTION / LIQUID
	α-solid	2.5% Cu	negligible α	
1650	liquid	9% Cu	50% L, from: $\dfrac{(7-5)(100)}{9-5} = 50\% \ L$	α-SOLID SOLUTION / LIQUID
	α-solid	5% Cu	50% α, from: $\dfrac{(9-7)(100)}{9-5} = 50\% \ \alpha$	
1565	liquid	14% Cu	negligible L	α-SOLID SOLUTION / LIQUID AT GRAIN BOUNDARIES
	α-solid	7—% Cu	essentially 100%	
1300	α-solid	5% Cu	98% α, from: $\dfrac{(95-7)(100)}{95-5} = 98\% \ \alpha$	α-SOLID SOLUTION WITH FINE β-PRECIPITATE
	β-solid	95% Cu	2% β, from: $\dfrac{(7-5)(100)}{95-5} = 2\% \ \beta$	
1100	α-solid	3% Cu	96% α, from: $\dfrac{(98-7)(100)}{98-3} = 96\% \ \alpha$	α-SOLID SOLUTION WITH FINE β-PRECIPITATE
	β-solid	98% Cu	4% β, from: $\dfrac{(7-3)(100)}{98-3} = 4\% \ \beta$	

(b) For an Alloy Containing 28.1 per cent Copper

1600	liquid	28.1% Cu	100% L	homogeneous melt
> 1434	liquid	28.1% Cu	100% L	homogeneous melt
< 1434	α-solid	8.8% Cu	77% α, from: $\dfrac{(63.9)(100)}{83.2} = 77\% \ \alpha$	α AND β OCCUR AS ALTERNATE LAMELLAE IN THIS EUTECTIC
	β-solid	92% Cu	23% β, from: $\dfrac{(19.3)(100)}{83.2} = 23\% \ \beta$	

(c) For an Alloy Containing 20 per cent Copper

Temperature	Phases Present	Compositions of Phases	Per Cent of Total Weight Represented by Phases	Microstructure
1600	liquid	20% Cu	100% L	homogeneous melt
1475	α-solid	8% Cu	20% α	
	liquid	23% Cu	80% L	
> 1434	α-solid	8.8% Cu	42% α	α-SOLID SOLUTION EUTECTIC LIQUID
	liquid	28.1% Cu	58% L	

(At 1434°F all liquid remaining in the system changes over to the solid eutectic mixture of the same composition and structure as for the alloy described in part (b).)

< 1434	α-solid (primary)	8.8% Cu	42% α	α-SOLID SOLUTION (I.E. PRIMARY α)
	eutectic solid	28.1% Cu	58% eutectic solid	
	α-solid in eutectic	8.8% Cu	77% of eutectic is α-solid, from: $\dfrac{(LM)(100)}{(KM)} = 77\%$ α	EUTECTIC SOLID MIXTURE (ALTERNATE LAYERS OF α AND β.)
	β-solid in eutectic	92% Cu	23% of eutectic is β-solid, from: $\dfrac{(KL)(100)}{(KM)} = 23\%$	
	total α-solid (i.e., in eutectic and primary α)	8.8% Cu	87% α, from: $\dfrac{(92-20)(100)}{92-8.8} = 87\%$ α	
	total β-solid (all in eutectic)	92% Cu	13% β, from: $\dfrac{(20-8.8)(100)}{92-8.8} = 13\%$ β	

As the temperature drops, the solid and liquid become richer in copper. Finally, at about 1565°F, the last remaining liquid, containing about 14 per cent copper, solidifies to form an α-solid solution which contains 7 per cent copper, the original composition of the melt. Below this temperature, until we reach 1375°F, the intersections of temperature lines with the composition line occur in the α-solid solution region. Hence, no changes in the structure of the alloy occur until 1375°F is attained. At this temperature the solvus line is crossed and the system enters a two-phase region where the β phase forms. The solvus line indicates that the solubility of copper in silver is diminishing, and the rejected copper forms some β particles. Since β is a solid solution of silver in copper, the rejected copper actually takes some silver with it as it precipitates. The composition of the β phase at 1300°F is determined by constructing the tie line *IJ* and dropping a perpendicular from *J*. Thus at 1300°F, β is made up of about 5 per cent silver dissolved in 95 per cent copper. As the temperature drops, more β forms from the α, and at 1100°F we have α of 3 per cent copper and β of 2 per cent silver in equilibrium. The amounts of the two phases present are:

$$\alpha = \frac{98-7}{98-3} \times 100 = \frac{91}{95} \times 100 = 95.8 \text{ per cent}$$

$$\beta = \frac{7-3}{98-3} \times 100 = \frac{4}{95} \times 100 = \ \ 4.2 \text{ per cent}$$

In actual nonequilibrium cooling of an alloy of this composition, very few structural changes would occur below this temperature, because the precipitation of β from α involves diffusion. Since diffusion occurs at slower speeds as the temperature drops, and since the temperature does decrease rather fast in actual practice, there is very little opportunity for diffusion to occur. Thus precipitation is sluggish if it occurs at all. Figure 4.3 is accompanied by idealized microstructures which show the approximate relative amounts of the phases which would be present if equilibrium cooling actually occurred so that diffusion and precipitation could take place. In actual practice, some coring would probably be present.

Consider next the eutectic alloy containing 28.1 per cent copper. At a temperature of 1600°F the eutectic composition is entirely liquid, and no changes occur until the eutectic composition cools to 1434°F. Here the intersection of composition and temperature lines places us on the intersection of the eutectic reaction isotherm with the two liquidus lines. A physical reaction occurs upon further cooling which is expressed by the equation:

$$\text{Liquid} \longrightarrow \alpha + \beta$$

The temperature always remains constant until the reaction, which is called the eutectic reaction, is complete. The ratio of α to β is a constant, but the ratio of solid to liquid depends upon the energy content of the system. When more and more of the latent heat of fusion is extracted, more solid forms from the liquid even though the temperature does not change. In this respect, freezing of the eutectic composition resembles solidification of a pure metal. When the temperature has dropped a minute amount below 1434°F, all the liquid has solidified and the system now consists of α and β. The composition of the α is given by a perpendicular from K, and is 8.8 per cent copper, while the β contains 92 per cent copper. The relative amounts of α and β are:

$$\alpha = \frac{63.9}{83.2} \times 100 = 76.8 \text{ per cent}$$

$$\beta = \frac{19.3}{83.2} \times 100 = 23.2 \text{ per cent}$$

Whenever the liquid eutectic composition for a particular alloy system freezes, the relative amounts and compositions of the solid phases formed are always the same. This produces what is known as the solid eutectic mixture. In the particular alloy under discussion, when the temperature drops further, α is precipitated from the β-solid solution of the eutectic mixture, and β is precipitated from the α-solid solution. In other words, both α and β tend to become pure metals.

Finally, consider solidification of the composition containing 20 per cent copper. At 1600°F this composition is liquid. Upon cooling, the first α-solid solution forms at 1500°F, and contains about 7.5 per cent copper. At a temperature of 1475°F, the equilibrium solid contains 8 per cent copper, and the liquid contains 23 per cent copper. At a temperature slightly higher than the eutectic we have liquid containing 28.1 per cent copper (i.e., the eutectic composition) in equilibrium with α-solid solution containing 8.8 per cent copper. The amounts of these two phases are:

$$L = \frac{11.2}{19.3} \times 100 = 58 \text{ per cent}$$

$$\alpha = \frac{8.1}{19.3} \times 100 = 42 \text{ per cent}$$

The freezing of the eutectic liquid proceeds at the eutectic temperature as described before. Below the eutectic temperature the structure consists of α crystals, known as primary crystals, which formed before the eutectic solidified, and these are surrounded by the solid eutectic mixture of α- and β-solid solutions. The percentage of eutectic solid mixture below 1434°F is the same as the percentage of liquid which existed slightly above 1434°F, and from which it formed. Thus there must be 58 per cent eutetcic and 42 per cent primary α. The eutectic mixture is made up of 76.8 per cent α and 23.2 per cent β. The total α just below the eutectic temperature amounts to 86.5 per cent of the entire system. Of the total, 13.5 per cent is β. As the temperature drops further below the eutectic point the α phase precipitates β, and the β phase precipitates α as mentioned previously.

Upon melting alloys containing some eutectic solid, the temperature rises until the eutectic temperature is reached. At this point the temperature remains constant until all the eutectic solid mixture has melted. The primary crystals melt when the temperature rises above the eutectic temperature.

Hypereutectics and hypoeutectics. The compostions just discussed were either at the eutectic composition (the lowest melting composition) or at the left of it. Those at the left are known as

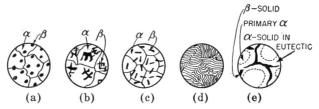

Fig. 4.4. Types of eutectic structures. (a) Nodular. (b) Chinese script. (c) Acicular. (d) Lamellar. (e) Divorced eutectic.

hypoeutectic mixtures, while those at the right are called hypereutectics. The solidification of hypereutectics follows the same pattern as described above for the hypoeutectics. In fact, if the composition axis is reversed, the hypereutectics becomes the hypoeutectics, and vice versa. The assigning of these names is merely a convention.

Kinds of eutectics. Eutectic alloys can have any one of the microstructures shown in Fig. 4.4. The silver-copper system just described is typical of eutectics which possess a lamellar microstructure. Other alloys exhibit eutectics of the nodular, Chinese-script, and acicular forms. There is no simple, rigid rule for predicting from the equilibrium diagram the type of eutectic structure which will be possessed by an alloy system. As might be expected, nodular, Chinese-script, and acicular eutectics most frequently form when the composition of the eutectic is close to the composition of either of the solid solutions which make it up. In this event, there is much more of one of the solid solutions than of the other in the eutectic mixture. Divorced eutectic structures occur when there is no distinct boundary between a primary solid solution and the portion of the same solid solution which occurs as part of a eutectic. A divorced eutectic structure is shown in Fig. 4.4(e).

4.6. Peritectics

In a sense, a peritectic system may be considered an inverted eutectic. A typical peritectic system is shown in Fig. 4.5, which represents a portion of the iron-iron carbide system. Principles previously discussed apply also to the interpretation of peritectic diagrams.

Consider an alloy of iron and carbon containing 0.18 per cent carbon. Upon cooling through the range 2766°F to 2719°F, solidification occurs, with formation of δ crystals. At 2719°F, δ and liquid exist in the amounts:

$$\delta = \frac{0.5 - 0.18}{0.5 - 0.1} = \frac{0.32}{0.40} = 80 \text{ per cent}$$

$$L = \frac{0.18 - 0.1}{0.5 - 0.1} = \frac{0.08}{0.40} = 20 \text{ per cent}$$

At 2718°F, the peritectic reaction occurs, and $\delta + L \longrightarrow \gamma$. The γ which forms contains 0.18 per cent carbon. The γ of this composition can form only if the liquid, which contains 0.5 per cent carbon, can react with δ containing 0.1 per cent carbon. Under equilibrium conditions all the δ and liquid are replaced at the peritectic temperature by homogeneous γ. When freezing occurs rapidly, the final structure at 2300°F may consist of cored δ which was not absorbed by the liquid at the peritectic temperature, a layer of homogeneous γ around the cored δ, and finally some cored γ as a matrix. This is shown in Fig. 4.5.

To illustrate freezing of another typical peritectic composition, consider an alloy containing 0.14 per cent carbon. Upon slow cooling from the liquid condition down to 2719°F, δ forms.   At 2719°F, 10 per cent of the system is a liquid containing 0.5 per cent carbon, and 90 per cent of the system is δ solid containing 0.1 per cent carbon.   At the peritectic temperature under equilibrium cooling, all the liquid and a good portion of the δ react to form γ.   Immediately below 2718°F half the system is δ which contains 0.1 per cent carbon.   The balance consists of γ containing 0.18 per cent carbon.   As the temperature drops, the δ disappears and is replaced by γ.

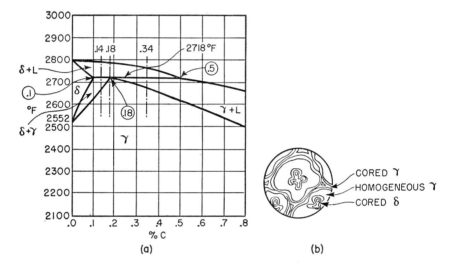

Fig. 4.5.   A peritectic system.   (a) A portion of the iron-iron carbide system.   (b) A possible structure resulting from the cooling of an alloy containing 0.18 per cent carbon.

Consider an alloy containing 0.34 per cent carbon.   At 2719°F this alloy consists of δ and liquid.   About 60 per cent of the system is liquid and 40 per cent is δ.   Under equilibrium cooling, some of the liquid and all the δ react to form γ solid having a composition of 0.18 per cent carbon.   At 2717°F, one-half of the system is liquid and one-half is γ.   When cooling occurs rapidly, there may be insufficient time at 2718°F for all the δ to react with the liquid to form γ.   As a result the final structure at 2600°F may consist of primary cored δ surrounded by a layer of homogeneous γ (which formed as a result of the peritectic reaction), which in turn is surrounded by cored γ.   The structure would be similar to that shown in Fig. 4.5(b), except that it would contain less primary cored δ and more cored γ.

Questions

4.1. As applied to equilibrium diagrams define: (a) state; (b) system; (c) phase; (d) component; (e) constituent; (f) equilibrium.

4.2. What is the outstanding characteristic of an isomorphous system?

4.3. The isomorphous diagram for copper-nickel alloys is given in Fig. 4.1. Given: 1000 pounds of an alloy containing 30 per cent nickel. For the equilibrium-cooled alloy, complete the table indicated below:

Tempera-ture	Phases present	Composi-tions of phases	Per cent of total weight represented by phases	Pounds of copper in phases	Pounds of nickel in phases	Micro-structure
2500°F						
2250°F						
2200°F						
2150°F						
2100°F						

Sketches should show approximately the correct proportions of the phases. The phases should also be identified.

4.4. Using the lever principle estimate the per cent liquid phase in: (a) equilibrium-cooled alloy and (b) the cored alloy at a temperature of T_4 on the diagram shown in Fig. 4.2. In the rapidly cooled alloy will there be more or less than equilibrium amounts of the solid phase at any given temperature when both solid and liquid co-exist?

4.5. Describe the nature of alloys which form eutectics, as indicated by their equilibrium diagrams.

4.6. The eutectic diagram for copper-silver alloys is shown by Fig. 4.3. Given: 1000 pounds of an alloy containing 350 pounds of silver, balance copper. For the equilibrium-cooled alloy prepare a table as shown in Question 4.3. Substitute for the temperatures in the table of Question 4.3 the following: 1800°F, 1700°F, 1435°F, 1433°F, and 1000°F.

4.7. What percentages of alpha and beta solid solution are present at 1433°F in the eutectic solid mixture of Question 4.6? Will these percentages be the same for the eutectic formed from any copper-silver alloy?

4.8. Sketch the appearance of: (a) lamellar; (b) Chinese script; (c) nodular; (d) acicular eutectic mixtures. What is a divorced eutectic?

4.9. The peritectic occurring in the iron-iron carbide diagram is shown in Fig. 4.5. For equilibrium cooling of an alloy containing 0.25 per cent carbon fill in the table below:

Temperature	Phases present	Compositions of phases	Per cent of total weight represented by phases	Sketch of structure at each temperature
2720°F				
2715°F				
2700°F				
2600°F				

4.10. Sketch an approximate structure of the alloy of Question 4.9 at 2500°F if rapidly cooled so that coring occurred. Identify the constituents in your sketch.

Bibliography

4.1. *Metals Handbook,* 1948 Ed. Cleveland: American Society for Metals.

4.2. Hansen, M., *Der Aufbau der Zweistofflegierungen.* Berlin: Julius Springer Verlag, 1936. Reproduced by Edwards Brothers, Ann Arbor, Michigan, 1943 by authority of the Alien Property Custodian.

CHAPTER 5

The Hardening of Metals

5.1. Hardness

Unless otherwise indicated, hardness in this book means indentation hardness or resistance to penetration. Hardness is intimately related to yield strength and, to a less extent, to tensile strength. Therefore the term "hardening of metals" means increasing the resistance to failure caused by loads which exceed the elastic limit. Treatments which increase hardness are among the most important metal processing operations, and are of considerable interest to engineers.

There are at least five distinct methods by which the hardness of metals can be improved:

(1) Reduction of grain size
(2) Cold working: mechanical distortion of the crystal structure
(3) Alloying: solid solutions and heterogeneous mixtures
(4) Precipitation hardening heat treatments
(5) Special heat treatments such as those used for steel.

The first four methods of hardening are discussed below in some detail. The heat treatment of steel is important enough to be classed separately and is taken up in a chapter of its own.

It is significant to note that distortion of the crystal structure is associated with all the methods of hardening. Increases in hardness are believed to result from the effect of distortion on the movement and blocking of dislocations.

REDUCTION OF GRAIN SIZE

5.2. Grain Size

Grain size can be controlled to a certain extent, in three primary means of fabrication: casting, electroforming, and powder metallurgy. Of these, the casting techniques offer the most common means of grain size control. By varying the cooling rate of the casting it is possible to make coarse- or fine-grained castings, the faster cooling rates yielding finer grain sizes. This is shown by a comparison of a sand-cast and die-cast part of the same shape and composition. The die casting, having cooled much faster, has a finer grain size. The difference in properties produced by different grain sizes is illustrated by the aluminum-silicon alloy containing 5 per cent silicon: [1]

Freezing Rate	Condition	Tensile Strength	Yield Strength	Brinell Hardness Number
Fastest	Die cast	30,000	14,000	..
Intermediate	Permanent mold cast	24,000	9,000	45
Slowest	Sand cast	19,000	9,000	40

The more rapidly cooled permanent mold castings of the aluminum alloy containing 3 per cent copper and 5 per cent silicon show a similar increase in hardness, compared to sand castings.[2]

	Tensile Strength	Yield Strength	Hardness, Rockwell E Scale	Compressive Yield Strength
Stress-relieved sand casting	29,000	18,000	67	19,000
Stress-relieved permanent mold casting	37,000	22,000	82	24,000

Control can be achieved also by supplying addition agents to the molten metal before pouring. (The effect of aluminum and titanium on steel has already been discussed. Although these deoxidizers do produce finer-grained steels, there are also secondary hardening effects involved which have no bearing on the topic under discussion.)

In powder metallurgy (see Chapter 14) grain size control is achieved by control of particle size, pressure used during compacting, and conditions of sintering.

In electrodeposition (see Chapter 15) control of grain size results from control of current density, agitation of the plating bath, use of

[1] Data from *Metals Handbook,* American Society for Metals, Cleveland, 1948, p. 825.
[2] *Ibid.,* p. 827.

lower plating temperatures, and use of addition agents in the plating bath.

Grain size can also be controlled by regulation of cold working and annealing cycles. In general, increasing the severity of cold work *prior* to annealing makes the grain size *after* annealing small. There are other factors involved in this method of grain size control which are explained in detail in Section 6.3. It is also possible to control the grain size by regulating the finishing temperature and the degree of hot working. The more severe the hot work and the lower the finishing temperature, the finer the final grain size.

The movement of dislocations (which allows glide or slip to occur when metals are loaded) is stopped by grain boundaries. Thus, dislocations accumulate at the grain boundary region. As explained in Section 3.9, an accumulation of dislocations results in an increase in strength. It has been found that there is less deformation at the grain boundaries than in the centers of the grains when plastic flow occurs at room temperature. Therefore, as the grain size decreases, the proportion of grain boundary region per unit volume of metal increases, and there is greater resistance to deformation.

COLD WORK

5.3. Cold Working

This term means, for most structural metals, inelastic deformation at or near room temperature. A more complete definition is given in Chapter 16. Cold working causes what is known as strain hardening and results in an increase in strength and decrease in ductility. The theory of dislocations, described in Section 3.9 explains why and how strain hardening occurs.

The *effect of prior cold deformation* on critical resolved shear stress has been investigated.[3] Critical resolved shear stress has always been found to increase with increasing prior cold work. For single crystals, there are no complicating features of grain boundary effects. Therefore a plot of shear stress versus shear strain for various single crystals shows how shear stress increases with increasing cold work. (See Fig. 5.1.) A zinc single crystal

---

[3] Schmid, W., and E. Boas, *Kristallplastizität*, J. Springer, Berlin, 1935, as reported in C. S. Barrett's *Structure of Metals*, 2nd Ed. McGraw-Hill Book Company, Inc., 1952.

which has undergone 500 per cent shear shows a sevenfold increase in the resolved shear stress required to continue shear in the same plane.   For the face-centered metals, the increase is even greater; i.e., they strain harden even more than the hexagonal metals.   The effect is similar for compressive or tensile shear, and the same results occur in polycrystalline materials as well as single crystals. Distortion of the crystal structure which accompanies this strain hardening is indicated by a study of x-ray diffraction patterns. Diffraction lines become broader and more diffuse with increasing amounts of cold work.

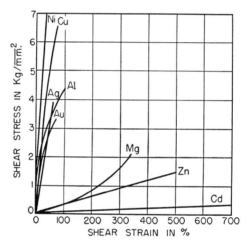

Fig. 5.1.   Strain hardening.   Curves show how the critical resolved shear stress increases with prior deformation for single crystals. [After E. Schmid and W. Boas, *Kristallplastizität.* Springer-Verlag (Berlin), 1935.]

Cold working increases not only the yield strength but also the tensile strength.   At the same time there is always a corresponding loss of ductility.   An example of this is found in the mechanical properties of commercially pure aluminum, known as 1100S.[4]

Increasing *Cold Work from* ↓	*Yield* *Strength*	*Tensile* *Strength*	*Elongation* *% in 2-in.* *Sample*	*Brinnell* *Hardness*
Fully annealed	5,000	13,000	45	23
	13,000	15,000	25	28
	14,000	17,000	20	32
	17,000	20,000	17	38
↓	21,000	24,000	15	44

[4] Data from *Metals Handbook,* American Society for Metals, Cleveland, 1948, p. 811.

SIMPLE ALLOYING

Simple alloying is intended to imply hardening resulting from effects of changes in chemical composition.   It is expressly intended by use of the term "simple alloying" to exclude any improvement in properties which may be effected by heat treatment.

5.4. Solid Solution Effects

It was stated in connection with the discussion of solutions that the hardness of one metal is increased when another metal is dissolved in it.   This common result of solid solution alloying can be traced to distortion produced in the crystal structure of the solvent metal by the acceptance of foreign atoms.   The foreign atoms tend to block the movement of dislocations and hence raise the resistance to glide or slip.   Two important generalizations can be stated regarding the effectiveness of alloy additions in achieving solid-solution hardening.   These are presented below.

Effect of the amount of solute present.   By studying an alloy system in which there is unlimited solid solubility of the two components in one another, it is possible to determine the effect of the amount of solute present.   This has been done for the silver-gold alloy system,[5] and also for the copper-nickel [6] system.   It has been observed that the hardness increases to a maximum at 50 atomic per cent of either component.   This represents maximum acceptance of silver atoms by the gold crystals, and vice versa, producing a corresponding maximum amount of distortion and maximum hardening effect.   This is illustrated in Fig. 5.2.

Effect of Relative Size of Solute and Solvent Atoms.   A study was made [7] of the change in hardness resulting from differences in size of solute and solvent atoms of a solid solution.   Copper was used as a solvent with various other metals as solutes.   The hardening effect was found to increase approximately in proportion to the distortion of the solvent crystal structure.   Distortion is dependent not only upon the relative sizes of the atoms but also upon the numbers of solute atoms present.   Therefore the hardening effect has

[5] Sachs, G., and J. Weert, *Z. Physik,* **62** (1930), p. 473.

[6] Osswald, E., *Z. Physik,* **83** (1933), p. 55.

[7] Brick, R. M., D. L. Martin, and R. P. Angier, *Preprint 37,* American Society for Metals, Cleveland, 1942.

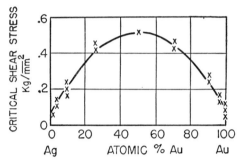

Fig. 5.2. **Solid-solution hardening.** A curve showing how the critical resolved shear stress varies with the composition of silver-gold alloys. The greatest hardening of gold occurs when the maximum amount of silver is in solution. The reverse of this statement is also true. [After G. Sachs and J. Weerts, *Zeitschrift für Physik*. Springer-Verlag (Berlin), 1943.]

been plotted (see Fig. 5.3) on the basis of equal numbers of atoms; that is, hardening per atomic per cent in solution versus the change in length (of one side of the face-centered cubic copper unit cell) for each atomic per cent in solution.

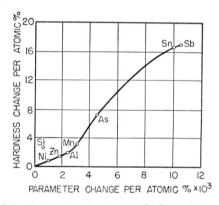

Fig. 5.3. **Solid-solution hardening and distortion of the crystal structure.** The solid-solution hardening of copper alloys is directly related to alteration of lattice parameter. [After R. M. Brick, D. L. Martin, and R. P. Angier, *Transactions of The American Society for Metals*. American Society for Metals.]

5.5. Effects of Heterogeneous Mixtures

The effects of changes in chemical composition which produce heterogeneous structures lend themselves to a generalization: *The properties of the alloy are largely governed by the amount and prop-*

erties of the continuous phase. The continuous phase is also called the matrix; it is the phase in which other phases exist as isolated regions or patches. If the continuous phase is hard and brittle, the alloy tends to be hard and brittle. On the other hand if the continuous phase is soft and ductile, the alloy has tendencies in this direction. The relative amounts of the continuous and isolated phases must also be considered in determining the effect of the continuous phase. It is also necessary to take into account particle shape of the discontinuous phase and the way in which these particles are distributed.

A striking example of this principle is found in steel which is abnormally high in sulfur. In high-sulfur steels, the sulfur tends to surround the grains, forming a network or continuous phase of iron sulfide. Iron sulfide is a constituent which is molten at the hot-rolling temperature of steel, so that steels having a sulfide network crack and tear apart at these temperatures. Manganese has a great affinity for sulfur, and if sufficient manganese is present it combines with the sulfur to form manganese sulfide. Manganese sulfide does not exist as the continuous phase, but instead is concentrated as small pools throughout the steel. Since there is no longer present a continuous network which softens at elevated temperatures, the high-temperature properties of the steel are improved. Thus, the addition of manganese removes a continuous phase and the harmful effects associated with it.

The effects of varying carbon content on the properties of non-heat-treated steels can be explained on the basis of the properties and amounts of the continuous phase which is present. This topic is discussed at length under the iron-iron carbide diagram.

The importance of the nature of the discontinuous phase is illustrated by a comparison of nodular and gray cast iron. The discontinuous phase is graphite in both cases. (See Fig. 7.7). In gray cast iron, the graphite exists as flakes, whereas in nodular iron, graphite is present as spherical particles or nodules. In both cases the graphite has negligible load-carrying capacity and could just as well be replaced by voids. The flakes act as sharp notches which intensify stress and reduce ductility. The nodules represent a much less abrupt change in cross section. Ductility is therefore much better in nodular cast iron (10 per cent elongation before rupture) than in gray cast iron (0 per cent elongation before rupture).

PRECIPITATION HARDENING

5.6. General Principles

A fourth method by which metals can be hardened is known as precipitation hardening. A slight variation of this is known as age hardening, but the essential features of both are the same. Age hardening is a process that increases hardness and strength, and ordinarily decreases ductility. It depends upon the slow precipitation of a constituent from a supersaturated solid solution at room temperature. Since the process occurs over long periods of time, it is called age hardening. When the same precipitation is carried out at elevated temperatures, it occurs with greater speed and is called precipitation hardening. All precipitation hardenable alloys

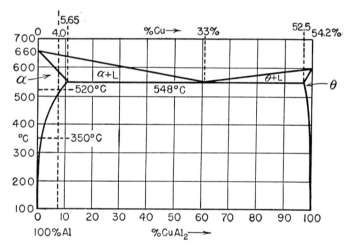

Fig. 5.4. Precipitation hardening. The equilibrium diagram for Al-CuAl$_2$ system is shown above. At the top of the diagram, compositions have been indicated in terms of per cent by weight of copper. The per cent by weight of CuAl$_2$ is plotted at the bottom of the diagram.

exhibit a decrease in solubility of one component in another with decreasing temperature.

When foreign atoms are present in a solvent structure to form a solid solution, they are believed to distort the structure and block the movement of dislocations. Thus, when the solid solution alloy is strained, dislocations accumulate, strength increases, and ductility decreases. In the precipitation hardenable alloys, the particles of precipitate increase the distortion of the solvent structure from which they form. Each particle of precipitated phase can be considered as a separate crystallite. The regions separating the particles of precipitate from the surrounding or matrix phase can be considered as grain boundary regions. Again, distortion blocks the dislocations and strength is increased and ductility decreased, in contrast to the behavior of the supersaturated solid solution from which the precipitation occurred.

The alloy containing 4 per cent copper and 96 per cent aluminum is a typical precipitation hardenable alloy. This composition provides an example of hardening by precipitation. Copper and aluminum react together to form an intermetallic compound which has the formula $CuAl_2$. In many respects $CuAl_2$ can be treated as a pure metal. It has a definite melting point, it is soluble in aluminum, forming a solid solution designated by the Greek letter α, and aluminum in turn is slightly soluble in solid $CuAl_2$. This latter solid solution is designated θ. Taking aluminum as one component and $CuAl_2$ as another component, the phase diagram for the system appears as in Fig. 5.4. It can be seen that $CuAl_2$ has a maximum solubility in aluminum at 548°C, 10.4 per cent by weight of $CuAl_2$ being soluble at this temperature. As the temperature drops, the solubility of $CuAl_2$ decreases; i.e., at 300°C the solubility of $CuAl_2$ in aluminum is only 0.83 per cent by weight. Consider a melt containing 7.4 per cent $CuAl_2$. Sand castings of this composition undergo coring, so that at 548°C some eutectic liquid still remains. When this freezes, a divorced eutectic forms in which much of the $CuAl_2$ solidifies as massive particles at the grain boundaries of the alpha grains.

Now if the sand cast alloy is reheated to 520°C and held at this temperature for a long enough time, the $CuAl_2$ precipitate dissolves in the α grains. This is known as solution heat treatment. If the solid solution is now very quickly cooled to room temperature, a supersaturated solid solution is formed in which the $CuAl_2$ remains dissolved. The supersaturated solution is not normal, and slowly decomposes with precipitation of very fine θ particles. Accompanying this precipitation is a gain in hardness and loss of ductility known as age hardening.

On the other hand, if the supersaturated alloy is reheated to an intermediate temperature of about 350°C, the time required for precipitation is reduced. This process is known as precipitation hardening. The various steps in the process are schematically shown in Fig. 5.5.

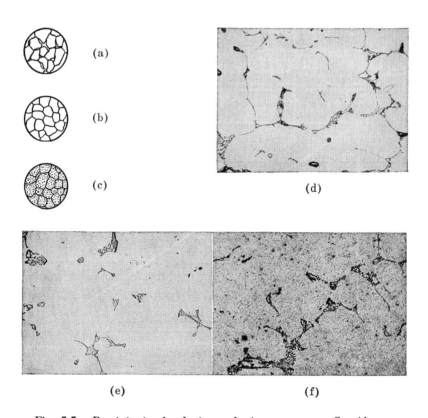

Fig. 5.5. Precipitation hardening and microstructure. Consider an alloy containing 4.0 per cent copper and refer to Fig. 5.4. (a) The sand-cast alloy contains large particles of θ phase at the grain boundaries. Precipitation of θ has occurred in this composition because of coring. The θ phase is actually a part of a divorced eutectic. (b) In the alloy after rapid cooling from 520°C, the θ phase has been dissolved. This is known as a solution heat-treated alloy in which a supersaturated condition exists. (c) If the solution heat-treated alloy is heated to 350°C (i.e., some temperature well below that used for solution heat-treating) the θ phase precipitates in a finely divided state throughout the grains and at the grain boundaries. In some alloys the precipitate is principally at the grain boundaries; in others it is distributed uniformly throughout the grains. Sometimes the precipitating phase forms selectively on certain crystallographic planes within the grains.

5.7. Factors Affecting Final Hardness and Speed of Hardening

It is fairly well established that, as aging proceeds, a sufficient number of atoms of the precipitating substances form crystal nuclei. These grow in size by diffusion of the supersaturated constituent toward them, and distortion of both the precipitate and matrix crystals occurs at the juncture of the two. Frequently, the size of the precipitated particles represents a condition somewhere between solid solution dispersion of atoms and that of microscopically visible particles. As aging proceeds, the particles become larger, the number of particles probably decreases, and the degree of supersaturation diminishes. The increase in the size of the particles and the decrease in their number relieve the strain which blocks dislocation movement. Thus overaging (i.e., heating for too long a time or at too high a temperature) causes softening. An optimum particle size seems to be associated with hardening. If the particles are too *small* they do not produce sufficient distortion of the matrix structure. If the particles are too *large,* the strains formerly associated with them disappear and simultaneously, relief of internal stresses and decrease in hardness occur.

There are various factors which have an important bearing on the progress and results of precipitation hardening. First consider the effect of the *concentration of the alloying elements* as shown by the copper-silver system. Figure 5.7 shows the Brinell hardness for various copper-silver alloys containing up to 7.5 per cent copper. The steepness of the initial portion of the curve is an indication of the speed of hardening. In this example, samples of the solution heat-treated alloy were heated at a constant temperature for increasing periods of time. The rate of hardening is related to concentration, and increases as the concentration increases. The reason for this is that nuclei formation and growth depend upon diffusion of the supersaturated component within the solid solution. Referring back to the discussion on diffusion, it is evident that diffusion within a solid solution is hastened by an increase in concentration gradient. When the first nucleus forms, it depletes the solid solution of solute in the immediate vicinity of the nucleus. This sets up a concentration gradient in which the concentration varies from nearly zero (near the nucleus) to the concentration of the supersaturated solution (at a distance from the nucleus). It is also seen from the curves of Fig. 5.6 that the maximum achievable hardness is greater for the higher concentrations. This presumably is due to a greater amount of precipitate of optimum particle size. However, overaging occurs earlier for the higher concentrations because diffusion occurs faster and the particles coalesce faster into sizes unfavorable to maximum hardness. Diffusion occurs more slowly at the lower concentrations, and hence a longer time is required for the same end results.

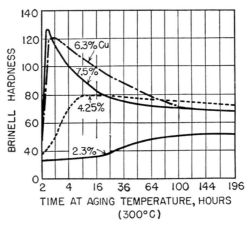

Fig. 5.6. Rate of aging versus concentration of solute. The time required for the aging cycle to run its course is decreased by an increase in the concentration of solute. That is to say, hardening and eventual softening occur faster at higher concentrations of solute. [After G. Sachs and K. R. Van Horn, *Practical Metallurgy*. American Society for Metals, 1947.]

A second factor having an important bearing on diffusion is *temperature*. The effect of temperature is shown in Fig. 5.7. It will be observed that the rate of hardening (initial slope of curve) increases with higher temperatures, but that the maximum hardness is lower for the higher temperatures. It is also apparent that overaging, as indicated by softening, sets in sooner in the case of the higher temperatures. The effect of temperature can be attributed to its effect on diffusion and annealing. Since precipitation hardening depends upon diffusion, its final results can be achieved in a shorter time by increasing the temperature of precipitation. Unfortunately, stress relief also occurs faster at elevated temperatures. Accompanying stress relief is a relaxation of the crystal distortions which are believed to be responsible for hardening. Therefore at higher precipitating temperatures, stress relief occurs as fast as additional precipitation can set up new stresses, and maximum possible hardness is never attained.

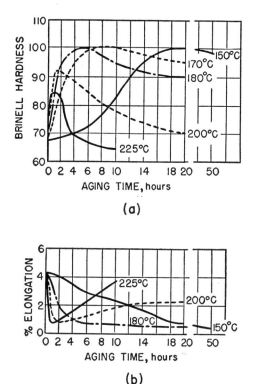

(a)

(b)

Fig. 5.7. Effect of temperature on speed of aging. The time required for the aging cycle to run its course is shortened by raising the temperature at which aging occurs. This is shown by a plot of hardness versus time, as in (a), and by a plot of elongation versus time, as in (b). Although the maximum hardness is reached in a shorter time at higher temperatures, the maximum hardness is lower for higher aging temperatures. [After G. Sachs and K. R. Van Horn, *Practical Metallurgy*. American Society for Metals, 1947.]

Questions

5.1. What is the term *hardening of metals* intended to mean as used in this text?

5.2. What are the five distinct methods of hardening metals?

5.3. Other considerations being equal, why does reduction of grain size effect an increase in hardness?

5.4. Explain how cold work achieves an increase in hardness.

5.5. Explain how solid-solution formation results in hardening of aloys. What factors will determine the degree of hardening?

5.6. What generalization can be made regarding the properties of heterogeneous alloys? Give an example which bears out this principle.

5.7. Distinguish between precipitation and age hardening. Discuss the mechanism proposed to explain precipitation hardening.

5.8. What factors affect the speed of and final hardness achieved by precipitation hardening? Explain why this is so.

Bibliography

5.1. Chalmers, Bruce, *Progress in Metals Physics,* Vol. 1 and Vol. 3. New York: Interscience Publishers, 1949 and 1952.

5.2. Hume-Rothery, William, *Electrons, Atoms, Metals, and Alloys.* London: The Louis Cassier Co., Ltd., 1955.

5.3. Barrett, C. S., *The Structure of Metals,* 2nd Ed. New York: McGraw-Hill Book Co., Inc., 1952.

5.4. Smith, Morton C., *Principles of Physical Metallurgy.* New York: Harper and Brothers, 1956.

5.5. Zener, C., "Metallurgical Designing," *Westinghouse Engineer,* Sept. 1956, pp. 146–151.

CHAPTER 6

Annealing: Recovery, Recrystallization, and Grain Growth

6.1. Cold Work and Annealing

Cold work occurs when a metal is deformed permanently in such a way that the grains are distorted, crystal planes are bent, and residual stresses remain in the piece upon removal of the load which produced the deformation. The hardness and yield strength are increased and ductility decreased by cold working. For most metals (with the notable exception of lead) cold work is accomplished simply by deforming the metal at room temperature. If the temperature at which deformation is carried out is raised beyond a certain value, cold work does not occur. This temperature, known as the recrystallization temperature, is principally dependent upon the metal involved and the rate of deformation. In general, the higher the melting point of the metal, the higher the recrystal-

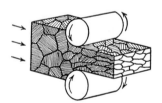

Fig. 6.1. Effect of cold work on grain shape. Cold rolling tends to elongate and flatten the grains. Other forms of cold work result in similar changes in grain size and shape.

lization temperature. If the recrystallization temperature is exceeded, hot work rather than cold work results. The effects of cold rolling on grain size and shape are shown in Fig. 6.1.

Some or all the effects of cold work can be removed by a process known as annealing, which consists of raising the cold-worked metal to a temperature which depends largely upon the metal involved, the severity of the cold deformation, the result to be achieved, and the time the metal is to be held at temperature.

6.2. The Progress of Annealing

Annealing under some circumstances has been observed to involve three steps, which are known as (1) recovery, (2) recrystallization, and (3) grain growth. Generally, the steps occur almost simultaneously and it is not possible to distinguish the changes accompanying each step. In the discussion which follows it is assumed they can be observed to occur as separate steps.

Recovery. Recovery is the least well understood of the three phases of annealing. It was stated that after cold working residual stresses are found in metals. An example of these residual stresses is found in cold-drawn wire, in which it has been observed that the outer fibers are in tension and the inner fibers in compression. This is illustrated by a cross section of such a piece of wire in Fig. 6.2. Residual tensile stresses in the surface of drawn brass car-

Fig. 6.2. **Cold work and residual stresses.** Residual stresses are introduced in cold-drawn wire as a result of the cold-working operation. The outer fibers at A will contain residual tensile stresses, and the inner fibers at B will be in compression.

tridge cases have led to the form of stress corrosion known as season cracking; this was mentioned earlier in this text. One of the principal effects of recovery is the removal of most of the residual stresses, and it is therefore useful in eliminating or minimizing stress corrosion caused by residual stresses. Recovery may also involve improvement in electric conductivity and other properties not important enough for mention here. Recovery does not involve appreciable changes in hardness, yield strength, or ductility.

Recrystallization. During recrystallization new equiaxed un-strained grains are nucleated in the metal. The nuclei for these grains seem to form largely at the grain boundaries of the distorted grains or at other discontinuities in the piece. The nuclei grow until new grains with new orientations have replaced the old grains. Accompanying recrystallization are significant changes in the me-chanical properties of the metal. Ductility is improved, while hardness and strength are sacrificed. Any residual stresses which may remain after recovery and before recrystallization are fully eliminated. The recrystallization temperature is always lower, the higher the purity of the metal, unless an impurity is present as a second phase; in the latter case, nucleation is promoted.

Grain growth. The final step in annealing involves growth of the new grains which formed during recrystallization. As the grain size increases, the metal becomes somewhat softer and more ductile, and eventually the grain size may exceed that which existed prior to deformation. Fig. 6.3 shows the microstructure of a sheet of cold-rolled brass and the changes brought about by recrystallization and grain growth.

6.3. Fundamentals of Annealing

As a result of studies of annealing processes, some basic discov-eries have been made, and three of these are taken up here in some detail.

It has been learned that *there is a relationship between the degree of cold work and the temperature of recrystallization.* If all other variables are held constant, as the amount of prior cold work in-creases there is a decrease in the temperature at which recrystalliza-tion occurs. This may be explained as follows: for recrystalliza-tion to occur (1) there must exist in the piece some points at which nucleation can occur, and (2) the atoms must be mobile enough to assume the positions of a new strain-free unit cell. Regions of re-sidual stress, grain boundaries, and discontinuities in the structure are believed to provide nucleating centers. Increasing the amount of cold work increases the number of each of these regions and hence enhances nucleation. Raising the temperature increases atom mo-bility and improves the probability that strain-free nuclei will form. Therefore recrystallization is dependent upon both temperature and

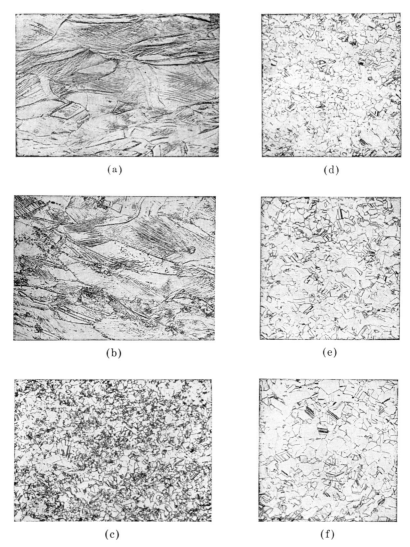

Fig. 6.3. Recrystallization of cold-worked brass. (a) The cold-worked structure. Other photomicrographs represent the structures which exist after annealing at 650°C for periods of time as indicated. (b) 15 seconds. (c) 30 seconds. (d) 60 seconds. (e) 2 minutes. (f) 4 minutes. (g) 10 minutes. (h) 30 minutes. (i) 60 minutes. (j) 90 minutes. In (b), nucleation has started and a few very small new crystals can be seen. These exist largely at the

the degree of cold work. For any particular temperature, there is a critical amount of cold work which must be exceeded in order for recrystallization to occur in a reasonable length of time. The rela-

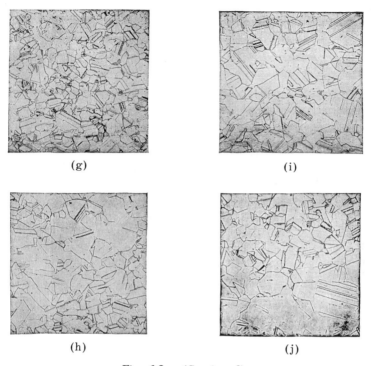

(g)   (i)

(h)   (j)

Fig. 6.3.   (Continued)

grain boundaries of the old grains. In (c), recrystallization is complete, although a ghost pattern of the previously existing grains can be faintly detected. The remaining pictures show growth of the grains as the time at temperature increases. Etchant: $H_2O_2 +$ NH_4OH. Magnification: $200\times$. [Courtesy of the School of Engineering, Metals Laboratory, University of Massachusetts.]

tionship between degree of cold work and recrystallization temperature is shown by a plot of the hardness of pieces of copper (cold worked different amounts) versus the temperature of annealing. A drop in hardness is indicative that recrystallization has occurred. Fig. 6.4 shows that when annealing time (the "reasonable time" mentioned above) is held constant, the temperature required for recrystallization increases as the amount of prior cold work decreases.

It has been determined that *there is a relationship between the time and temperature of annealing.* If other variables are fixed, the same degree of annealing may be achieved by using a long time at low temperature or a short time at high temperature. Thus, the temperature of recrystallization can be depressed by using

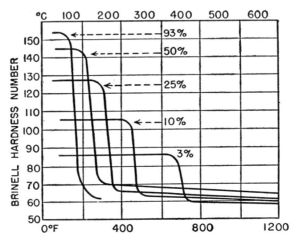

Fig. 6.4. Annealing temperature decreases with increasing prior cold work. The temperature required for annealing cold-worked metal is lowered by increasing the severity of the cold work which preceded annealing. This is shown by annealing several pieces of copper which had previously received different amounts of reduction by cold rolling. The percentages indicate the decrease in thickness produced by the rolling operation. [After G. Sachs and K. R. Van Horn, *Practical Metallurgy*. American Society for Metals, 1947.]

longer times of annealing. It is approximately correct to say that for every 10°C (18°F) increase in annealing temperature, the annealing time is halved. Fig. 6.5 shows the relationship between time and temperature of annealing for cold-worked copper. In this illustration, a decrease in tensile strength indicates the progress of annealing. Although of limited practical application, the rates of annealing and of grain growth are related to temperature by an equation of the form:

$$E = Ae^{-Q/RT}$$

(See Section 3.14 and reference [*6.3*].)

The *variables which affect final grain size* after annealing is completed have been studied. It has been learned that the final grain size is largely dependent upon G/N relationships similar to those which determine the grain size of crystals forming from a melt. Probably the *most important single factor in determining the final grain size* for a given time and temperature of annealing is the degree of prior cold work. Fig. 6.6 illustrates the effect of prior cold work on the grain size of low-carbon steel after it has been recrystallized at 950°C.   Below 7 per cent deformation in this case there is insufficient deformation to produce recrystallization at the temperature used.   At 7 per cent deformation, the critical amount is barely achieved.   At this point, the degree of cold work has introduced only a very small number of nucleating centers, and hence N is small, G/N is relatively large, and grain size is large.[1]   Beyond 7 per cent, additional amounts of deformation serve to increase the number of points at which nuclei can form, but there is no effect on the rate of grain growth.   Therefore N increases while G remains fixed and G/N becomes smaller, and a smaller grain size results.   Temperature also has an effect on final grain size, but it

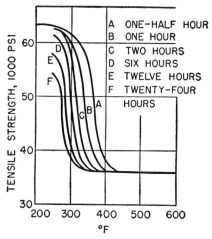

Fig. 6.5.   **Time-temperature relationship during annealing.**   Time and temperature are inversely related for annealing, i.e., the same effect can be achieved in a shorter time at a higher temperature than at a lower temperature.   This is shown by annealing studies carried out on copper which had previously undergone a 93 per cent reduction.   [After G. Sachs and K. R. Van Horn, *Practical Metallurgy.* American Society for Metals, 1947.]

is less significant than is the amount of prior cold deformation. After recrystallization is complete, *higher temperatures* increase the rate of growth of the larger of the existing grains, which absorb the smaller grains.   No new nuclei form at this stage of the process. *Longer times* at temperature promote grain growth, which proceeds

---

[1] When G/N is applied to recrystallization, N stands for the number of nucleating centers.   In respect to solidification, N indicates the rate of nucleation.

fairly rapidly at first, but eventually seems to stop for all practical purposes. *Insoluble impurities* have been observed to exert effects on grain size, but the nature of their effect is not thoroughly understood, and generalizations are rather dangerous in this case.

The *rate of cooling* from the annealing temperature is often erroneously considered to have an effect on the microstructure. This is not true unless phase changes occur within the range of cooling. *Properties* may be altered by very rapid cooling rates even though the *microstructure* is unaffected. Very rapid cooling rates are likely to produce residual stresses because of uneven cooling of the piece. In simple shapes made of alloys which do not undergo phase changes, rapid cooling produces residual compressive stresses in the surface. These probably improve fatigue strength. Extremely slow cooling rates can be considered equivalent to an increase in time at annealing temperature.

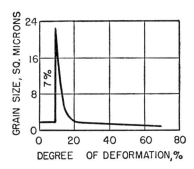

Fig. 6.6. Effect of degree of prior cold deformation on grain size after annealing. The plot is for a low-carbon steel annealed at 950 °C. [Adapted from *Metals Handbook*. American Society for Metals, 1948.]

Single crystals. The basic dependence of the final grain size on the degree of prior cold work has provided the basis for producing single crystals, which are useful in fundamental research. Single crystals are made by controlling the amount of cold work prior to annealing. The alloy of Fig. 6.6 would require about 7 per cent deformation, so that only one nucleating center would be produced, thus achieving a very large grain size upon annealing.

6.4. The Instability of the Cold-Worked Condition

Cold-worked metals are unstable because of their high internal energy. Micro- and macro-residual stresses exist throughout the mass, and in addition there are submicroscopic stresses. The latter accompany distortion of crystallographic planes such as occurs at the grain boundaries or within the grains of cold-worked metals. These stresses are associated with high internal energy, and since energy always tends to be dissipated, there is a tendency for the atoms in the crystal structure to rearrange themselves in positions which are stress-free and strain-free. Annealing involves such a relocation of atoms. It proceeds at an infinitesimally slow rate, well below the so-called recrystallization temperature for a cold-worked piece of metal. By raising the temperature, the mobility of the atoms is increased and their relocation is facilitated so that annealing occurs faster at higher temperatures. The end result of annealing a piece of metal would seem to be a single crystal in which all the atoms are located in their ideal crystallographic positions and in which there are no grain boundary regions of crystal imperfection. This, however, is disputed by work [2] which indicates that grain growth ceases when all the grains in a metal have flat faces making 120° angles with adjacent faces, regardless of grain size.

6.6. Creep, Strain Hardening, and Annealing

There is still another less important variable which has not been mentioned in connection with annealing. For larger original grain sizes, greater amounts of cold deformation are required to produce equivalent recrystallization temperatures and times. This can be used to explain the increased creep strength of coarse-grained metals over fine-grained metals. Softening and annealing may be considered to be progressing in cold-worked metals, even at temperatures below the recrystallization temperature. The speed of annealing at these temperatures is very slow. As the temperature is raised, the speed of annealing increases. Consider a piece of metal which is being deformed by a load at room temperature. Strain hardening and deformation occur simultaneously, and therefore the rate of strain hardening (related to the rate of deformation) is a great deal faster than the rate of annealing. Thus the load is balanced at a certain deformation and deformation stops as long as the load is held constant. Since the rate of softening or annealing is increased by a rise in temperature (strain hardening is apparently instantaneous with deformation and hence its rate is

[2] Harker, D., and E. R. Parker, *Preprint 38*, American Society for Metals, Cleveland, 1944.

independent of temperature), eventually such a temperature is reached that for a constant load there is a constant rate of deformation. This is truly plastic behavior, and is the condition which exists during the secondary stage of creep. Strain hardening in this instance is not sufficient to overcome the effects of softening or annealing, and so the load cannot be balanced at a permanent deformation. Let us recall that larger original grain sizes require greater amounts of deformation to produce equivalent recrystallization times and temperatures. This being so metals of coarser grain size can undergo a greater amount of deformation, and therefore more strain hardening, before softening sets in at the particular temperature of loading.

6.7. Homogenizing Anneals

Annealing is also carried out for the purpose of producing a more homogeneous metal structure. As a result of dendritic segregation during freezing, there is a tendency for the low-melting portions of an alloy to become concentrated at the grain boundaries. Segregation of this type can be eliminated by heating the metal to an elevated temperature, thus speeding diffusion so that a uniform composition occurs in a reasonable time. This is known as a homogenizing anneal. It is particularly applicable to cast structures, in which case it not only improves the uniformity of composition, but also relieves any residual stresses which may result from the casting technique. A slight amount of prior cold work improves the speed of diffusion in a homogenizing anneal by increasing the number of crystal imperfections along which diffusion is believed to occur most easily.

6.8. Full Annealing

The full annealing of steel is discussed under the topic of the operations of heat treatment of steel. Full annealing involves a change in properties because of phase changes in the steel. It is not dependent upon cold working of the metal for its results. Unlike the other forms of annealing which have been described, rate of cooling has an important bearing on the final properties of fully annealed steel. In fact, if the rate of cooling is appreciably faster than furnace cooling, the process cannot be termed a full anneal.

Questions

6.1. What changes accompanying cold work identify the deformation as such rather than as hot work?

6.2. How is annealing accomplished and what effect does it have on the properties of cold-worked metals?

6.3. What relationship exists between the degree of cold work and the temperature of recrystallization? Explain why this relationship exists.

6.4. What is the relation existing between time and temperature of annealing?

6.5. What is the most important single factor in determining the final grain size of an annealed cold-worked piece? Why? What other factors have an effect on final grain size? Do ordinary cooling rates from the annealing temperature have an effect on properties and microstructure of the annealed metal?

6.6. Discuss the proposed explanation as to why coarse-grained metals have greater creep strength than fine-grained metals.

6.7. What is meant by a homogenizing anneal?

Bibliography

6.1. *Metals Handbook.* Cleveland: American Society for Metals, 1948.
6.2. Symposium, *Working of Metals.* Cleveland: American Society for Metals, 1937.
6.3. Larson, F. R., and J. Salmas, "A Time-Temperature Relationship for Recrystallization and Grain Growth," *Trans. ASM,* **46** (1954).

CHAPTER 7

Phase Changes in Iron and Steel

EQUILIBRIUM PHASE CHANGES AND THE IRON-IRON CARBIDE DIAGRAM

7.1. Significance of the Diagram

Although the iron-iron carbide diagram has limited application in actual practice, the ability to interpret it is of importance: it provides a fundamental approach to the principles of alloying, hot working, and heat treating of steel. Using the diagram, it is possible to establish a correlation between the properties and microstructures of slowly cooled plain carbon steels. Studies made of the modifying effects on the diagram of many alloying elements have led to a better understanding of the properties and microstructures of the alloy steels. These concepts are discussed more fully in the following sections.

7.2. Equilibrium Cooling

The iron-iron carbide diagram states the compositions of the phases which are present at various temperatures as a result of equilibrium cooling or heating of iron and carbon alloys. Strictly speaking, equilibrium cooling or heating means a change in temperature at an infinitestimally small rate. Thus equilibrium changes represent a condition which is approached but never reached. In this text, the term "equilibrium cooling" signifies a very slow cooling rate, such as might be achieved in a well-insulated furnace.

7.3. Phases and Constituents

The phases which may be present under equilibrium conditions in the iron-iron carbide system are liquid, α-iron, γ-iron, δ-iron, and cementite. The *liquid phase* may consist of any combination of iron and carbon, within the composition limits of the diagram. *Cementite,* or iron carbide (Fe_3C) is a chemical compound containing 6.7 per cent carbon. It is one of the components of the system, and as such indicates the maximum amount of carbon which may be present. (100 per cent cementite is equivalent to 6.7 per cent carbon.) Cementite is an extremely hard, brittle phase of complex crystal structure. Iron, the other component of the diagram, exists in three allotropic forms. Delta iron is a body-centered cubic structure which exists only at high temperature. Alpha iron, which is the form present at room temperature, also has a body-centered cubic structure. It is known as ferrite, and is a soft ductile phase. Gamma iron, or austenite, has a face-centered cubic structure. It is sometimes considered to be slightly harder and less ductile than ferrite, although a comparison is difficult to make. Gamma iron exists in a temperature range between α iron and δ iron, though there is overlapping, as can be seen from the diagram. All three forms of iron dissolve carbon, and the letters α, γ, and δ are used to represent both pure iron and the solid solutions of carbon in iron.

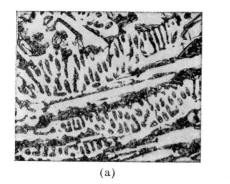   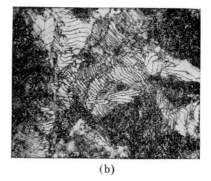

(a)   (b)

Fig. 7.1. Eutectic and eutectoid structures in iron-carbon alloys. (a) A white cast iron showing a eutectic structure known as *ledeburite* (1500×, nital etch). (b) A eutectoid steel showing the structure known as *pearlite* (1500×, nital etch). [Courtesy of the School of Engineering, Metals Laboratory, University of Massachusetts.]

The above-mentioned phases are also constituents. In addition there are two other constituents, namely ledeburite and pearlite. The decomposed eutectic structure is called *ledeburite,* and has the spotted appearance shown in Fig. 7.1(*a*). It occurs only in cast iron. *Pearlite* is a very important constituent found in both steel and cast iron. It is the eutectoid structure and is composed of alternate layers of ferrite and cementite. (See Fig. 7.1(*b*).) Pearlite has hardness and ductility values between those of ferrite and cementite.

Martensite and bainite are also constituents found in steel. Neither is an equilibrium constituent, and therefore they are not discussed at this point.

7.4. Systems Shown on the Diagram

Reference to Fig. 7.2 shows that the iron-iron carbide diagram actually consists of a peritectic, a eutectic, and a eutectoid system. The δ region and the peritectic reaction near 2700°F (1485°C) are not significant in correlations of structure and properties, because

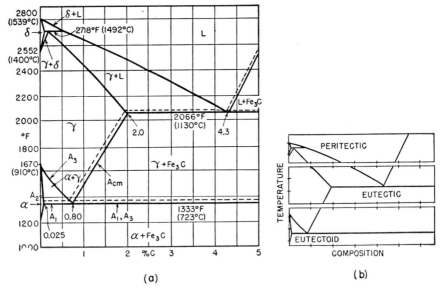

(a)   (b)

Fig. 7.2. The iron-iron carbide diagram. The iron-iron carbide diagram shown in (a) actually consists of a peritectic, eutectic, and eutectoid reaction as shown in the analysis of (b).

under ordinary conditions of processing plain carbon steel the peritectic structure is replaced by reasonably homogeneous austenite which undergoes further changes. However, the δ ⟶ γ transformation is of significance in certain alloy steels, as is pointed out later. It is for this reason that the δ region and the peritectic are shown.

7.5. Arrest Points and Phase Boundaries

Certain lines on the iron-iron carbide diagram are given designations such as A_1, A_3, A_{cm}. These lines are so identified, because they represent points of inflection in the heating or cooling curves for particular compositions. The A stands for the word "arrest" which indicates an arrest in the rate of change of temperature of a specimen to which heat is supplied or removed at a steady rate. An A_2 line exists, but has no significance in regard to phase changes. It represents a change in magnetic properties of iron and steel. On some diagrams A_{r1}, A_{c1}, and A_{e1} are used in place of A_1. Similar substitutions exist for A_3. This usage arises from the fact that the lines are displaced by heating or cooling the steel at faster than equilibrium rates. For instance, upon fairly rapid heating, the A_1 and A_3 lines are displaced upward, and become the A_{c1} and A_{c3}. The subscript c stands for the French word "chauffrage" which means heating. Upon cooling, the A_1 and A_3 lines are displaced downward, and are designated A_{r1} and A_{r3}. In this instance the r stands for the French word for cooling, i.e., "refroidissement." The true equilibrium lines are designated A_{e1} (or simply A_1) and A_{e3} (or A_3). They exist between the lines representing conditions of fairly rapid cooling or heating. The extent of the displacement of the lines from their equilibrium positions depends upon the degree of departure from equilibrium conditions. Thus, on two different diagrams, the A_{r1} lines might exist at different locations, because they represent different cooling rates.

7.6. Slow Cooling

Consider next the slow cooling of several different alloys of iron and carbon for which properties and microstructure are correlated. (Refer to Figs. 4.5 and 7.3.)

When a *steel containing 0.3 per cent carbon* cools from above 2800°F (1593°C), freezing starts at about 2770°F (1523°C), with the formation of δ crystals having a composition of approximately 0.05 per cent carbon. As the temperature drops, more δ forms, and less liquid remains. Slightly above 2718°F (1492°C) the δ contains

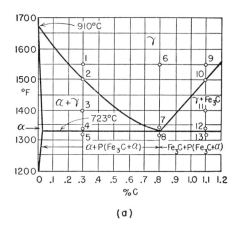

1700
910°C
1600
1500 °F
1400
723°C
α→
1300
1200
0 .1 .2 .3 .4 .5 .6 .7 .8 .9 1.0 1.1 1.2
% C

γ

6   9
1   10
2   11
α+γ 3   γ+Fe₃C
4   7   12
5   8   13
α+P(Fe₃C+α)   Fe₃C+P(Fe₃C+α)

(a)

Fig. 7.3. Equilibrium structures of iron-carbon alloys. The structures resulting from slow cooling of several iron-carbon alloys are shown here. In (a), the critical portion of the iron-iron carbide diagram has been reproduced. The small numbers appearing on the diagram correspond to the numbers of the sketches appearing in (b), (c), and (d). Part (b) represents the structures for an alloy containing 0.3 per cent carbon, (c) the structures for 0.8 per cent carbon, and (d) the structures for 1.1 per cent carbon.

TOTAL C = .3%

TEMPERATURE AND MICROSTRUCTURE	MICROCONSTITUENTS AND THEIR COMPOSITIONS	PERCENTAGES OF MICROCONSTITUENTS PRESENT
1550°F (843°C) ①	$\gamma = .3\% C$	$100\% \gamma$
1500°F (816°C) ②	$\gamma = .3 + \% C$ $\alpha \cong .01\% C$	$100 - \% \gamma$ $0 + \% \alpha$
1400°F (760°C) ③	$\gamma = .53\% C$ $\alpha = .02\% C$	$\frac{.28}{.51} \cong 55\% \gamma$ $\frac{.23}{.51} \cong 45\% \alpha$
1334°F (724°C) ④	$\gamma = .8\% C$ $\alpha = .025\% C$	$\frac{.275}{.775} \cong 36\% \gamma$ $\frac{.5}{.775} \cong 64\% \alpha$
1332°F (722°C) ⑤	PEARLITE = .8% C $Fe_3C = 6.7\% C$ $\alpha = .025\% C$ $\alpha = .025\% C$	36% P $12\% Fe_3C$ $88\% \alpha$ $64\% \alpha$

(b)

190

TOTAL C = .8% C

TEMPERATURE AND MICROSTRUCTURE	MICROCONSTITUENTS AND THEIR COMPOSITIONS	PERCENTAGES OF MICROCONSTITUENTS PRESENT
 1550°F (843°C) ⑥	$\gamma = .8\% C$	100% γ
 1334°F (724°C) ⑦	$\gamma = .8\% C$	100% γ
 1332°F (722°C) ⑧	PEARLITE = .8% C $Fe_3C = 6.7\% C$ $\alpha = .025\% C$	100% P $.775/6.675 \rightleftharpoons 11.6\% Fe_3C$ $5.9/6.675 \rightleftharpoons 88.4\% \alpha$

(c)

TOTAL C = 1.1% C

TEMPERATURE AND MICROSTRUCTURE	MICROCONSTITUENTS AND THEIR COMPOSITIONS	PERCENTAGES OF MICROCONSTITUENTS PRESENT
 1550°F (843°C) ⑨	$\gamma = 1.1\% C$	100% γ
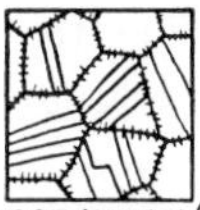 1500°F (816°C) ⑩	$\gamma = 1.1 - \% C$ $Fe_3C = 6.7\% C$	100 - % γ 0 + % Fe_3C
 1400°F (760°C) ⑪	$\gamma = .93\% C$ $Fe_3C = 6.7\% C$	$\frac{5.6}{5.77} \rightleftharpoons 97\% \gamma$ $\frac{.17}{5.77} \rightleftharpoons 3\% Fe_3C$
 1334°F (724°C) ⑫	$\gamma = .8\% C$ $Fe_3C = 6.7\% C$	$\frac{5.6}{5.9} \rightleftharpoons 95\% \gamma$ $\frac{.3}{5.9} \rightleftharpoons 5\% Fe_3C$
 1332°F (722°C) ⑬	PEARLITE .8% C $Fe_3C = 6.7\% C$ $\alpha = .025\% C$ $Fe_3C = 6.7\% C$	95% P 12% Fe_3C 88% α 5% Fe_3C

(d)

Fig. 7.3.   (Concluded)

0.1 per cent and the liquid 0.5 per cent carbon. The δ crystals are probably cored crystals. From the lever principle it can be determined that approximately one-half the mass is solid (δ) and one-half liquid. At 2718°F (1492°C) the δ and the liquid undergo the peritectic reaction, and a new phase, γ, appears. Immediately below 2718°F (1492°C), the phases in equilibrium are γ + L, in which the γ has the composition 0.18 per cent carbon, while the liquid still contains 0.5 per cent carbon. Therefore a shift has taken place as follows:

	Above 2718°F (1492°C)		Below 2718°F (1492°C)	
Phase	δ	L	γ	L
Carbon content of phase	0.1%	0.5%	0.18%	0.5%
Amount of phase	50%	50%	60%	40%

Thus additional solid has formed and all the δ has disappeared. The remaining liquid freezes as the temperature drops, and finally at 2680°F (1472°C) the last liquid, which contains about 0.8 per cent carbon, solidifies to form austenite whose final composition is the same as that of the initial liquid, namely 0.3 per cent carbon. If any coring exists, it is probably eliminated as a result of rapid diffusion at the high temperatures involved. When a temperature of 1550°F (844°C) is reached, the austenite may be considered to be homogeneous. At about 1500°F (817°C), ferrite, a new phase, commences to precipitate from the austenite. Nucleation of the new phase occurs principally at the grain boundaries of the existing austenite grains, as shown in Fig. 7.3(*b*). As the temperature gets closer to 1333°F (723°C) the composition of the ferrite approaches 0.025 per cent carbon, and the composition of the austenite approaches 0.8 per cent carbon. The amounts of the phases change accordingly, as shown in Fig. 7.3(*b*). At 1333°F (723°C) the remaining austenite undergoes a transformation to the eutectoid structure known as pearlite. *Pearlite is always formed from austenite under equilibrium conditions at 1333°F (723°C). Since austenite at this temperature always contains 0.8 per cent carbon, the pearlite into which it changes always contains 0.8 per cent carbon, and pearlite is always made up of alpha and cementite in the ratio of 88 per cent alpha to 12 per cent cementite.* This can be determined by use of the lever principle, using 0.8 per cent carbon as the location of the fulcrum, 0.025 per cent as the composition of the α, and 6.7 per cent as the composition of cemenite. Thus at temperatures below 1333°F (723°C), the final structure for a total composition 0.3 per cent carbon consists of a large (64 per cent) continuous α phase with a smaller (36 per cent) amount of pearlite. *The amount of pearlite is the same as the amount of the austenite from which it formed, i.e., γ which existed slightly above 1333°F (723°C).* It is present in the alloy under consideration as isolated *islands* of pearlite in a *sea* of ferrite. The islands are more frequently referred to as "pearlite colonies," and the sea as a *matrix*. The structure existing immediately after the transformation of austenite to pearlite does not change appreciably upon cooling to room temperature.

For a *total composition of 0.8 per cent carbon,* freezing starts at about 2670F° (1466°C), and is completed at about 2480°F (1361°C), possibly with the formation of a cored γ structure. Upon slowly cooling this to the neighborhood of 1333°F (723°C), the effects of coring are substantially removed, and a reasonably homogeneous austenite containing 0.8 per cent carbon exists at 1334°F (724°C). At 1333°F (723°C), the austenite changes over to a completely pearlitic structure of composition and make-up as previously described. *Under conditions approaching equilibrium,* the transformation of austenite to pearlite occurs at a constant temperature; in fact, *the temperature cannot drop until the transformation is complete.* For this particular composition there is no massive continuous phase corresponding to the ferrite in the 0.3 per cent carbon alloy. The pearlite in this, as in all cases of slow cooling, consists of 88 per cent α and 12 per cent cementite, and has a total carbon content of 0.8 per cent.

Upon cooling molten *steel containing 1.1 per cent carbon,* freezing commences at approximately 2630°F (1443°C). If a cored structure results, it is substantially eliminated upon slowly cooling this mass to slightly above 1500°F (817°C). At this temperature the structure should consist of homogeneous austenite. As the temperature drops and the A_{cm} line is crossed, cementite starts to precipitate from the austenite. The formation of the new phase follows the same pattern as the precipitation of ferrite from austenite, i.e., most nucleation occurs at the grain boundaries. Thus a network of cementite, outlining the austenite grain boundaries, forms as more and more cementite comes out of solution. At a temperature of 1334°F (724°C), the structure consists of austenite and cementite. Examination of the diagram shows that the austenite contains 0.8 per cent carbon dissolved in iron. The cementite is a chemical compound containing 6.7 per cent carbon. Applying the lever principle, the amounts of austenite and cementite can be calculated to be about 95 per cent γ and 5 per cent cementite. As the temperature is lowered past 1333°F (723°C), the austenite transforms into pearlite, as it always does at this temperature. The cementite network is unaffected by a decrease in temperature. Therefore the final structure consists of 95 per cent pearlite with a thin network consisting of 5 per cent cementite. Since slowly formed pearlite always has the same composition and structure, this pearlite must contain 88 per cent α and 12 per cent cementite.

The three steel compositions just described are typical of the three classes of steels known as the eutectoid, hypoeutectoid, and hypereutectoid compositions. Eutectoid steels always contain 0.8 per cent carbon and consist entirely of a pearlitic structure. The hypoeutectoid steels contain less than 0.8 per cent carbon and have a structure consisting of pearlite colonies surrounded by a ferritic matrix. The hypereutectoid steels have a carbon content greater than 0.8 per cent and consist of pearlite colonies surrounded by a cementite matrix. The size of the ferrite network in hypoeutectoid steels decreases with increasing carbon content. At 0.8 per cent carbon, the ferrite network disappears entirely. Beyond 0.8 per cent carbon a cementite network appears, the size of which increases with increasing carbon content. This can be confirmed by reference to the iron-iron carbide diagram and by use of the lever principle. The matrix phase is called the proeutectoid constituent. This name arises from the fact that the matrix forms immediately prior to the formation of the eutectoid constituent. The nature and amount of proeutectoid constituent depends upon the carbon content of the slowly cooled steels. In steels which are cooled faster than equilibrium cooling, the quantity of proeutectoid constituent is influenced by the cooling rate.

7.7. Correlation of Properties, Microstructure, and Carbon Content

Recall for the moment the properties of the various constituents found in steel. Refer also to the statement in Section 5.5 regarding heterogeneous alloys. Since a hypoeutectoid steel contains a continuous phase of soft, ductile ferrite, it is reasonable to expect the hypoeutectoids to be soft and ductile. Furthermore, as the carbon content increases and the amount of free (i.e., in the matrix) ferrite decreases, the steel becomes harder and less ductile. That this is the actual case can be seen by referring to Fig. 7.4. In the hypereutectoid steels a hard, brittle cementite matrix exists. These are therefore very hard, brittle steels. However, the tensile

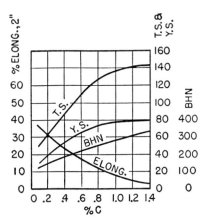

Fig. 7.4. **The properties of hot-worked steels versus carbon content.** It should be noted that these curves are for hot-worked carbon steels. Curves for equilibrium cooled steels would differ slightly from those shown. [Adapted from *Metal Industries Catalogue.* The Reinhold Publishing Corporation, 1947.]

strength of cementite is somewhat lower than might be expected from its hardness. Thus increasing amounts of free cementite produce less increase in tensile strength than in hardness.

7.8. Changes Occurring Upon Heating Steel

When steel is heated from room temperature to the austenite range or above, changes occur in the microstructure in the reverse order of those just described. In addition, there are important changes in grain size which are described below.

References to the grain size of steel apply to the austenite grain size which existed prior to the precipitation of the proeutectoid constituent or the formation of pearlite. In steels whose composition is reasonably close to 0.8 per cent carbon, the size of the previously existing austenite grains is indicated by the proeutectoid network, which is nucleated at the grain boundaries of the austenite. Thus, before formation of pearlite, the austenite grain boundaries are outlined by ferrite or cementite. A practical estimate of austenite grain size can be made from the microstructure. The importance of austenite grain size in heat-treating considerations will be indicated subsequently.

Consider heating a steel which has a carbon content of 0.3 per cent. When this alloy is heated slowly from room temperature, the first significant change occurs at 1333°F (723°C). Here the pearlite is transformed to austenite. The austenite grains are nucleated at discontinuities, and since there is a discontinuity at the boundary between each lamella of cementite and ferrite in pearlite, the opportunities for nucleation are considerable. Thus the transformation of each pearlite colony produces many austenite grains. Therefore there are many more austenite grains in a piece of steel immediately following heating above 1333°F (723°C), than there were in the original piece of steel upon its initial cooling. By alternately heating and cooling a piece of steel near its critical temperature, a very fine austenite grain size may be produced.

If the steel is held for a long period of time at temperatures above 1333°F (723°C), the small austenite grains grow. The same result is achieved by heating the steel to very high temperatures for shorter periods of time. Thus control of grain size is a practical possibility in steel even though no cold work is involved. If a large grain size is desired, the steel should be heated into the austenite region for a long time. If a small grain size is desired, the steel should be heated and cooled several times above and below its critical temperature. The effect of heating and cooling on grain size is illustrated in Fig. 7.5.

7.9. White Cast Iron and Malleable Cast Iron

Steels are usually considered to be alloys of iron which contain less than 2 per cent carbon. Most steels contain appreciably less than this amount. Alloys having a carbon content greater than 2 per cent are called cast irons. Of the several varieties of cast irons, white cast iron is the only one whose properties and structure are indicated by the iron-iron carbide diagram.

White Cast Iron. Consider the freezing and cooling of an alloy of iron and carbon containing about 2.5 per cent carbon. Austenite

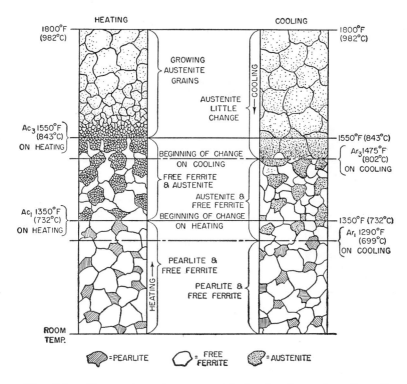

Fig. 7.5. Changes in grain structure during heating and cooling of a 0.25 per cent carbon steel. [After C. G. Johnson, *Metallurgy.* The American Technical Society, 1948.]

nuclei commence to form in this alloy at about 2400°F (1317°C). As cooling proceeds, the amount of solid austenite increases until at 2066°F (1130°C) the eutectic solid forms from the remaining liquid. The eutectic solid in this case consists of globules of austenite in a cementite matrix (Fig. 7.6). Since the A_{cm} line in the iron-iron carbide diagram slopes to the left, as cooling progresses below 2066°F (1130°C), the primary austenite (i.e., dendrites) as well as the eutectic austenite must precipitate cementite. Thus the quantity of cementite increases as the temperature approaches the eutectoid temperature. At 1333°F (723°C), the austenite undergoes the typical transformation to pearlite. The final structure consists of large pearlite colonies (from the primary austenite dendrites), plus small pearlite colonies (from the eutectic austenite) in a matrix of eutectic cementite. The small pearlite colonies and the surrounding cementite produce the structure called

ledeburite.   As can be seen in Fig. 7.7 (a), white cast iron contains
a massive cementite matrix, which produces a material having
high hardness, low ductility, and fairly low strength.   White cast

TEMPERATURE AND MICROSTRUCTURE	MICROCONSTITUENTS AND THEIR COMPOSITIONS	PERCENTAGES OF MICROCONSTITUENTS PRESENT
 2200°F (1204°C)	LIQUID=3.6% C (DARK) γ = 1.7% C (LIGHT)	42% LIQUID (DARK) 58% γ (LIGHT)
 2067°F (1131°C)	LIQUID= 4.3% C (DARK) γ=2.0% C (LIGHT)	22% LIQUID (DARK) 78% γ (LIGHT)
 2065°F (1129°C)	LEDEBURITE = 4.3% C CONTAINING Fe_3C=6.7% C (MATRIX) γ=2.0% C (SMALL POOLS) γ=2.0% C (LARGE POOLS)	22% LEDEBURITE (MATRIX PLUS SMALL POOLS) 78% PRIMARY γ (LARGE POOLS)
 ROOM TEMPERATURE	LEDEBURITE = 4.3% C CONTAINING Fe_3C (MATRIX) PLUS PEARLITE (SMALL POOLS) PEARLITE PLUS EXCESS Fe_3C FROM γ ORIGINALLY CONTAINING 2.0% C WHICH HAS UNDERGONE THE EUTECTOID DECOMPOSITION	

Fig. 7.6. **Microstructures resulting during the cooling of an alloy
containing 2.5 per cent carbon.**   [Refer to Fig. 7.2 (a).]

iron is desirable for resistance to wear and abrasion.   Its low
ductility and impact strength render it unsuitable for structural
parts.   White cast iron is important as an intermediate step in
the production of malleable iron castings.

Malleable iron castings are made in the United States by heating the white cast iron to 1700°F (927°C) for about 50 hours, followed by slow cooling. The castings are packed in a neutral slag or scale during heating and cooling. Decomposition of cementite is promoted by the long heating period. In malleable iron castings, cementite which existed in both the matrix and in the pearlite of the white cast iron structure is decomposed to graphite and ferrite. The final structure is illustrated in Fig. 7.7(*b*). Malleable cast iron has good machinability and is a great deal more ductile than both white and gray cast iron. Its mechanical properties compare favorably with those of low-carbon steels. In addition the white cast irons, from which malleable castings are made, can be poured at lower temperatures and give better reproduction of patterns than do steel castings.

7.10. Gray Cast Iron

The iron-iron carbide diagram actually represents metastable conditions, because cementite decomposes into graphite and iron at high temperatures. The phase diagram representing this decomposition is known as the iron-carbon or iron-graphite diagram. It is quite similar to the iron-iron carbide diagram and is indicated by the dotted lines in Fig. 7.2. The microstructure of gray cast iron represents complete or partial graphitization of cementite. Therefore the structure of gray cast iron can be predicted better from the iron-carbon diagram. However, satisfactory approximations can be made using the iron-iron carbide relationships.

The formation of gray cast irons, i.e., the promotion of graphitization is accomplished most readily by the following:

1. Increasing the carbon content.
2. Increasing the quantities of silicon and nickel. These two elements promote graphitization and are known as graphitizers. Strictly speaking, the presence of these elements invalidates the use of the simple binary iron-carbon diagram. (Opposed to graphitizers are alloying elements which stabilize carbides and cementite. These are known as carbide formers, and include titanium, vanadium, molybdenum, tungsten, and chromium. See section 9.2.)
3. Increasing the time the casting is at high temperatures, i.e., decreasing the cooling rate.

The cooling of a gray cast iron containing about 4 per cent carbon involves formation of primary austenite dendrites. At about 2075°F (1135°C) a eutectic forms in which the matrix is also austenite. Throughout the matrix are flakes of graphite whose size and distribution may vary quite widely. As the temperature drops, the austenite continues to precipitate graphite, and at approximately 1333°F (723°C) the austenite to pearlite transformation occurs. However, if cooling is sufficiently slow, a partial or complete decomposition of austenite into ferrite and graphite may occur. Thus, the final structure may consist of:

1. Graphite imbedded in pearlitic matrix (fairly rapid cooling).
2. Graphite imbedded in pearlite and ferrite [intermediate cooling rates. See Fig. 7.7 (d)].
3. Graphite imbedded in ferritic matrix [extremely slow cooling rates. See Fig. 7.7 (c)].

A superior product results when the matrix is a mixture of pearlite and ferrite, as this provides strength combined with machinability. The graphite flakes are actually small stress raisers and hence gray cast irons are extremely brittle. However, the presence of carbon in the form of graphite is believed to account for the two outstanding characteristics of gray cast iron, namely, *superior machinability* and *damping capacity.*

By careful control of composition and cooling rate it is possible to make castings in which both gray and white cast iron structures are present. Thin sections of castings of this type cool fast enough to produce the chilled structure of white cast iron. Thick sections cool more slowly and have a gray cast iron structure. Introduction of chill blocks in the mold may produce local areas of white cast iron. This is useful in casting machine-bases, where hardness in a wearing surface is to be coupled with the ability to absorb machine vibrations.

7.11. Alloy Cast Irons

In more recent years there have been some advances in the field of *alloy cast irons*. Some of these developments gain their advantage over more conventional cast irons by the improved strength of their pearlitic and ferritic matrix. This improvement can be appreciated if gray cast iron is considered as having the same

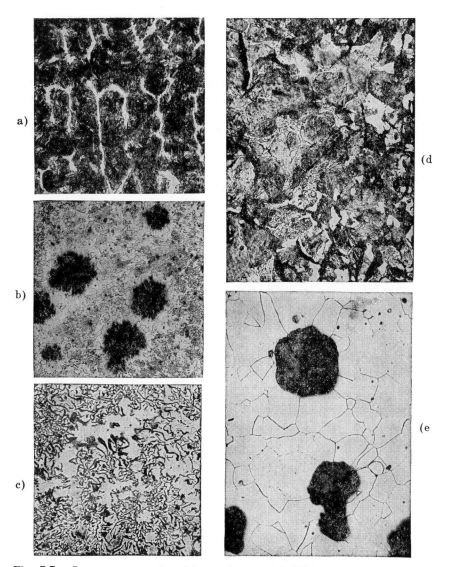

Fig. 7.7. Some structures found in cast irons. (a) White cast iron consisting of dark etching pearlite surrounded by a white cementite network. The pearlite colonies were formerly primary austenite dendrites. Etchant: nital. Magnification: 200×. (b) Malleable iron in which the cementite has partially decomposed into large black nodules of graphite surrounded by white ferrite. The matrix is lamellar pearlite. Etchant: nital. Magnificant: 75×. (c) Gray cast iron consisting of flakes of graphite in a matrix of ferrite. (d) Gray cast iron in which graphite flakes are imbedded in a matrix of pearlite and ferrite. Steadite (white with small black specks) is at some of the former austenite grain boundaries. (e) Ductile cast iron in the annealed condition consists of nodules of graphite in ferrite matrix. Etchant: nital. All at 200×. [Courtesy of the School of Engineering, Metals Laboratory, University of Massachusetts.]

structure as steel, in which fine particles of graphite are distributed. In these alloy cast irons a combination of alloying elements is used, so that a balance is attained between the carbide formers and graphitizers. This has led to the use of the term "balanced compositions." Some of these alloy cast irons are a little more than balanced on the chill side, so as to prevent graphitization during heat treatment. Where heat treatment is applicable a further improvement in properties will result.

There are also some *special-purpose high-alloy irons* used for high temperature resistance (14 per cent nickel—2 per cent chromium—"Niresist"), high corrosion resistance (25–30 per cent chromium), and good resistance to acids (13–14 per cent silicon—"Duriron").

The *nodular cast irons* are another noteworthy development. A typical nodular structure is shown in Fig. 7.7(e). In these irons, alloying elements control the size, shape, and distribution of graphite particles. Ductility is greatly improved by the nodular form of the graphite, as compared to the brittleness produced by the flaky graphite which occurs in gray cast iron. The degree of stress intensification produced by the nodules is much smaller than that produced by flakes. Elongations of 10 per cent at fracture are attainable, and at the same time good strength, machinability, and damping capacity are maintained. For successful production of nodular cast irons the composition, particularly with respect to a low sulfur content, must be closely controlled. In one process, the iron is innoculated with an alloy of magnesium when the hot metal flows into the ladle from the cupola furnace. The first alloy addition is followed by a second ladle addition of ferrosilicon. In the United States magnesium alloyed with copper, with nickel, or with iron, copper, and silicon is used for the first alloy innoculation. In England, cerium alloys are used successfully.

EFFECTS OF NONEQUILIBRIUM COOLING

7.12. Moderate Departures from Equilibrium

It was stated earlier in this chapter that fairly rapid temperature changes in steel produce a shift in the positions of the A_1 and A_3 lines of the iron-iron carbide diagram. The displacement of the lines is significant in that it indicates a change in the temperatures at which phases undergo transformation. For instance, cooling at faster than equilibrium conditions depresses the temperatures of ferrite precipitation and pearlite formation in hypoeutectoid steels.

When steel is cooled at a rate slightly exceeding the equilibrium rate, two significant changes occur in the *microstructure:*

1. In steels of other than eutectoid composition, there is *less proeutectoid constituent formed than under equilibrium conditions.* Quickly cooled hypoeutectoid steels contain smaller amounts of free ferrite, and hypereutectoid steels have less free cementite than when slowly cooled. The net effect is to produce a microstructure which is more nearly like that of eutectoid steels, i.e., entirely pearlitic.
2. Regardless of composition, the *pearlite laminations become finer with faster cooling rates.*

These effects on microstructure are shown in Fig. 7.8.

The changes in microstructure pointed out in the preceding paragraph are accompanied by changes in the *properties* of steel. Since finer pearlite produces a stronger, harder steel, rapid cooling results in an improvement in properties because it yields a finer pearlitic structure. In hypoeutectoid steels, rapid cooling reduces the amount of ferrite matrix, which has the effect of increasing strength and at the same time reducing ductility. In hypereutectoid steels, the reduction in the size of the cementite network tends to cause a drop in the hardness value and significantly improves the machinability of the hypereutectoids.

Work on the austenite-pearlite transformation has shown that rapid cooling both depresses the transformation temperature and shortens the *time required for the transformation.*

7.13. Radical Departures from Equilibrium

If the cooling rate is great enough, no pearlite at all is formed. Instead, a nonequilibrium constituent known as martensite is produced. Under suitable conditions where the quench is interrupted before transformation has started, still another constituent known as bainite may form. Studies of this nonequilibrium behavior led to the conclusion that the temperature at which austenite decomposes determines (1) *the time required for the decomposition and* (2) *the nature of the decomposition products. This conclusion is graphically presented in what are called time-temperature-transfor-*

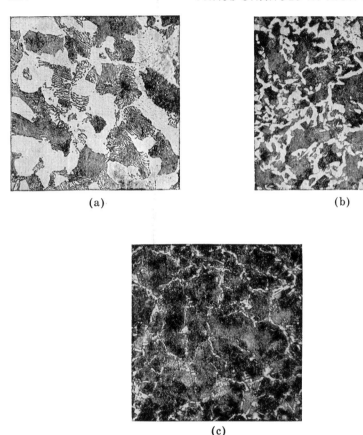

(a)   (b)

(c)

Fig. 7.8.   Effects of various cooling rates on the structure of SAE
1045 steel.   (a) Furnace cooled.   (b) Cooled in an air blast.   (c)
Cooled in oil.   Two principal effects can be detected.   The amount
of proeutectoid constituent decreases with increasing cooling rates,
i.e., there is less free ferrite in the more quickly cooled samples.
The pearlite becomes finer with increasing cooling rates.   In hypoeutectoid steels, both of these tendencies increase the strength and
decrease the ductility of rapidly cooled steel.   The ferrite network
in (c) outlines the original austenite grains, making an estimate of
grain size possible in this structure.   Etchant: nital. Magnification:
500×.   [Courtesy of the School of Engineering, Metals Laboratory,
University of Massachusetts.]

mation diagrams.   Other names for the same curves are: *T-T-T*
diagrams, isothermal transformation diagrams, *S* curves, and
double *C* curves.   The first two terms are preferred.   Some typical
T-T-T diagrams are shown in Fig. 7.9.

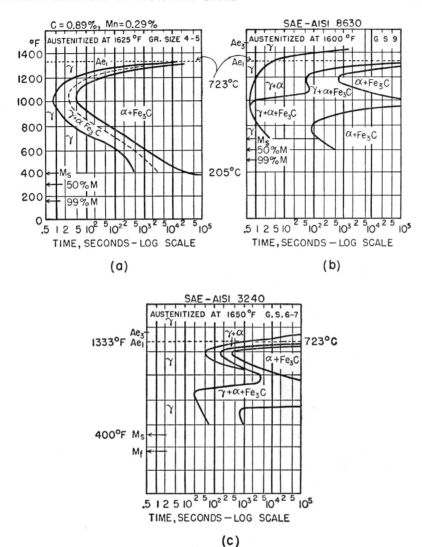

Fig. 7.9. Typical time-temperature transformation curves. (a) Eutectoid steel. [Adapted from *Metals Handbook*. American Society for Metals, 1948.] (b) SAE-AISI 8630. [Adapted from *Metals Progress*. American Society for Metals.] (c) SAE-AISI 3240. [Courtesy of The International Nickel Company, Inc.]

7.14. T-T-T Diagrams: Formation of Pearlite and Bainite

Probably the most efficient way to gain an understanding of isothermal transformation diagrams is to study their derivation.

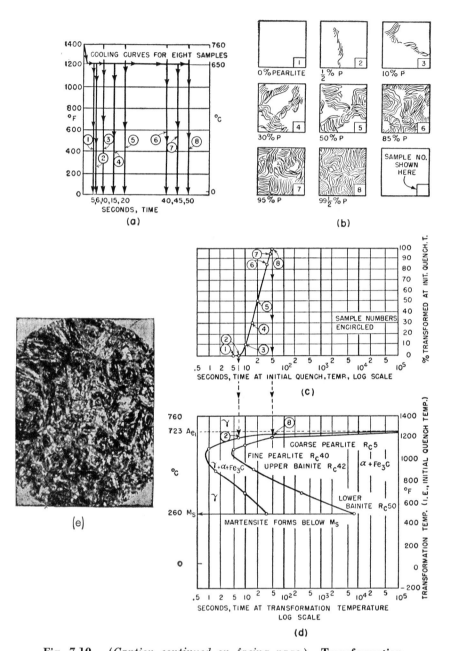

Fig. 7.10. (*Caption continued on facing page.*) **Transformation above the M_s temperature.** (a) Cooling cycles for several samples quenched so as to determine the rate of transformation at 1200°F. (b) The structures of the several samples cooled as indicated in (a). (c) A plot of the per cent pearlite formed in the several samples of (b), which had been held for various times at 1200°F. Time is

206

If the derivation is understood they can be interpreted with little difficulty.

Let us select a eutectoid composition for the derivation of a *T-T-T* diagram. This choice simplifies the problem somewhat, as there is no proeutectoid constituent to confuse the metallographic results. The advantages of this simplification are apparent in the description which follows.

A large number of small samples is cut from a single piece of steel whose composition is 0.8 per cent carbon. A number of these are heated to a definite temperature above 1333°F (723°C) (i.e., in the austenite range) for a standard length of time. A few samples are then removed from the furnace and quenched in a bath of molten salt held at 1200°F (650°C). Since the samples are very small, they are for all practical purposes instantaneously cooled to the quenching temperature. The first of these is allowed to remain at 1200°F (650°C) for 5 seconds and then removed from the salt bath and quenched in iced brine. A second sample is removed from the salt bath at 6 seconds and quenched in brine. The third sample is removed and quenched at 10 seconds, and so on, so as to produce for eight samples the cooling cycles indicated in Fig. 7.10(*a*). The eight samples are then ground, polished, and etched with picric acid. The microstructures obtained are shown in Fig. 7.10(*b*). In the first sample there is no evidence of pearlite, indicating that austenite does not start to transform to pearlite at 1200°F (650°C) within 5 seconds. This sample is not attacked by the etchant because its structure is entirely martensitic, and martensite is only very slowly etched by picric acid. (Pearlite, bainite, and tempered martensite are all rapid-etching constituents; fresh martensite is slow-etching.) The second sample, which was held at 1200°F (650°C) for 6 seconds shows just a trace of pearlite.[1] (Thus, after

---

plotted on a log scale. (d) A plot showing the time at which transformation of austenite starts and finishes at various temperatures. The two points at 1200°F. correspond to the samples numbered two and eight in (c). Time is plotted on the same scale in (c) as in (d). The hardness and type of microstructure resulting at various transformation temperatures is indicated. (e) The appearance of bainite is shown in the photograph. Etchant: nital. Magnification 1000×. [Courtesy of Ralph G. Kimball.]

[1] When 0.5 per cent of the entire structure is pearlitic, transformation is considered to have started. This is purely an arbitrary assumption, based on the smallest amount of pearlite which can be identified with certainty.

6 seconds at 1200°F (650°C), austenite commences to transform to pearlite.)   The matrix is martensite, which is not attacked by the etchant during metallographic preparation.   The third sample, held for 10 seconds at 1200°F (650°C), shows 10 per cent pearlite and 90 per cent martensite in its final structure.   As can be seen from the microstructures, the longer the samples are held at 1200°F (650°C), the closer the structure approaches that of 100 per cent pearlite.   The second sample (0.5 per cent pearlite) and the eighth sample (99.5 per cent pearlite) represent the start and finish of the austenite transformation.   These data are plotted on a pair of co-ordinates in which the vertical axis represents the per cent transformation at the temperature of the first quenching bath. The horizontal axis is a plot of the time the samples were held in the first quench.   For greater convenience, time has been plotted on a logarithmic scale, which has the effect of compressing the diagram to a reasonable size.   At the same time good detail is retained in the areas of the plot representing short periods of time.

The procedure described above is repeated with large numbers of samples, held for varying lengths of time at quenching tempera-tures between 1333°F (723°C) and 500°F (260°C).   The data are plotted as described above, and a line is drawn through all the points representing the start of transformation.   Another line is drawn through all the points representing completion of transformation. The curve of Fig. 7.10(d) is the result.

The data and samples taken at different temperatures show some interesting features.   The austenite which transforms at tempera-tures near 1333°F (723°C), produces a soft (R_c 5), coarse pearlite. As the temperature of transformation drops, the pearlite formed is finer and of greater hardness.   In the vicinity of 1100°F (593°C) the pearlite is so fine that it cannot be resolved at ordinary mag-nifications.   Finally in the neighborhood of 1000°F (538°C) a new constituent known as bainite [2] rather than pearlite is formed from austenite.   At lower transformation temperatures the bainite formed is increasingly different from pearlite.   It becomes more needlelike or acicular, and has a much greater hardness than pearlite.   The appearance of bainite is shown in Fig. 7.10(e). Both bainite and pearlite are two-phase constituents consisting of α-iron and cementite.   In bainite the cementite is much more finely dispersed than in pearlite.

[2] Named in honor of one of its codiscoverers, E. C. Bain.

7.15. T-T-T Diagrams: Formation of Martensite

During very rapid cooling from the austenite range, any unde-composed austenite transforms to martensite as cooling proceeds below 500°F. Martensite is the slow-etching constituent mentioned earlier, which is present in the microstructures in Fig. 7.10(b). Any martensite which forms at a particular temperature *forms instantly (for all practical purposes) from austenite,* and the lower the final temperature the greater the percentage of martensite. This is quite different from the austenite-to-pearlite transformation, where the amount transformed depended upon time at temperature. The nature of martensite formation has been investigated by the procedure described below.

In studying the formation of martensite, use is made of the difference in appearance between freshly formed martensite and tempered martensite. Fresh martensite refers to martensite which has recently been formed from austenite and has undergone no further treatment. Tempered martensite is formed from fresh martensite by heating to some elevated temperature below 1333°F (723°C) for a time interval which depends upon the temperature selected. Fresh martensite when polished and etched is white (it is sometimes called "white martensite"), while tempered martensite is yellow. The yellow color deepens with increasing tempering times and temperatures.

Fresh martensite is a supersaturated solid solution of carbon in body-centered tetragonal iron. The unit cell of this structure has edge lengths of about 2.84 Å and 3.00 Å (at room temperature) when the martensite contains about 0.6 per cent carbon. The a and c values of the unit cell vary with changes in the carbon content of the structure. Fully tempered martensite consists of iron carbide and ferritic iron, in which the iron is a body-centered cubic structure having a unit cell whose edge length is about 2.87 Å (at room temperature). The face-centered cubic austenite from which martensite or ferrite plus carbide forms has an edge length of about 3.57 Å (at room temperature).

The experimental procedure for studying martensite formation requires a series of small samples about $\frac{1}{32}''$ thick, taken from the same stock used for studying the transformations to bainite and pearlite. The samples are heated to the austenite range and then quenched. The first sample is quenched to 500°F (260°C) and then immediately reheated to 1300°F (704°C), where it is held for a few seconds and then quenched in iced brine. If any martensite forms at 500°F (260°C) it is tempered and darkened by reheating to 1300°F (704°C). The retained austenite is not affected during reheating, and upon being given the final quench in brine it is con-

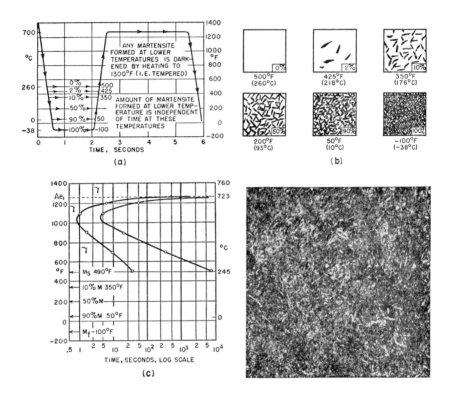

Fig. 7.11. Transformation below the M_s temperature. (a) The cooling cycles required for the determination of the portions of a T-T-T diagram below the M_s point. The percentages indicate the amount of martensite formed at the various initial quenching temperatures. The same percentages are also noted in (b), which shows the microstructures of thin samples, cooled as shown in (a). The percentages are determined by estimating the amount of dark, tempered martensite formed during heating, after the initial quench. The balance of the structure is white (or fresh), untempered martensite, formed upon quenching the austenite which remained at 1300°F. (c) The complete T-T-T diagram, showing the region below the M_s temperature. The transformation of austenite to martensite depends upon temperature and is independent of time. (d) The structure of martensite is shown in the photograph. Etchant: nital. Magnification: 500×. [Courtesy of the School of Engineering, Metals Laboratory, University of Massachusetts.]

verted to fresh martensite. When polished and etched, the sample has a structure consisting entirely of fresh martensite. Therefore no transformation from austenite to martensite could have taken place at 500°F (260°C). A second sample is quenched from the austenite range to 490°F (245°C), reheated to 1300°F (704°C) for a short time, and then quenched in brine. This sample shows the first traces of tempered martensite, indicating that transformation of austenite had just started at 490°F (245°C). The quenching cycles and resulting microstructures for the remaining samples are shown in Figs. 7.11(a) and 7.11(b). The percentage of tempered martensite increases as the initial quenching temperature drops toward —100°F (—73°C), when for all practical purposes it reaches 100 per cent. This is shown in Fig. 7.11(b). By working with another set of samples, it is possible to vary the time of holding at the initial quenching temperature. It has been found that the amount of martensite formed at the initial quenching temperature is independent of the holding time. In other words, the time required for transformation is so short as to be negligible. Thus transformation of austenite to martensite is dependent only on temperature; it is independent of time at temperature. It is now possible to complete the *T-T-T* diagram for a eutectoid steel, i.e., to consider changes occurring below 490°F (245°C).

FACTORS AFFECTING THE POSITION AND SHAPE OF T-T-T DIAGRAMS

Let us take the *T-T-T* diagram for eutectoid steel as a standard or reference curve. Studies have been made to determine the factors which affect the shape and position of the curve. The three most important considerations are: (1) alloy content, (2) carbon content, and (3) austenitic grain size.

7.16. Alloying Elements and T-T-T Diagrams

Addition of alloying elements to steel affects both the position and shape of the curve. All the common alloying elements except cobalt can cause the curve to be displaced to the right. See Figs. 7.12(a), 7.9(b), and 7.9(c). Hence, the use of alloys in steel (other factors being equal) makes possible the formation of martensite at slower speeds of cooling. However, in order for the alloying elements to accomplish this, it is necessary that they be in solid solution in the austenite before quenching. If the alloying elements are present as insoluble particles (often carbides), they may actually shift the curves to the left. This makes formation of martensite more difficult because the insoluble particles nucleate ferrite plus carbide, making it possible for pearlite or bainite to form in a shorter time at any given temperature.

When the steel contains alloying additions, the shape of the

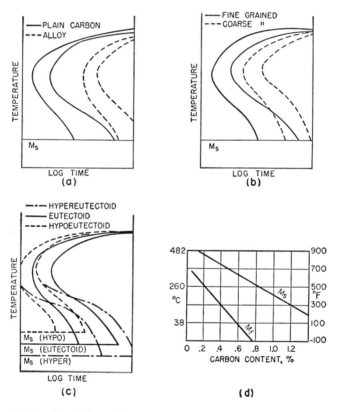

Fig. 7.12.   Variables affecting the *T-T-T* curve.   (a) The effect of dissolved alloying elements on the transformation of austenite is a displacement of the curve to the right. (b) Coarse-grained steels transform more slowly than fine-grained steels. (c) For all practical purposes carbon contents above or below 0.8 per cent carbon cause the steel to transform in shorter times at the critical temperature near 1000°F. (d) An important effect of increasing carbon content is to decrease the M_s and M_f temperatures. This increases the tendency toward quench cracking. [Part (d) adapted from *Metal Progress*. American Society for Metals, 1946.]

T-T-T diagram may be changed quite radically from the standard curve for a plain carbon eutectoid composition. Some alloy elements displace the upper portion of the curve more than the lower portion, or vice versa. Some displace the portion of the curve in the range around 1000°F (538°C) far to the right. This gives rise to the "double C curve" shown in Fig. 7.9(*c*). Occasionally the time required to finish transformation of austenite to pearlite or bainite is so great that only the time required for the start of transformation is indicated. No generalizations can be made regarding the effect of the alloying elements on the shape of the curve, excepting to say that its shape probably is changed by their presence. The alloying elements, with the exception of cobalt, have a tendency to lower the M_s point. Manganese and nickel exert the greatest effect in this regard.

7.17. Carbon Content and T-T-T Diagrams

Variation in the carbon content in steel affects the *position of T-T-T curves* and also the *temperature at which formation of martensite starts (M_s) and is finished (M_f).* For hypoeutectoid steels, the curve is farther to the left than for eutectoid steels. At very low carbon contents (less than 0.3 per cent), the curve is so far to the left that, for most purposes, it is impractical to attempt to cool fast enough to produce martensite. For hypereutectoid steels the curve is shifted to the right. However, this depends upon complete solution of all carbides before quenching starts. Since this is rarely attained in commercial practice, it is usually considered that for carbon contents of more than 0.8 per cent, the curve is actually displaced to the left. Thus, for practical purposes the most easily hardened of the plain carbon steels is the eutectoid composition. The net effect of carbon content is indicated in Fig. 7.12(*c*).

The M_s and M_f temperatures are both lowered by increasing carbon content. This is shown in Fig. 7.12(*d*). From this plot it can be seen that austenite, particularly in the high-carbon steels, can be retained down to or below room temperature. Since the formation of martensite from austenite is accompanied by an appreciable volume change, the high carbon steels show a greater tendency to crack as a result of quenching. This is because at the low temperatures of their transformation, there is little opportunity for relief of the stresses arising from the volume changes.

7.18. Austenite Grain Size and T-T-T Diagrams

The finer the austenite grain size, the further the T-T-T curve is displaced to the left. Thus a fine-grained steel must be cooled more quickly than a coarse-grained steel if the formation of pearlite is to be avoided. It has been mentioned that aluminum is used as a deoxidizer in the making of steel. This practice tends to produce a fine austenite grain size, and hence a steel which is more difficult to harden. This effect of aluminum is distinct from its effect as an alloying element.[3] The effects of grain size are schematically shown in Fig. 7.12(b).

It should be pointed out that while coarse grain sizes render a steel more easily hardened, they also reduce ductility, toughness, and impact strength. Coarse-grained steels also undergo more distortion than fine-grained steels upon quenching. Quench-cracking tendencies are thus promoted by coarse grain sizes. Therefore, coarse-grained steels are generally considered undesirable even though they have greater hardenability. Heating for a long time at the austenitizing temperature or using excessive temperatures for austenitizing produces coarse-grained steels.

7.19. Measurement of Austenite Grain Size

Grain size is so important a consideration that it will be worth while to mention a few methods of measuring it. One device for determining the austenitic grain size has already been mentioned. This consists of heating a piece of steel to the heat-treating temperature, followed by cooling it at a suitable rate. If the steel is not of the eutectoid composition, the proeutectoid constituent, which forms at the grain boundaries of the austenite, indicates where the grain boundaries previously existed. A comparison is then made with ASTM grain size standards to determine austenite grain size. This method is limited to hypereutectoid steels and hypoeutectoid steels. Figure 7.8(c) illustrates how the ferrite in a hypoeutectoid steel, when cooled at a satisfactory speed, can be used to indicate the old austenite grain boundaries.

---

[3] Consider two steels of the *same grain size* and carbon content, one containing aluminum as an alloying element and the other not. The aluminum-bearing steel is easier to harden.

For steels of approximately eutectoid composition, grain size can be determined by an iced brine quench of a sample one inch in diameter. Near the center of the specimen, where the cooling rate is slowest, a mixed structure consisting of pearlite and martensite forms. During the formation of this structure, pearlite is nucleated at the grain boundaries of the austenite grains. Since there is insufficient time for much more than a thin network of pearlite to form, the remaining austenite is transformed to martensite at the M_s temperature. Thus the pearlite outlines the austenite grains from which it formed.

Another method of determining austenite grain size consists of using Vilella's etching reagent.[4] In this procedure, fully hardened and slightly tempered steel (500°F (260°C) for 15 minutes) is polished and etched by immersion. A repolishing and re-etching follows. Differences in the orientation of the austenite grains are transferred to the martensite, and show up rather clearly, making an estimate of grain size possible. This method is applicable to most plain carbon and low-alloy steels.

Still another method involves the use of Shepherd grain size fracture standards. A sample of the steel to be studied is notched, heated to the heat-treating temperature, quenched, and then fractured by impact. The appearance of the fracture indicates the austenite grain size because fracture occurs along the previously existing austenite grain boundaries. The fracture is compared with the ASTM Shepherd grain size standards and a grain size reading is obtained. A fine-grained steel might have a reading between 8 and 10, and would be very silky in appearance. A very coarse-grained steel has a lower reading in which the facets of individual grains can be detected by the naked eye.

HARDENABILITY AND CONTINUOUS COOLING CURVES

7.20. Concept of Hardenability

The depth to which hard martensite can be formed in a piece of suitably heat-treated steel depends upon:

---

[4] One gram picric acid, 5 cc concentrated hydrochloric acid, and 95 cc ethyl alcohol.

1. The time and temperature of heating prior to quenching.
2. The effectiveness of the quenching medium in removing heat.
3. The physical character of the piece, i.e., principally its size and shape.
4. The hardenability of the steel.

Hardenability is that property of the steel itself which exerts its influence upon the depth of hardness developed on quenching (independently of the heat-treating procedure, heat-treating technique, and the size and shape of the piece).

7.21. The Jominy Test

Hardenability is readily measured by the Jominy test,[5] in which the first three factors listed above are standardized. A steel bar of prescribed dimensions (see Fig. 7.13) is subjected to a standard heat treatment followed by a standard quenching practice. Shallow flats are then ground on the quenched bar, and hardness readings are taken at $\frac{1}{16}$-inch intervals from the quenched end of the bar. These are plotted against distance from the quenched end as in Fig. 7.13(c). Steels having good hardenability show higher hardness values at the same distance from the quenched end than those having poor hardenability. Steels with good hardenability are known as deep-hardening steels, while those with poor hardenability are said to be shallow-hardening. Hardenability as indicated by the Jominy test is related to T-T-T diagrams. A steel having good hardenability has its transformation curve displaced further to the right than one with poor hardenability. Thus the factors discussed earlier as affecting the position and shape of the T-T-T diagrams are actually factors which affect hardenability.

Data are available showing cooling velocities developed in the Jominy bar at various distances from the quenched end. This information is sometimes indicated along the upper horizontal axis of the Jominy test plot, as shown in Fig. 7.13(c). In practical applications of the Jominy test the cooling rate data are of considerable interest.

---

[5] Named after the man who was responsible for the development of the test, W. E. Jominy, a metallurgist with the General Motors Corporation. Other useful tests are Grossman's critical diameter, the S-A-C rating of Burns, Moore, and Archer, and the Shepherd P-F and disk tests.

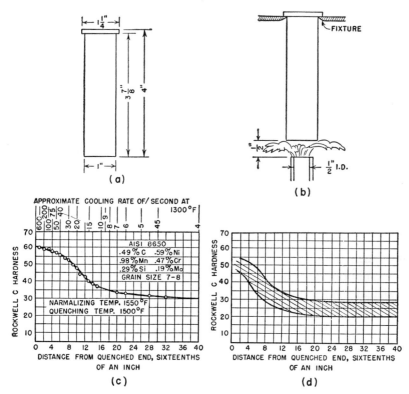

Fig. 7.13. The Jominy test. (a) A sketch of the standard Jominy test bar. The cross-section of the bar is round. (b) The Jominy test bar is held in a quenching fixture so that its lower end is one-half inch above the open end of the pipe which carries the quenching water. The water flow is adjusted so that when flowing freely, the column of water rises two and one-half inches. The temperature of the water is maintained at $75 \pm 5°F$. (c) A typical Jominy plot showing hardness readings at various distances from the quenched end. Cooling rates developed at different points along the length of the bar have been experimentally determined, and are noted along the top of the plot. [Adapted from *Metals Handbook*. American Society for Metals, 1948.] (d) The hardenability band for SAE-AISI 8630-H. [Adapted from *Metal Progress*. American Society for Metals, 1950.]

7.22. Standard Hardenability Bands

The American Iron and Steel Institute in cooperation with the Society of Automotive Engineers has set up standards of hardenability based on the Jominy test. Steels meeting these standards are designated with the usual AISI-SAE number followed by an H.

Since there is a possibility of a variation in the actual composition and in grain size, the hardenability of steels so designated may vary somewhat. Thus the specifications take the form of a hardenability band appearing on the Jominy plot rather than a single line. A steel meeting the composition requirements and yielding Jominy data falling within the band is said to meet the specifications. The hardenability band for an AISI-SAE 8630-H steel is shown in Fig. 7.13 (d).

7.23. Application of Jominy Results

The Jominy test is useful in determining what steel to use in order to achieve a specified hardness in a part, using a particular heating and quenching sequence. This is accomplished by obtaining Jominy data on a particular heat of steel. Then a sample part made from the same heat is hardened, and the hardness is measured at critical points in the part. From these values and the Jominy plot for the steel, it is possible to determine the cooling rates developed by the quench used, at critical points in the part. Applying the cooling velocity data to a series of hardenability bands for standard steel compositions, it is possible to select a steel and suitable quench which will develop in the part the desired hardness at significant locations.

7.24. Continuous Cooling Curves

In actual practice steel parts are of such size and shape that temperature changes on quenching are far from instantaneous. Rather, in an actual quenching operation, the temperature drops quickly at first, followed by a somewhat slower rate as the temperature of the object approaches that of the bath. Thus the T-T-T diagrams are not, strictly speaking, applicable to the prediction of structures resulting from the continuous cooling associated with most heat treating. The T-T-T diagrams show what structures result from transformations occurring at a *constant* temperature rather than a *continuously changing* temperature. To accommodate the conditions existent in actual heat treating, continuous cooling diagrams are available.[6] The continuous cooling curve occupies

---

[6] These may be derived from T-T-T diagrams or from end quench tests similar to the Jominy test. See Grange, R. A. and G. C. Kiefer, *Trans. ASM*, **29** (1941), p. 85; Liedholm, C. A., *Metal Progress*, **45**, January 1944, p. 95.

a position downward and to the right with respect to the *T-T-T* diagram. If a known cooling velocity is applied to a continuous cooling diagram, the resulting structure can be more accurately predicted than from a *T-T-T* diagram. However, reasonably accurate predictions of structure are possible with *T-T-T* diagrams because the actual difference between the two is not excessively great. The relationship between the continuous cooling diagram and the *T-T-T* diagram for AISI-SAE-8630-H steel is shown in Fig. 7.14. Also shown in this figure are some superimposed cooling curves, representing the velocities of cooling developed at various points in a Jominy test bar. For a particular piece of steel cooled at a certain rate, the resulting structure can be estimated by noting areas of the diagram through which the cooling curves pass. This is also indicated in Fig. 7.14. Using the method described in the preceding paragraph in connection with applications of the Jominy test,

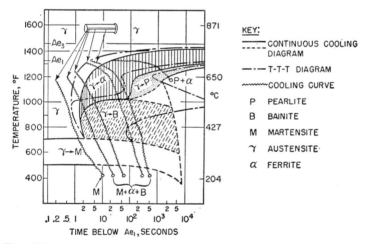

Fig. 7.14. Relationship between *T-T-T* and continuous cooling diagrams. The *T-T-T* diagram and continuous cooling diagram for SAE-AISI 8630-H are shown in the above plot. The cooling curves corresponding to various cooling rates at different points along the Jominy bar are indicated along with the resultant structure. [Adapted from *Metal Progress*. American Society for Metals, 1950.]

it is possible to determine the cooling rates developed in parts subjected to specific quenches. Application of the cooling rate data to a *T-T-T* diagram or a continuous cooling diagram facilitates the selection of a particular steel in terms of a certain microstructure and hardness.

DEPTH OF HARDNESS DEVELOPED IN STEELS

The hardness developed in a piece of steel is determined not only by hardenability but also by the speed with which heat is removed from the metal. The speed of heat removal is dependent upon (1) the effectiveness of the quenching medium in removing heat and (2) the physical character of the piece being heat treated.

7.25. The Quenching Medium and Depth of Hardness

The effectiveness of the quenching medium is contingent upon (1) the kind of quenching medium, (2) its temperature, and (3) the degree of agitation, if any. Various quenching media have been studied as to their effectiveness at different temperatures. A few of the results are shown in the table below:

Table 7.1

Cooling Rate at Center of 4 mm Diameter Nichrome Ball
Quenched from 1580°F

Quenching Medium	Cooling Rate Relative to that for Water at 65°F in Temperature Range Indicated *	
	1328–1022°F	At 392°F
Aqueous 10% NaOH	2.06	1.36
Aqueous 10% NaCl	1.96	0.98
Water at 32°F	1.06	1.02
Water at 65°F	1.00	1.00
Mercury	0.78	0.62
Rapeseed oil	0.30	0.055
Glycerin	0.20	0.89
Water at 122°F	0.17	0.95
Air	0.028	0.007
Vacuum	0.011	0.004

* The cooling rate for water at 65°F is 3260°F per second through the range from 1328°F to 1022°F and 810°F per second at 392°F. Table reproduced by permission from *Metals Handbook* (Cleveland: American Society for Metals, 1948).

Thus it can be seen that not only the kinds of quenching media, but their temperatures and the temperatures of the objects being quenched are important. The degree of agitation is also worthy of consideration. The more vigorous the agitation, the greater the cooling rate. For instance, the cooling rate of an air stream may be about double that of still air depending on the velocity and temperature of the moving air.

The cooling action of most liquid quenches occurs in three fairly well-defined stages. During the first stage the piece is so hot as to produce and sustain a blanket of vaporized liquid around itself. Cooling is fairly slow through this vapor film. In the second stage, the vapor film breaks down continuously, and as fresh liquid comes into contact with the hot metal surface fresh vapor bubbles form which condense in the cooler surrounding liquid. Heat extraction during this stage depends partly upon the latent heat of vaporization of the medium. Heat removal occurs at its maximum rate during boiling. The final phase of cooling occurs when the metal is no longer hot enough to cause boiling of the liquid. Heat extraction is now accomplished mainly by conduction and convection through the liquid, and is fairly slow.

7.26. The Physical Character of the Piece and Depth of Hardness

The speed of heat extraction, and in turn the hardness developed in a piece, are partly dependent on the physical character of the piece. This should include at least two major considerations: (1) the surface/mass ratio of the piece and (2) the surface condition of the piece.

The ratio of the surface of the piece to its mass is significant because heat can be removed only by passing through the surface. The total quantity of the heat in the object is directly proportional to its mass or to its volume (assuming an absence of voids). Therefore a large surface/mass ratio provides greater opportunity for cooling than a small ratio. The greater the surface/mass ratio, the greater the proportion of the mass which can be hardened by a given quench. Neglecting minor variations in surface smoothness, the surface/mass ratio depends upon (1) the size of the piece and (2) the shape of the piece. The dependence upon size is readily perceived if two spheres are considered, one with a radius of R, and the other with a radius of $2R$. The surface increases as the square of the radius ($A = 4\pi R^2$) while the mass and volume increase as the cube of the radius ($V = \frac{4}{3}\pi R^3$). Thus as size increases, there is a disproportionate increase of mass with respect to surface. In larger objects, the surface/mass ratio is lower than in smaller objects of the same shape. Other factors being equal, small objects are therefore easier to harden throughout.

Consider for a moment *different shaped objects, all of which occupy the same volume.* One cubic foot in the shape of a cube has a surface of 6 square feet. The same volume in the shape of a rectangular parallelopiped, 6 inches high, 2 feet long, and 1 foot wide, has a surface of 7 square feet. If the same volume is rolled out into a thin strip, the surface approaches infinity as thickness approaches zero. With a little speculation, it is readily seen that shape has an important bearing on surface/mass ratio. In general, the more rounded the contours of a shape and the more nearly the shape approaches that of a sphere, the lower the surface/mass ratio.

The condition of the surface of the piece must not be neglected. Minor variations in surface smoothness can have an effect on speed of heat extraction, although this is rarely a consideration of importance. (Strictly speaking, variations in surface smoothness should be considered as variations in shape.) A more frequent cause of variation in response to a prescribed heat treatment is the nature and amount of scale present on the surface of the steel at the time of quenching. In certain instances scale has been found to imepede heat transfer from metal to quenching bath, resulting in a decrease in hardenability.

Questions

7.1.   Name and describe the phases and constituents which may be present in alloys of iron and carbon.

7.2.   What is meant by the symbols A_1, A_3, A_{cm}, A_{c3}, A_{r1}, and A_{c3}? What determines the distance between A_{e1} and A_{r1}?

7.3.   Into what constituent does austenite always transform when it is slowly cooled below 1333°F? What is the carbon content of this constituent? What phases are present? What are the compositions of the phases and how much of each is present?

7.4.   Given a steel containing 95 per cent austenite at 1334°F, what two possible compositions could the steel have? How much pearlite will be present in both of these steels when slowly cooled to 1332°F?

7.5.   Where are ferrite and cementite nucleated when they precipitate from austenite grains?

7.6. Fill out tables similar to those of Fig. 7.3 for a plain carbon steel: (a) containing 0.4 per cent carbon; (b) containing 1.0 per cent carbon.

7.7. On the basis of the properties, amounts, and distribution of constituents in slowly cooled steels, explain the curves shown in Fig. 7.4.

7.8. What is the meaning of the expression *grain size of steel?* How can it be estimated for hypoeutectoid and hypereutectoid steels?

7.9. Discuss the changes in grain size which may occur upon heating steel to various temperatures above A_1.

7.10. Correlate the microstructure with the properties of white cast iron.

7.11. Explain why certain properties of malleable iron are better than those of white cast iron.

7.12. Why is it not possible to predict the exact structure of gray cast iron from the iron-iron carbide diagram?

7.13. How can graphitization be promoted in gray cast iron? Sketch the possible microstructures of gray cast iron. Identify the phases in the sketches.

7.14. What are the outstanding service properties of gray cast iron?

7.15. What is meant by a *balanced composition* as applied to cast irons?

7.16. What advantages do nodular cast irons have over gray cast iron? Explain.

7.17. Compare the microstructure and properties of a hypoeutectoid equilibrium-cooled steel with one cooled at a rate slightly greater than equilibrium cooling, though not severely quenched.

7.18. How does rapid cooling affect: (a) the temperature of transformation; (b) the time required for transformation?

7.19. Describe the determination of a *T-T-T* diagram for a steel of eutectoid composition. Make sketches to assist in your description.

7.20. How could you demonstrate that the formation of martensite is independent of time?

7.21. Discuss the factors affecting the position and shape of *T-T-T* curves.

7.22. What is the effect of carbon content on M_s and M_f temperatures?

7.23. Describe suitable methods for determining the grain size for a steel of eutectoid composition. What are Shepherd grain size fracture standards? How are the latter used?

7.24. What determines the depth of hardening in a piece of heat-treated steel?

7.25. Outline the method used for Jominy testing and explain what the results show. What are standard hardenability bands?

7.26. A machine part is to be made of AISI 8650. After quenching, it was found that two critical areas on the part had hardnesses of

R_c55 and R_c35. What cooling rate was developed at these areas by the quench? Supposing the minimum hardness required at these two places was R_c57 and R_c45, how could the specifications be met?

7.27. What is the difference between a continuous cooling curve and a *T-T-T* diagram? What are the relative positions of *T-T-T* and continuous cooling curves with respect to the temperature-time axes?

7.28. Upon what factors does the speed of heat removal from a piece of steel depend?

7.29. What determines the effectiveness of a given quenching medium in removing heat? For plain carbon steels is the rate of heat removal at 1000–1300°F more important than the rate of heat removal near 400°F? Why?

7.30. How is the depth of hardening affected by the physical character of the piece?

Bibliography

7.1. Reed, E. L., *Photomicrographs of Iron and Steel*. New York: John Wiley & Sons, Inc., 1929.

7.2. Bain, E. C. and E. S. Davenport, "Transformation of Austenite at Constant Subcritical Temperature," *Tran. AIME*, **90** (1930), pp. 117.

7.3. Symposium, *Hardenability of Alloy Steels*. Cleveland: American Society for Metals, 1938.

7.4. Boyles, Alfred, *The Structure of Cast Iron*. Cleveland: American Society for Metals, 1938.

7.5. Bain, E. C., *Alloying Elements in Steel*. Cleveland: American Society for Metals, 1948.

7.6. Grossman, M. A., *Elements of Hardenability*. Cleveland: American Society for Metals, 1952.

CHAPTER **8**

Heat-Treating Equipment and Operations

HEAT-TREATING EQUIPMENT

A few paragraphs will be devoted to heat-treating equipment before the actual operations of heat treating steel are discussed. This equipment can be classified under three functional headings:

1. Temperature-measuring and -controlling devices.
2. Equipment used for heating metals.
3. Apparatus for quenching and controlled cooling.

Much of the equipment described is also used for the heat treating of nonferrous as well as ferrous metals. This includes annealing, solution heat treating, and age hardening.

8.1. Temperature-Measuring and -Controlling Devices

These devices occupy a position of great importance with respect to heat treating. However, most of this equipment is similar to other industrial temperature controls, and is well discussed in texts where the principal interest is along these lines. They are too complex for more than a cursory mention here. For heat treating, the most widely used temperature measuring and controlling devices are actuated by thermocouples. These operate through amplifying circuits to open and close valves or electric contacts which control the flow of fuel or current. The amplifying circuit may also position a rheostat or transformer controller. Radiation and optical pyrometers are likewise used, but to a lesser extent. Heating equipment and quenching apparatuses are unlike other temperature measuring and controlling devices in that they are applied only to heat treating. Descriptions of them are somewhat harder to find, and hence they are discussed in more detail in the following paragraphs.

8.2. Heating Devices

There are many different designs of equipment for applying heat to metals. Two fundamental differences in design are based upon the means by which heat is transferred to the metal. That is, heat may be carried from the source to the metal through (1) gaseous surroundings, or through (2) liquid surroundings.[1] These two major classes of furnace are further subdivided as to the particular heat-transfer agent used, the source of heat, and the particular design of furnace. All these considerations enter into the applicability of a particular furnace for specific uses.

8.3. Hot Gases and Their Effects on Metallic Substances

The first furnaces used for heat treating were those in which the work was surrounded by air or by the raw products of combustion. Air consists of about 20 per cent oxygen and 80 per cent nitrogen. The nitrogen is inert and hence is a useful ingredient in furnace atmospheres. In contrast to this, oxygen is very reactive at high temperatures, attacking ferrous alloys severely, and discoloring many others, e.g., copper-base alloys. When in contact with steel, oxygen forms an iron oxide scale. Oxygen also reacts with the carbon at the surface of the steel to form carbon dioxide. Carbon is removed faster than it can be replenished from the interior of the steel, and a thin decarburized skin forms which does not harden upon quenching.

The **raw products of combustion** vary depending upon the fuel used and how completely it is burned. Under all conditions of combustion, nitrogen is a major component of the products of combustion. The presence of nitrogen is desirable since it is inert. If excess air is used to insure complete burning, oxygen will be present to cause the difficulties described above. Carbon dioxide and water vapor are also common products of combustion. Carbon

[1] Induction heating, which is a very special method, involves the production of heat within the metal by inducing current flow in it. Induction heating is taken up again in Section 8.21.

dioxide reacts with the iron atoms in steel to form scale and carbon monoxide:

$$CO_2 + Fe \longrightarrow FeO + CO \qquad (8.3\text{-}1)$$

It also decarburizes steel by reaction with carbon to form carbon monoxide:

$$CO_2 + C_\gamma \longrightarrow 2CO \qquad (8.3\text{-}2)$$

where C_γ represents carbon dissolved in austenite. Water vapor, the other common product of combustion, is also oxidizing with respect to iron:

$$H_2O + Fe \longrightarrow \text{Iron oxides} + H_2 \qquad (8.3\text{-}3)$$

and with respect to carbon in steel:

$$H_2O + C_\gamma \longrightarrow CO + H_2 \qquad (8.3\text{-}4)$$

Whether carbon dioxide causes oxidation in accordance with equation (8.3-1) depends upon the concentrations of carbon dioxide and carbon monoxide present at a particular temperature. The concentration of a gas present in a mixture is indicated by the proportion of the total pressure of the mixture which is contributed by the gas in question. Concentration is thus expressed in partial pressures or percentages. The partial pressures of water vapor and hydrogen, as indicated by equation (8.3-3) determine whether oxidation occurs in the presence of these gases. Increases in the partial pressures of carbon monoxide or hydrogen shift the respective equilibria from right to left, as written, and thus decrease oxidizing tendencies.

A furnace atmosphere containing hydrogen, water vapor, carbon monoxide, carbon dioxide, and nitrogen may oxidize, reduce, or behave neutrally, depending upon the equilibria reached by both reactions (8.3-1) and (8.3-3). Fig. 8.1 affords a specific example. Let us assume that natural gas has been partially burned to produce an atmosphere containing percentages by volume as follows:

14   per cent hydrogen
2.8 per cent water vapor
5   per cent carbon dioxide
10 per cent carbon monoxide
balance nitrogen

The ratios of the percentages by volume are the same as the ratios of the partial pressures. Equilibrium data for various ratios are shown for different temperatures for the two reactions indicated above. From the gas analysis, the ratio of water vapor to hydrogen is 0.2, while the ratio of carbon dioxide to carbon monoxide is 0.5.

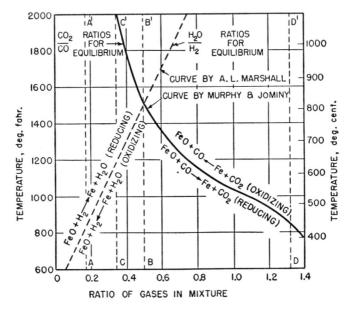

Fig. 8.1. Theoretical equilibrium relations among iron, iron oxide, hydrogen, and water vapor and among iron, iron oxide, carbon monoxide, and carbon dioxide. [Adapted from *Metals Handbook*. American Society for Metals, 1948.]

Consider only the effects of water vapor and hydrogen at 1750°F (955°C) : there is a strong tendency to prevent oxidation since the coordinates intersect above the dotted line of Fig. 8.1. Slow cooling of the steel in the furnace, at the same atmosphere at temperatures below 900°F (482°C), would produce an oxidizing effect. Let us now consider the added effect of the carbon dioxide and carbon monoxide portion of the atmosphere. At 1750°F (955°C) there would be a slight tendency toward oxidation, but this would probably be overcome by the strong reducing effects of reaction (1). Upon cooling in the furnace, the CO_2-CO reaction becomes strongly protective, while the H_2O-H_2 reaction becomes mildly oxidizing, so that protection is realized as the temperature drops.

Effect of diluent. The effect of an inert gas such as nitrogen is interesting. The attainment of equilibria is always slowed by the presence of a diluent gas. The equilibrium reached may or may not be affected depending upon the relative volumes of products and reactants. The reactions represented by (8.3-1) and (8.3-3) are not affected by a diluent because the volumes of gaseous products and gaseous reactants are equal to one another. Consider, however, the following carburizing reactions:

$$2\,CO \longrightarrow C_\gamma + CO_2 \tag{8.3-5}$$

and

$$CH_4 \longrightarrow C_\gamma + 2\,H_2 \tag{8.3-6}$$

If nitrogen is present as a diluent it discourages carburizing tendencies of an atmosphere made up of carbon monoxide and carbon dioxide. When present in a methane-hydrogen atmosphere, nitrogen encourages carburization. This can be determined from the equations for the equilibrium constant.

For equation (8.3-5), $K_{(3)} = (CO_2)(C_\gamma)/(CO)^2$, and for equation (8.3-6), $K_{(4)} = (H_2)^2(C_\gamma)/(CH_4)$, where K is the equilibrium constant for the particular reaction involved, and the terms in parentheses indicate the concentrations of the various substances expressed in appropriate units. Solving for (C_γ) we have for (8.3-5), $(C_\gamma) = K_{(3)}(CO)^2/(CO_2)$, and for (8.3-6), $(C_\gamma) = K_{(4)}(CH_4)/(H_2)^2$. Assuming an atmosphere of 95 per cent CO and 5 per cent CO_2, then $(C_\gamma) = K_{(3)}\dfrac{(95)^2}{5} = K_{(3)}9025/5 = 1805K_{(3)}$. If the same atmosphere is simply diluted with four times its volume of nitrogen, the percentages of CO and CO_2 become 19 per cent and 1 per cent, respectively. Substituting again we have $(C_\gamma) = K_{(3)}(19)^2/1$ so that $(C_\gamma) = 361K_{(3)}$. Thus the percentage of carbon in the steel will be one-fifth the original value when equilibrium is reached, i.e., the carburizing potential of a CO_2-CO mixture is lowered by dilution with N_2.

Consider next, the reaction of equation (8.3-6); the equilibrium produced by a gas containing 99.5 per cent H_2 and 0.5 per cent CH_4 gives $(C_\gamma) = (0.5)/(99.5)^2 (K_{(4)}) = 0.00005K_{(4)}$. If the same gas is diluted with four times its own volume of nitrogen, the percentage of CH_4 becomes 0.1, while that of H_2 becomes 19.9 (C_γ) now equals $(0.1)/(19.9)^2 = 0.00025K_{(4)}$. In this case, dilution by an inert gas has increased the carburizing potential by five times.   In both cases the extent of the dilution was the same.

It is emphasized that dilution *always* slows down the speed of a reaction as does a decrease in temperature.

The complexity of the problem of atmosphere control can be appreciated by considering a few of the other reactions [2] which may go on in a furnace:

Table 8.1

Possible Reactions in Atmosphere Furnaces

Reaction	Effects when Proceeding to Right	Effect of Diluent on Position of Equilibrium
$CO_2 + Fe \rightleftarrows FeO + CO$	Oxidizing	No effect
$H_2O + Fe \rightleftarrows FeO + H_2$	Oxidizing	No effect
$2CO + 3Fe \rightleftarrows Fe_3C + CO_2$	Carburizing	Shifts to left
$CO_2 + Fe_3C \rightleftarrows 3Fe + 2CO$	Decarburizing	Shifts to right
$H_2O + C \rightleftarrows CO + H_2$	Decarburizing	Shifts to right
$2H_2 + Fe_3C \rightleftarrows 3Fe + CH_4$	Decarburizing	Shifts to left
$CH_4 + 3Fe \rightleftarrows Fe_3C + 2H_2$	Carburizing	Shifts to right

8.4.   Atmosphere Control

Although the control of furnace atmospheres is complex in theory, actual practice has reduced it to a set of fairly simple techniques.   The most widely used atmospheres are generated by partially burning gaseous or vaporized liquid fuels.   If the fuel is burned with sufficient air to sustain combustion it produces what is called an exothermic atmosphere.   Exothermic atmospheres are used to a greater extent than any other kind of atmosphere for industial heat treating.   If fuel is catalytically reacted with less than enough air to sustain combustion, external heat must be supplied and the atmosphere is called endothermic.   Both exothermic and endothermic atmospheres are chilled to remove most of the water vapor formed by combustion.   Carbon dioxide, which is practically nonexistent in endothermic atmospheres (see Fig. 8.2), can be removed from exothermic atmospheres by amine solution absorption. Carbon monoxide can be removed from endothermic and exothermic

[2] *Metals Handbook*, American Society for Metals, Cleveland, 1948, p. 296. Last column added by author.   A diluent gas always shifts the equilibrium to the side of the equation having the largest total number of mols of gases.

gases by reaction with steam which converts carbon monoxide to carbon dioxide:

$$H_2O + CO \longrightarrow CO_2 + H_2$$

The excess water vapor and carbon dioxide are then respectively removed by chilling and absorption processes.

Endothermic gas may be enriched by metering a small quantity of propane or methane to increase the carburizing potential. Anhydrous ammonia is added along with the hydrocarbon if both carbon and nitrogen are to be introduced at the surface of the steel being heat treated. Such a procedure is known as carbonitriding. Ammonia may also be added by itself for nitriding.

The compositions of endothermic and exothermic atmospheres are indicated by Fig. 8.2. In actual practice, an endothermic atmosphere consisting of 20 per cent CO, 40 per cent H_2, and 40 per cent N_2 is a popular one. The dew point of such a composition is adjusted to the carbon content of the steel being heat treated so that the atmosphere is neutral, i.e. it tends to neither carburize nor decarburize the given composition. An equilibrium curve for carbon content of the steel at 1700°F (955°C) versus the dew point is shown by Fig. 8.3. If the steel being heat treated has a carbon content of 0.4 per cent carbon, the dew point of the gas is maintained at 40°F (4°C). If the steel should have a carbon content of 0.8 per cent carbon, the dew point would be dropped to 26°F (−3°C). In effect, very close control is easily achieved by control of the dew point.

Instruments are available for conveniently measuring and controlling dew points automatically. One device is based on the principle that inorganic salts become electrically conducting when moist. A hygroscopic salt is used in the instrument which, upon becoming moist, allows current to flow through a heating unit. The heat so generated tends to dry the salt and lower its conductivity until an equilibrium temperature is reached. This temperature depends upon the moisture content of the surrounding atmosphere. Measurements of the equilibrium temperature are used to operate the controls which regulate the dew point of the atmosphere.

Other sources of controlled atmospheres are bottled hydrogen, nitrogen, helium, argon, and ammonia. Ammonia is often catalytically cracked or dissociated into hydrogen and nitrogen:

$$2\,NH_3 \longrightarrow 3\,H_2 + N_2$$

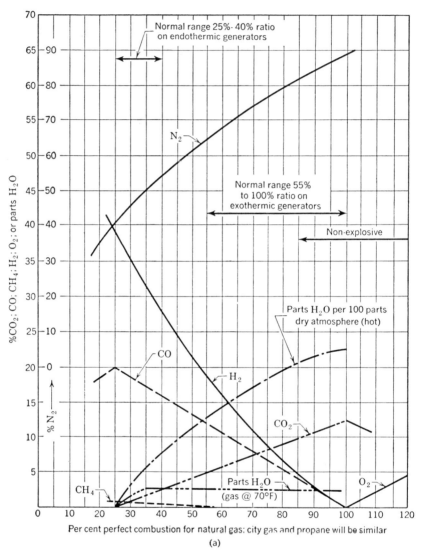

Fig. 8.2. Controlled atmospheres. (*Caption continued on facing page.*)

Ammonia is also burned to produce water vapor and nitrogen, the undesirable water vapor being subsequently removed by chilling. The bottled gases are prohibitively expensive for most industrial applications where protection is the major requirement. For instance, dissociated ammonia costs about 10 times as much per cubic foot as an endothermic gas containing 20 per cent CO, 40 per cent H_2, and 40 per cent N_2.

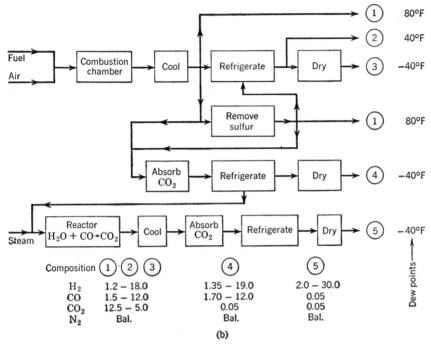

(a) Typical compositions of exothermic and endothermic atmospheres. (b) Schematic diagram showing how various atmospheres are produced. [Reproduced with permission from C. H. Vaughan, "A Survey of the Types of Furnace Atmospheres," *Steel Processing and Conversion*, February, 1957.]

Steam is used during tempering operations (described later) to produce an oxide coating on high-speed steel cutting tools at temperatures near 1000°F (538°C). The tightly adherent coating consists of a layer of hard, porous Fe_3O_4 only 0.0001 in. thick. The porosity of the oxide film allows it to retain cutting fluid, thus improving cutting lubrication and prolonging the life of the tool. Steam atmospheres are also used for annealing of cold-worked copper-base alloys and for solution treatment of aluminum-base alloys.

8.5. Heating of Atmosphere Furnaces

Atmosphere furnaces may be heated by a variety of methods. The *smaller furnaces* are frequently *electrically* heated. Electric heaters consist essentially of high-resistance material in a variety

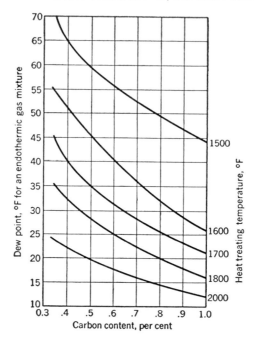

**Fig. 8.3. Equilibrium carbon content versus dew point for an
endothermic gas mixture.**

of forms such as rods, ribbons, or wire. Heating of the piece is
accomplished by convection and radiation. Radiation transfers
a larger share of the heat as operating temperatures rise. Many
furnaces are equipped with fans to aid circulation of the air, for
quicker, more uniform heating. If a protective atmosphere is used,
the excess gas is allowed to escape and burn. Care must be exercised to prevent explosive mixtures from accumulating in a tightly
closed furnace.

Fuel-fired furnaces may be heated by burning oil, tar, producer
and blast furnace gases, or natural gas. Firing is accomplished in
a variety of ways. Some furnaces are fired *directly,* with the burners projecting directly into the heating chamber. In other furnaces, the burners are separated from the heating chamber by
baffles. This is known as *indirect firing.* In neither instance is
there an opportunity for atmosphere control, and applications are
limited accordingly. Where protective atmospheres are required,
muffles or *radiant tube* heaters are used. In a muffle furnace, the
burners are located outside a permanently installed container into

which the work is placed.   A controlled atmosphere is maintained in the muffle, excess gas being allowed to escape and burn.   In radiant tube furnaces, the burning air-gas mixture flows through tubes which pass through the heating chamber.   The atmosphere in the heating chamber may be regulated as desired without interference from the burning gases.

Both electric and fuel-fired furnaces are available in several distinct designs.   The furnaces may be designed as *batch* or *continuous* furnaces.   Among the batch furnaces are box, pit, bell, elevator, and car bottom furnaces.   These are diagrammatically represented in Fig. 8.4(*a*).   The continuous designs include rotary hearth, belt conveyor, roller hearth, pusher, and shaker furnaces.   The rotary hearth furnace is illustrated in Fig. 8.4(*b*).   In the belt conveyor, the work is placed on an endless belt moving within the heating chamber.   At the far end of the furnace the work is dropped into a quenching bath.   In the roller hearth furnace, the work is carried on power-driven rolls.   Pusher furnaces are designed so that the work pieces are pushed through at a steady rate.   In some applications of pusher furnaces there is contact between adjacent workpieces.   In other instances the work is loaded on trays which are pushed through the furnace.   The shaker furnace consists of a reciprocating hearth which moves the pieces through the furnace. Continuous furnaces may be equipped with several different temperature zones such as a preheat, heat, and cooling zone, through which the work must pass.

8.6.   Characistics of Liquid Heat-Transfer Furnaces

Furnaces in which the work is surrounded by a liquid medium have become increasingly popular in recent years.   *Salt baths* are the most common furnaces of this type.   Many different salts are available for different operating ranges and for achieving different surface effects.   In most cases a mixture of salts is used rather than a pure salt.[3]   Salt baths can be used for carburizing, cyaniding, nitriding, and interrupted quenching, as in martempering and austempering, and tempering.   These heat-treating operations are described in the last half of this chapter.   They permit heating for hardening without allowing scaling or decarburization.   There

[3] A list of various salts and their uses is given on p. 284.   *Metals Handbook*, 1948 ed., American Society for Metals, Cleveland.

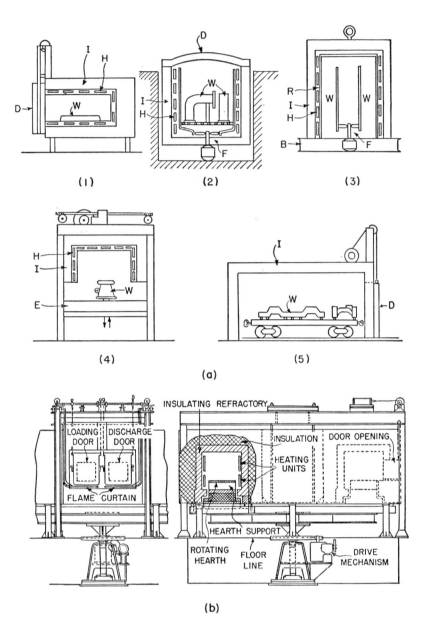

Fig. 8.4. Batch-type and continuous-type furnaces. (a) Diagrams of some of the principal types of batch furnaces. The letters identify the following: *D*—door or access, *I*—insulation, *H*—heating elements, *W*—work piece or work space, *F*—fan for forced circulation, *R*—retort (actually a removable muffle), *B*—furnace base, *E*—elevator serving as the furnace bottom. The names of the furnaces are (1) box furnace, (2) pit furnace, (3) bell furnace, (4) elevator furnace, and (5) car bottom furnace. In the bell furnace, the insulating bell-like cover can be lifted and removed so that the retort

are several advantages resulting from the use of salt baths which are worthy of mention. Foremost among the advantages is the fact that heating is much more rapidly accomplished in salt baths than in atmosphere furnaces. Thermal shock is prevented to a certain extent by the formation of a solid, insulating layer of salt around the cold workpiece when it is first immersed in the hot salt. Avoidance of scaling and decarburization is easily accomplished since the parts being heated are not in contact with air. Non-oxidizing salts are used, and any oxidizing compounds which form in the salt baths must be removed occasionally. Failure to remove oxidizing compounds produces decarburization. Another advantage of salt baths is their suitability for selective heating of portions of a workpiece. The speed of heating in a salt bath makes possible localized heating before the entire piece becomes hot. An additional advantage is the buoyancy of salt, which makes heavy pieces easier to handle. A salt bath leaves a layer of salt on pieces, which must be removed. After quenching in water the last traces of this salt are usually removed by washing in order to prevent any tendency to corrode. See Fig. 8.5.

Lead is another liquid medium used in heat-treating furnaces. It has an operating range between 650°F (343°C) and 1700°F (927°C), whereas salts operate from about 325°F (163°C) to 2450°F (1342°C). Heating rates developed in lead baths are about the same as those developed in salt baths, and very much greater than in atmosphere furnaces. Unless protected from atmospheric oxidation by a cover of carbonaceous material or a suitable salt, lead baths pick up oxygen. Unprotected lead baths produce dirty stock. The buoyancy of lead is so great that steel and other metals being heat treated must be forcibly submerged. Lead is well suited to localized heating of workpieces. Because of its temperature range it is useful for tempering, annealing, and low-temperature hardening operations. A lead bath does not leave a film on the parts unless the lead has been contaminated with tin.

Oil baths, heated by immersion heaters, *are used for tempering.* Oil tempering baths are for low-temperature work only, the maximum safe operating temperature being about 600°F (315°C) depending upon the oil used.

---

and work can be put in place. (b) A continuous type furnace known as the rotary open hearth furnace. [Part (b) adapted from *Metals Handbook.* American Society for Metals, 1948.]

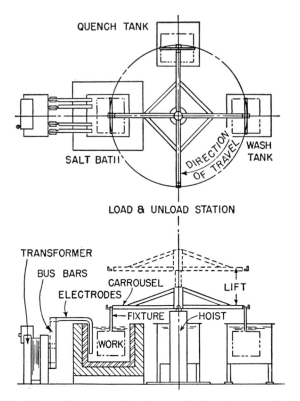

Fig. 8.5.   Carousel-type mechanism applied to immersed-electrode salt-bath furnace. [Adapted from *Metals Handbook.* American Society for Metals, 1948.]

8.7. Heat Sources for Liquid Heat-Transfer Furnaces

Salt and lead baths are contained in square, rectangular, or round pots.   Heat is supplied to salt and lead baths by *external gas or oil firing,* or by externally located *electric resistance units.*   Salt baths, having high internal resistance, are also commonly heated by *immersion electrodes.*   This method cannot be used for lead because its electric conductivity is too high.   A special advantage of the immersion electrode heater is the effect of electromagnetic forces which cause circulation of the salt.   These forces cause the molten salt to be sucked in between the electrodes and forced downward, counter to the direction of thermal convection.   Therefore good mixing is achieved and uniform temperatures are developed throughout the bath.

8.8. Quenching Apparatus

Cooling devices and furnaces for the controlled extraction of heat have already been discussed briefly. Atmosphere furnaces may be used for slowly cooling metals, such as in the annealing of steel. Salt and lead baths are used not only for heating to hardening temperatures, but also for interrupted quenches. An application has already been discussed under the general topic of derivation of *T-T-T* diagrams. Other applications are for martempering and austempering, which are described later in the chapter. Water- and oil-quenching tanks may simply be large metal containers. If the volume and nature of the work demands, agitation, recirculation, and cooling equipment are used. Quenching presses are used in which dies hold the part to its desired shape while it is quenched. These devices which minimize or prevent distortion have been successfully used in the quenching of gears, long flat bars, and similar shapes.

HEAT-TREATING OPERATIONS FOR STEEL

8.9. Box Annealing or Process Annealing

This is simply a recrystallization and stress relief anneal of cold-worked steel, accomplished by heating to some temperature below A_{c1}. Box and process anneals do not involve a pearlite-austenite transformation. They apply particularly to low-carbon steels which are the most common cold-working grades.

8.10. Full Annealing

Full annealing, or more often simply "annealing," is a heat treatment in which the steel is heated about 100°F (55°C) above the A_{c3} temperature, then slowly cooled in the annealing furnace. Note that for hypereutectoids this does not take the steel to a region where austenite alone exists. Annealing is often applied to hot-worked pieces which are air cooled after working, so that there has been little opportunity for complete precipitation of the proeutectoid constituent from austenite. Furthermore, since sections of varying thickness cool at different speeds, they exhibit different mechanical properties. This is due to the differences in fineness of pearlite and varying amounts of proeutectoid. The objectives of annealing, in the approximate order of importance, are:

(1) *Softening.* In hypoeutectoid steels containing lamellar pearlite, maximum softness results if the soft ferrite network is permitted to reach a maximum size, and if the pearlite laminations are allowed to become very coarse. Both of these structures are promoted by heating above A_{c3}, followed by a slow cool to room temperature. (See Fig. 7.8.) In the hypereutectoid steels, before annealing, there is often less than an equilibrium amount of cementite. Since this is desirable for greater softness, heating to any temperature in excess of A_3 would simply allow a larger amount of cementite to precipitate upon slow cooling. In both eutectoid and hypereutectoid steels, softness is achieved by formation of coarse pearlite upon slow cooling from the austenitic condition.

(2) *Grain size refinement.* The nonuniform and sometimes large grain sizes resulting from hot working are eliminated by reheating the steel to the austenite range. The grain size in castings is also refined. Upon slow cooling a more uniform spacing of pearlite lamellae also results.

(3) *Residual stress relief.* Any stresses which remain in the steel as a result of prior processing are relieved upon full annealing.

(4) *Homogenization.* The heating period and slow cooling involved in annealing allow diffusion to occur, and thus tend to eliminate segregation and nonuniform distribution of components.

8.11. Normalizing

In normalizing, the steel is heated well into the austenite range, then given a mild quench in still air. Normalizing accomplishes the following:

(1) *The amount of proeutectoid net work is reduced.* In hypereutectoid steels this is the result of dissolving the cementite at high temperatures and preventing its subsequent precipitation by a mild air quench. Hypereutectoid compositions are thus rendered more suitable for spheroidization, because of elimination of the massive network of cementite which does not readily spheroidize. (The significance of spheroidizing is explained below.) In hypoeutectoid steels, the size of the ferrite network is reduced and pearlite is ren-

dered finer.   (See Fig. 7.8(b).)   In eutectoid steels the only change
in microstructure is an increase in the fineness of pearlite.   Both
hypoeutectoid and eutectoid steels are made stronger and less ductile by normalizing.

(2) *Homongenization and Grain Size Refinement.*   Same as for
annealing.

(3) *Pearlite is rendered finer* than in the annealed condition.
(See Fig. 7.8.)

(4) *Improvement of machinability of low-carbon (<0.3 per cent
carbon) steels* by decrease in the amount of soft, ductile ferrite.
(See section 18.7.)

8.12. Spheroidizing

When steel is heated to temperatures below A_1 for long enough
periods of time, the lamellar cementite in pearlite becomes spheroidal.   That is, under the influence of diffusion, the cementite
lamellae coalesce into spheres.   These are embedded in a matrix
of ferrite.   Spheroidizing places a steel in the softest possible condition.   It is widely used for high-carbon steels, to render them
more machinable.   After machining to shape, the steel is in an
ideal condition for heat treating, because the carbides dissolve in
austenite most readily when in the finely dispersed spheroidal condition.   Spheroidizing is also the end result of prolonged tempering
of martensitic steels.   As tempering proceeds, carbide particles, at
first distributed on a submicroscopic scale, grow to larger sizes
until they can be seen even at fairly low magnifications.   This
amounts to a spheroidizing treatment.   A spheroidized structure is
shown in Fig. 8.6.

Fig. 8.6.   Spheroidized   structure.
Etchant: picric acid in alcohol.
Magnification: 500×.   [Courtesy
of the School of Engineering,
Metals Laboratory, University of
Massachusetts.]

8.13. Tempering

Tempering is an operation which is applied only to hardened steels. After being hardened, steel is usually tempered. Tempering is also known as *drawing* or *drawing back*. The operation involves heating the hardened steel to some temperature below A_1. (Usually the temperatures for spheroidizing are higher than those used for tempering.)

The principal objectives of tempering are:

(1) *To achieve increased toughness.* Fresh martensite has practically no resistance to impact loads and has poor notched strength. Tempering improves the ductility, toughness, and impact strength of martensite. This is illustrated in the plot of Fig. 8.7.

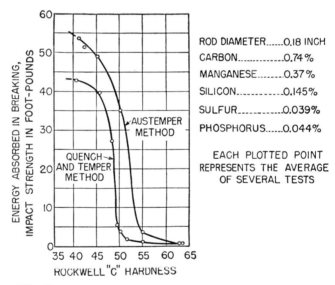

Fig. 8.7. **The toughness of austempered and quenched and tempered steel compared.** The toughness of the austempered steel is greater than that of conventionally heat-treated steel of the same hardness. [Adapted from *Suiting the Heat Treatment to the Job.* Carnegie-Illinois Steel Corporation, 1946.]

(2) *To relieve residual stresses.* In this respect, tempering is similar to annealing. Residual stresses may be present in any piece of metal as a result of a quenching operation. Even if no changes in phase are involved, rapid cooling of a piece of metal produces

compressive stresses in those sections which are cooled first.   The
compressive stresses are opposed by tensile stresses which arise in
the last portions to cool.   Thus thin sections and outer surfaces
tend to be in compression, while thick sections and inner regions
tend to be in tension as a result of rapid cooling alone.   Where
there are phase changes (as in the quenching of steel), accompanied by variations in density, the picture becomes somewhat more
complicated.   Consider for a moment Fig. 8.8.   Suppose an irregularly shaped piece of steel of cross section as indicated is quenched.
Section A, being thinner, cools and contracts faster than section B.

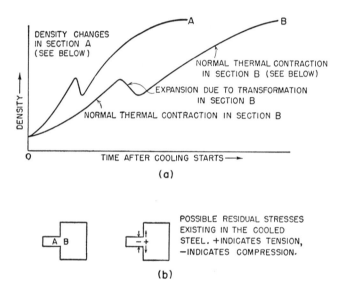

(a)

(b)

Fig. 8.8.   Residual stresses in quenched steel.   (a) Shows how a
piece of steel of uneven cross-section might undergo changes in density at nonuniform rates, upon cooling from above the critical
temperature.   Normal contractions resulting from cooling are opposed by expansion accompanying the formation of martensite.   Opposing stresses are thus set up, and if the cooling and transformation temperature are such that these cannot be relieved, residual
stresses will exist in the cooled piece, possibly as shown in (b).

The steel in section A also reaches the M_s temperature before that
of section B, and hence is the first material to undergo the martensite transformation.   Martensite has a lower density than the
austenite from which it is formed.   Therefore, as indicated in the
plot, section A undergoes an expansion while section B is still undergoing thermal contraction.   Section A again contracts when the

martensite transformation is complete. Finally section B reaches the M_s temperature, and starts to expand at a time when the density of A is fairly stable. This temporarily places A in tension, and B in compression. When B has completely transformed, it tends to contract, leaving the piece in compression at A and tension at B. Thus residual stresses are set up by the opposing forces of normal contraction (upon cooling) and expansion (upon transformation). These residual stresses are relieved by tempering.

The stresses, as mentioned before, may be serious enough to cause distortion or even cracking. If the martensite transformation occurs at a sufficiently low temperature, the steel is no longer plastic, and it cannot yield, so that cracking results. At high carbon contents which lower the M_s and M_f temperatures, this problem becomes more serious. Manganese and nickel also lower the M_s temperature appreciably.

(3) *To stabilize structure and dimensions*. It is quite common to find some *retained austenite* in quenched steels. The instability of austenite under some conditions leads to changes in the dimensions and the microstructure of steels. Tempering either eliminates the retained austenite or stabilizes it, and by these means renders it harmless. The amount of retained austenite which is present depends upon several factors, the most significant of which are listed below:

   (a) *The alloying elements present*. Certain elements have been found more effective than others in encouraging retention of austenite. In general the strong carbide formers exert the least effect, but no strict rule may be stated.

   (b) *The austenitizing temperature*. The higher the austenitizing temperature [below about 1900°F (1037°C)], the greater is the percentage of retained austenite. This seems to be related to the homogeneity of the austenite and grain size.

   (c) *The quenching rate*. The higher the cooling velocity the lower is the percentage of retained austenite.

The amounts of retained austenite may be as high as 100 per cent, as in the case of Hadfield's steel, which contains 1.2 per cent carbon and 12 per cent manganese. In plain carbon, water-quenched, tool steels 5 to 10 per cent retained austenite is common. Even in 0.2 per cent carbon steel, up to 2 per cent retained austenite may remain after quenching in iced brine. After hardening, steel is likely to consist mainly of fresh martensite (see Section 7.15) with smaller amounts of austenite.

Freshly formed martensite is unstable and tends to decompose slowly into cementite and ferrite at room temperature. Since martensite is a structure of lower density than steel consisting of α and cementite, a contraction accompanies its decomposition. The rate of decomposition is considerably speeded by using elevated temperatures. If the tempering temperature is too low, or the time too short to complete the process, the decomposition of martensite continues at room temperature at the normal room temperature rate.

Retained austenite in the steel undergoes decomposition at room temperature to form martensite. Upon tempering, the retained austenite decomposes to whatever products are formed isothermally at the tempering temperature. That is, the *T-T-T* diagram again becomes effective. Upon subsequent cooling, after tempering, the retained austenite becomes quite stable, so that it transforms very, very slowly at room temperature. When austenite, which is the most dense structure found in steel, undergoes transformations to other products, an expansion occurs.

Thus tempering achieves structural stability by hastening the decomposition of martensite and by causing either decomposition or stabilization of retained austenite. Dimensional changes are thus minimized or eliminated. It should be pointed out that stability and dimensional changes are of greatest importance in gages and similar devices where tolerances are small. Whether there is a net expansion or net contraction depends upon the relative amounts of martensite and retained austenite which transform.

The three most important considerations in tempering are: (1) The temperature used, (2) the time at temperature, and (3) the effect of alloying elements in resisting softening and causing brittleness under certain conditions. The rate of cooling usually has no effect on the results obtained excepting that residual stresses are introduced by very rapid cooling. Of course, at slower and slower rates of cooling the results are affected as they would be by increasing the time at temperature. Tempering is most often carried out by varying the temperature rather than the time at temperature, although much the same results can be achieved in either way. In actual practice the control of temperature is sometimes accomplished by observing the changes in the color of the piece as it is heated. The colors developed are due to the formation of an oxide film on the surface of the metal. This is adequate for some work, but in most instances more precise means are used. Tempering is usually carried out immediately after quenching so as to stabilize structure and dimensions and avoid the formation of cracks. If cracks do not immediately develop as a result of quenching, they frequently appear in untempered pieces some time after the quenching operation. This may involve a matter of hours, days, or weeks.

(1) *Effect of Varying Tempering Temperatures.* Increasing the tempering temperature, but holding the time constant, results in increasing softening of the tempered steel. This is shown in Fig. 8.9(a). For steels containing more than 1 per cent carbon, it is interesting to note that there is an initial increase in hardness of the

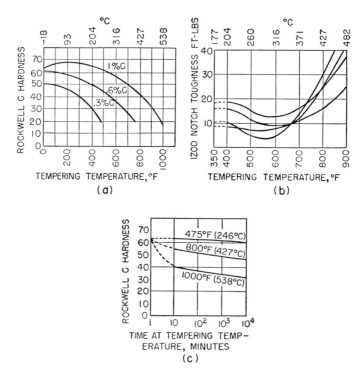

Fig. 8.9. **Variables in tempering.** (a) The effect of temperature on final hardness, shown for steels of different carbon contents. The time at temperature is held constant for this plot. (b) The loss of notch toughness in Izod test specimens for several alloy steels after tempering at 600°F. (c) The effect of time at tempering temperature on final hardness. The effects of different temperatures are also indicated. [Part (b) after E. C. Bain, *Alloying Elements in Steel.* American Society for Metals, 1948.]

steel at low tempering temperatures. This finally gives way to softening of the steel at higher tempering temperatures. It has been observed that the higher the temperature of tempering, the greater the amount of retained austenite that is transformed to martensite on cooling to room temperature. If low tempering temperatures are used (i.e., 300–600°F), the retained austenite is stabilized, and transformation to martensite cannot be accomplished even by refrigeration. As the temperature is raised toward 400°F (204°C) the fresh martensite is converted to a complex carbon-rich phase called ε-carbide and a body-centered tetragonal martensite containing 0.25 per cent carbon in solid solution:

$$M \longrightarrow \varepsilon\text{-carbide} + M\ (0.25C)$$

Epsilon-carbide is not cementite. Above 400°F (204°C) the ε-carbide and M (0.25C) decompose into cementite and ferrite:

$$\varepsilon\text{-carbide} + M\ (0.25C) \longrightarrow Fe_3C + \alpha$$

In alloys steels containing sufficient quantities of strong carbide-forming alloying elements, Fe_3C may finally be replaced by the stable complex carbides of these elements. While tempering has as one of its principal objectives the improvement of notched impact strength, it actually results in lowered values for this property under some conditions. The *plain carbon and low-alloy* steels show a decrease in toughness (known as *blue brittleness*) when tempered in the temperature range near 600°F (315°C). Precipitation of iron carbide in massive form around the martensite needles is believed to be the cause of blue brittleness. This is shown in Fig. 8.9(*b*).

(2) *Effect of Varying Time at Temperature.* Substantially the same effect can be achieved by using a shorter time at high temperature as by using a longer time at low temperature. The rate of softening increases at higher and higher temperatures, as indicated by the increase (numerical) in the slope of the lines in the plot of Fig. 8.9(*c*).

(3) *Effect of Alloying Elements.* A notable effect of alloying elements is to increase resistance to softening as a result of tempering. The alloying elements exerting the greatest tendency in this respect are the strong carbide formers such as titanium, vanadium, molybdenum, tungsten, and chromium. The elements are more effective in resisting softening, the higher the original quench-

ing temperature, as shown in Fig. 8.10(a). Not only is softening resisted, but in some cases there is an increase in hardness at higher tempering temperatures. This is known as secondary hardness and is graphically illustrated in Fig. 8.10(b). Secondary hardness is similar to aging, in that the increase in hardness occurs in less time the higher the tempering temperature. This is indicated

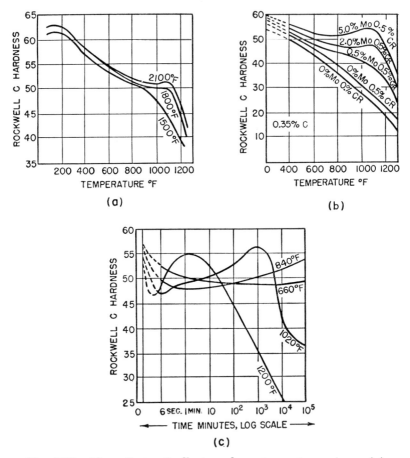

Fig. 8.10. The effects of alloying elements on tempering. (a) Softening with increasing tempering temperature of a Cr-Mo-V steel, as influenced by degree of carbide solution. The degree of carbide solution depends on the hardening temperature (time at temperature being held constant). (b) Softening with increasing tempering temperature, as influenced by chromium and molybdenum content. (c) Softening with increasing time interval in a quenched steel containing 5 per cent Mo and 0.35 per cent C. Note the difference between Figs. 8.10(c) and 8.9(c). [After E. C. Bain, *Alloying Elements in Steel*, American Society for Metals, 1948.]

in Fig. 8.10(c). Resistance to softening is an indication that creep resistance in a steel may be good. If a steel fails to have good resistance to softening at high tempering temperatures, it probably has poor creep resistance. The resistance to softening which the strong carbide formers impart to steel is also the source of the high hot-hardness of steel cutting tools at red heat.

There is an instance, in addition to the one mentioned above, in which tempering reduces toughness as indicated by impact strength. When many of the alloy steels, particularly the deep-hardening chromium-nickel steels, are cooled slowly from high tempering temperatures [i.e., near 1200°F (650°C)] through the range 700–800°F (371–427°C) a form of brittleness known as temper brittleness develops. This can be prevented by quenching from the tempering temperature.

Other effects of alloying elements in rendering steels brittle because of tempering have already been discussed.

Normalized versus Quenched and Tempered Steels. A comparison of steels of the same composition, in which the same tensile strength has been developed by normalizing in one case, and by quenching and tempering in the other case, shows that the quenched and tempered steel is superior. The quenched and tempered steel has better ductility and toughness and a higher yield strength than normalized steel of the same tensile strength.

8.14. Master Tempering Curves

Using principles similar to those outlined in Section 3.14 which were applied to stress-rupture predictions, one can predict tempering response. The parameter which governs the relationship between time and temperature of tempering is

$$T(c + \log t)$$

where T is the absolute temperature (°F + 460), t is time in hours and the logarithms are to the base 10. The term c is a constant which has values between 15 and 20, but for which a value of 18 is most universally useful.

The plot of Fig. 8.11 provides an easy means for determining the value of the parameter $T(c + \log t)$ when the value of c is taken as 18. The values of the parameter, taken from Fig. 8.11, for one-hour tempering times, are shown in Table 8.2.

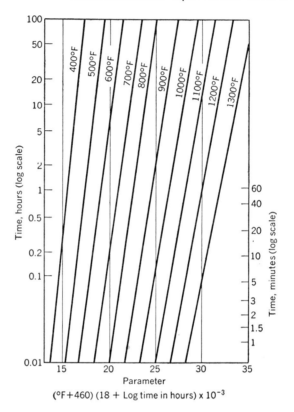

**Fig. 8.11. Plot of relationship between parameter and tempera-
ture and time, for C = 18.** [Reproduced with permission from
R. A. Grange and R. W. Baughman, "Hardness of Tempered Martensite in Carbon and Low Alloy Steels," *Trans. ASM*, 1956.]

Table 8.2

Temperature °F	Parameter × 10⁻³
400	15.5
500	17.3
600	19.1
700	20.9
800	22.7
900	24.4
1000	26.2
1100	27.9
1200	29.8

Supposing that a fully hardened SAE-AISI 4340 heat gave hardness
values, after one hour's tempering, as follows:

Table 8.3

Temperature-Time-Hardness Relations for SAE-AISI 4340 Steel

Temperature °F	R_c Hardness
400	54.8
500	52.2
600	49.5
700	49.0
800	45.9
900	43.3
1000	39.9
1100	37.2
1200	32.3

Using the information of Tables 8.2 and 8.3, a master curve can now be constructed for the tempering response of SAE-AISI 4340 as shown in Fig. 8.12. This plot can be used to determine what tempering time-temperature specifications would produce, for fully hardened SAE-AISI 4340, any as-tempered hardness within the range R_c 32–55. For instance, suppose a hardness of R_c 46 was required using a time cycle of one-half hour, what temperature should be used? From Fig. 8.12, R_c 46 is seen to correspond to a parameter of 22.7×10^3. Substituting this into the expression for the parameter

$$(°F + 460)(18 + \log 0.5) = 22.7 \times 10^3$$

and solving for °F

$$°F = \frac{22.7 \times 10^3}{18 + 9.698 - 10} - 460$$

$$°F = 822$$

Using Fig. 8.11 and published tempering data for steels, one can construct master tempering curves as needed. The curves can be used to determine the amount of additional tempering necessary to bring an undertempered piece to specified hardness. They can also be used to calculate the hardness of hardened steel members subjected to high temperatures for long periods of time. The curves thus represent an improved technique for predicting tempering behavior and response to elevated temperature service. The curves also have been successfully used to predict, on the basis of composition alone, the as-tempered hardness for various time-temperature combinations. This is described in section 8.8.

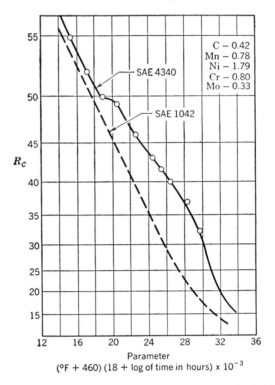

C – 0.42
Mn – 0.78
Ni – 1.79
Cr – 0.80
Mo – 0.33

SAE 4340

SAE 1042

R_c

Parameter
(°F + 460) (18 + log of time in hours) x 10^{-3}

Fig. 8.12. Hardness of tempered martensite in SAE-AISI 4340 steel. [Reproduced by permission from R. A. Grange and R. W. Baughman, "Hardness of Tempered Martensite in Carbon and Low Alloy Steels," *Trans. ASM*, 1956.]

Limitations to use of master tempering curves. Response to tempering is significantly affected by the composition of the steel, the size of the pieces being tempered, the presence of high-temperature transformation products, and the presence of retained austenite. In an SAE-AISI medium-alloy structural steel such as 4340, variations in R_c hardness of ± 2.5 points can be expected. That is, a steel whose composition was on the high side might have a tempered hardness 5 points higher than the same steel whose composition was on the low-side, even though both met composition specifications. In general, as the size of the pieces being tempered increases, the larger the piece the lower the actual hardness obtained from a given quenching and tempering sequence. Thus, if master tempering curves are constructed from published literature, such curves would be rigorously applicable only to pieces of exactly the same composition and size and heat treated in the same way as the material used for obtaining the published data. In actual practice, to overcome such limitations, it is desirable to quench and temper some sample pieces from each heat being used. Negative or positive corrections are then made on the master tempering curves, in the form of lines drawn parallel to the master plot. In this way, curves constructed from published data can be extended to apply to heats, sizes, and heat-treating procedures different than those which the published data represent.

8.15. Austempering

The interrupted quenching process shown schematically in Fig. 8.13 (a) is known as austempering. As can be seen from the diagram, in order for the process to be successful the piece must be cooled rapidly enough to prevent the formation of pearlite. The quench is interrupted at a transformation temperature which produces acicular bainite. The piece is held at this temperature until the transformation of austenite to bainite is complete. The resulting transformation product may be as hard as the martensite produced by conventional quench and temper methods. In addition, a comparison of bainite with quenched and tempered martensite of equal hardness has shown that the bainitic structure has greater ductility and impact strength. This is illustrated in Fig. 8.7. Austempering is applied to small parts such as shoe shanks, or shapes of small cross section such as wire, in which it is possible to prevent formation of pearlite during the initial stages of cooling. Obviously, the hardenability of the steel is of primary importance for successful austempering.

8.16. Martempering

The heat treatment known as martempering is illustrated in Fig. 8.13 (b). Martempering is successfully applied to steel sections or irregular shapes which are likely to crack during conventional quenching. The initial quench is the same as that for austempering, except that the steel is not held at the quenching temperature long enough to allow any bainite to form. Instead, it is held only long enough to allow for equalization of the temperature throughout the piece. When this is achieved, it is slowly cooled to room tem-

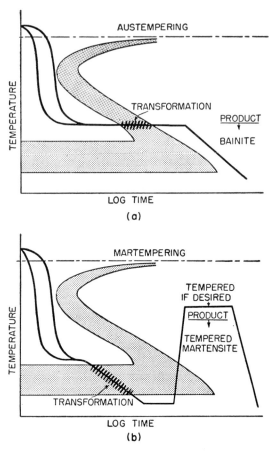

Fig. 8.13. Schematic indication of differences between austempering and martempering. [Adapted from *Suiting the Heat Treatment to the Job*. Carnegie-Illinois Steel Corporation, 1946.]

perature, during which transformation occurs slowly and uniformly to martensite. Thus the high stresses (as explained earlier) which accompany conventional quenching to martensite are avoided. The final product has some of the properties of tempered martensite, and a tempering operation is not always necessary. However, where further tempering is desirable, the workpiece can be reheated for this purpose. The hardenability of the steel bears directly on the applicability of martempering. Martempering will not be successful if appreciable transformation occurs before the M_s temperature is reached during the final cooling operation.

SURFACE HARDENING METHODS FOR STEEL

There are numerous surface hardening treatments which are usually intended to provide a hard, wear-resistant surface or case on a relatively soft, tough core. Another name for these treatments is case hardening.

8.17. Carburizing

One of the oldest and most widely used case-hardening methods is carburizing. It is also called case carburizing. Carburizing is applied to low-carbon, plain carbon steels, though frequently low-alloy, low-carbon steels are also carburized. It involves increasing the carbon content of the surface, so that upon suitable heat treatment the surface will respond by hardening. In pack carburizing, the piece is surrounded with solid carbonaceous materials (often charcoal to which barium carbonate has been added as an energizer). Gas carburizing involves placing the piece in a furnace atmosphere having a suitable concentration of a hydrocarbon gas. Salt baths [4] containing potassium and sodium cyanides as the active ingredients are also used (liquid carburizing). Temperatures of about 1700°F (927°C) are used for periods of time up to about 75 hours, depending upon the depth of case required. The depth of case is usually under 0.100 inch. Gas carburizing produces a case about 0.05 inch deep in about 50 hours at 1725°F (941°C). This temperature is high enough to make the steel austenitic so that the carbon dissolves and diffuses rapidly. Higher temperatures are avoided because of the danger of excessive grain growth and distortion of the piece by creep. Carbon pickup alone increases the surface hardness, relative to the low-carbon core. By proper heat treatment, however, the properties of both case and core can be further improved. The piece may be directly quenched upon removal from the carburizing unit, to produce a martensitic case and hypoeutectoid core. This is not the best treatment, because at the high temperatures of carburizing the austenite grain size increases; thus maximum ductility and toughness are not realized.

[4] Liquid carburizing results in a small amount of nitrogen pickup in the surface steel. This is not harmful; in fact, the hardness is improved by it.

Furthermore, quenching from such a high temperature may involve damage to the work. To avoid these difficulties, the steel may be quenched in oil after carburizing, then reheated above A_1, and then quenched in water. This latter method, known as the double quench method, has several advantages. First, precipitation of a massive carbide network is prevented by the oil quench, while at the same time the more severe strains of a direct water quench are avoided. Upon reheating to above A_1, fine-grained austenite is formed, which produces maximum toughness and fully hardens to

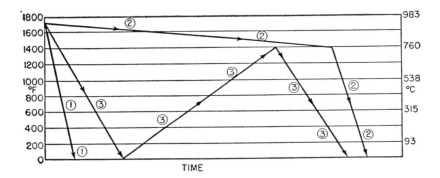

Fig. 8.14. Three possible heat treatments after carburizing. ① shows a direct quench from the carburizing furnace to develop full hardness, at the same time avoiding the formation of massive, free cementite, which would lower the ductility. However, the carburizing operation results in coarsening of the austenite grain size, and the transformation products of this structure do not attain maximum ductility and toughness. The case is martensitic; the core has a hypoeutectoid structure. ② is a furnace cool to 1400°F (760°C), which avoids the severe stresses of the direct quench, but allows precipitation of an undesirable cementite network. The grain size of the austenite prior to transformation is too large to produce a piece having maximum ductility and toughness. The case consists of massive cementite and martensite, and the core has a hypoeutectoid structure. ③ A double quench avoids the severe strains of the direct quench by using oil rather than water for initial cooling. Furthermore, it prevents the formation of massive cementite as in the case of ②. Upon reheating to slightly above the eutectoid temperature, the austenite grain size is reduced, producing a piece having maximum toughness and ductility upon subsequent transformation. During the reheating, the temperature and time are adjusted so as to minimize cementite precipitation. The case is martensitic, and the core has a hypoeutectoid structure. Still another possibility is to control the carbon content of the case so that the hypereutectoid structures are avoided. If this is done, cycle ② can be used without danger of massive cementite precipitation.

martensite at the surface upon receiving the final water quench.   A third possible heat treatment for carburized parts involves slow cooling to just above A_1 followed by a quench from this temperature. While this avoids severe straining of the part, it produces undesirable massive cementite particles in the case, and the large austenite grains transform to a product lacking toughness.   These are the three most important possibilities in the way of heat treatment. They are represented in Fig. 8.14.

8.18. Cyaniding

If the salt baths used for carburizing are operated at temperatures between 1300°F (704°C) and 1500°F (817°C) [rather than near 1700°F (927°C)] the steel tends to pick up appreciable quantities of nitrogen as well as carbon.   This is known as cyaniding, a process which has been successfully applied to alloy and carbon steels.   Because of the lower temperatures used, diffusion is slower than in carburizing baths.   Gas cyaniding, more accurately called carbonitriding, is carried out in a furnace whose atmosphere consists of a hydrocarbon gas and ammonia.   Cyaniding is used as an economical means of producing a *thin* (i.e., up to about 0.008-inch) case.   The nitrogen which is absorbed forms needlelike nitrides which impart added hardness to the case.   In order to obtain maximum hardness from the high carbon content of the case, quenching is usually used.

8.19. Nitriding

As has been mentioned and can be seen from the iron-iron carbide diagram, carbon is almost insoluble in ferrite.   Therefore if the same baths used for carburizing are operated below the A_1 temperature, carbon pickup is prevented, but not nitrogen pickup. This is essentially what happens in salt bath nitriding.   The energizing and other salt additions used in carburizing are eliminated from cyaniding baths, which may be mixtures of potassium cyanide and sodium cyanide.   Gas nitriding, which is also common, is carried out by heating the steel to below A_1 for periods of time up to 75 hours, while salt bath nitriding may require only 1½ hours. Parts to be nitrided are usually rough machined to shape, hardened by quenching, then given a high-temperature [1100°–1200°F (593°–

650°C)] temper.   The part is then finish machined or ground to final dimensions, and finally nitrided.   (A nitrided case is very difficult to machine or grind.)   The nitrided layer is inherently hard and does not require quenching or other heat treatment.   Thus, one significant advantage of this process is the fact that the tendencies toward cracking and distortion are avoided.   Since there is no chance of distortion, finish machining is possible prior to nitriding. A very high hardness is developed in the nitrided case, and is of such a nature that the hardness is retained at elevated temperatures.   In addition, the case imparts good fatigue strength and resists certain types of corrosive media.   However, nitriding is limited in use by its high cost.   Entering into the cost picture are special alloy steels which must be used.   These steels always contain appreciable amounts of aluminum (approximately 1 per cent) along with other elements.   In addition, the time required to develop an appreciable thickness of case is long and involves expense, as does also the ammonia used.

8.20. Flame Hardening

In flame hardening, an oxyacetylene or similar gas flame is passed over the surface to be hardened.   Quenching immediately after heating may be accomplished by a jet of water or air, or by immersion in conventional quenching liquids.   Sometimes still air is sufficient as a coolant.   The temperature developed at various locations in the piece can be controlled by the speed of travel and intensity of the flame.   The severity of quench can be adjusted by varying the time interval between heating and quenching, and by the selection of quenching medium.   Mechanized equipment has been developed for automatic flame hardening of large numbers of similarly shaped parts.   Flame hardening is particularly suited to surface hardening of parts whose size renders furnace treatments impractical.   It also applies to any part where hardening throughout is not desired.   It has been very widely used for hardening gear teeth. The small portion of metal actually heated and quenched is also an advantage, because this reduces distortion to a minimum.   Since flame hardening produces hardness by the formation of martensite, the composition of the steel is a prime consideration.   It must be capable of being hardened without any dependence on change of composition of the surface layers. This may involve some added cost, as compared to carburizing or cyaniding. Flame hardening may require tempering or mild [400°F (204°C)] stress-relief anneals following the hardening operation.

8.21. Induction Hardening

This process accomplishes much the same results as flame hardening. However, instead of using a flame for heating, an induction coil carrying high-frequency (600 to 2,000,000 cycles per second) current is used. The coil surrounds the piece to be hardened but does not touch it. Induction heating can produce a very rapid rise in temperature. In a steel rod 1½ inches in diameter a rise of 1300°F (722°C) in 10 seconds is readily achieved. For most surface hardening, the time involved is in the order of 2 to 3 seconds. When the proper temperature has been achieved to the desired depth, the power is shut off and the part is quickly cooled. Quenching is accomplished by dropping the part into a conventional quench tank or by using a quenching spray. Induction hardening involves high initial cost. Each job requires its own timing sequence and coils, and therefore the process is better suited to mass production of small parts. Speed, cleanliness, and freedom from scale and distortion are among the advantages of induction hardening. It might also be mentioned that induction heating is used for bringing pieces to forging heat, for soldering, brazing, for sintering of powdered metal compacts, and for stress relieving and tempering. It may be used for heating nonferrous as well as ferrous metals.

8.22. Summary

A table listing the various heat treatments, how they are accomplished, their applications, and their effects is reproduced on page 260.

Table 8.4. Heat Treating Summary

Process	How Accomplished	Application	Changes in microstructure	Changes in properties
1. Box or Process Annealing	Heat to below A_{c1}.	Cold-worked low-carbon steels.	Recrystallization of cold-worked metal. (No pearlite to austenite transformation.)	Softening, restoration of ductility, and stress-relief.
2. Full Annealing (Annealing)	Heat above A_{c3}, then slow furnace cool.	Hot-worked (i.e. forged, hot-rolled, etc.) steel. Cast steels.	Maximum ferrite and coarse pearlite produced. Refines grain structure of hot-worked steels. Homogenizes structure.	Maximum softness and ductility, stress relief.
3. Normalizing	Heat to austenite range, cool in still air.	Hot-worked and cast steels. High-carbon steels before spheroidizing.	Less proeutectoid than in annealed steels (important for spheroidization of hypereutectoids), fine pearlite produced. Refine grain structure (of hot-worked steels and castings). Homogenizes structure.	Stronger and less ductile than annealed steels. May have slight residual stresses. Improves machinability of some hypereutectoid steels.
4. Spheroidizing	Heat to below A_{c1} for long time.	High-carbon steels to be machined or heat treated.	Fe_3C in lamellar pearlite and *thin* Fe_3C network becomes spheroidal.	Renders high-carbon steels soft and machinable. Carbides in finely dispersed spheroidal condition dissolve readily in γ; steel is thus rendered suitable for heat treatment.
5. Tempering	Heat to below A_{c1} for short time.	Hardened steels only.	Martensite darkens. Eventually carbides coalesce. Spheroidization is the end result if tempering temperatures are maintained for long times. Microstructure is stabilized.	Increases toughness and ductility if properly carried out. Increases softness (undesirable). Relieves residual stresses of hardening. Stabilizes dimensions.
6. Hardening	A. Conventional —heat to γ range and quench in brine, H_2O, oil, or air, to obtain martensite. B. Austempering—heat to γ range and quench in molten salt or lead to produce isothermal transformation between M_s and 1000°F (538°C) to produce bainitic structure. C. Martempering—heat to γ range and quench to just above M_s, hold to equalize temperature throughout, then cool to room temperature to get martensite.			

260

Questions

8.1. What are the three functional classes of heat-treating equipment?

8.2. What major differences exist in the equipment used to apply heat to metals?

8.3. (a) What gases are commonly found in raw products of combustion and what is the effect of each on steel?

(b) Refer to Fig. 8.1. A furnace atmosphere consists of 6 per cent carbon dioxide and 10 per cent carbon monoxide, 84 per cent nitrogen. What is the maximum temperature to which a low-carbon steel could be heated in this atmosphere without oxidizing? If H_2O and H_2 were introduced in the ratio of 3 to 10, would a greater or lesser degree of protection be offered at 1300°F (704°C)?

8.4. Under what conditions does a diluent gas have no effect on shifting the equilibrium of a reaction? Under what conditions is the equilibrium shifted by the presence of a diluent, and in what way is it shifted?

8.5. (a) Distinguish between an endothermic and exothermic gas.

(b) Given an endothermic atmosphere containing 20 per cent CO, 40 per cent H_2, and 40 per cent N_2, what dew point should be used for neutral hardening of a steel containing 0.6 per cent C?

(c) How is dew point measured?

(d) For what purpose are steam atmospheres used in heat treating of steel?

8.6. What two heat sources are used in atmosphere furnaces? Distinguish between box, pit, bell, elevator, and car-bottom furnaces.

8.7. What two major classes of heat-transfer agents are used in furnaces relying on liquid heat-transfer media? What are the advantages and limitations of each?

8.8. Describe the different heat sources used for heating furnaces embodying liquid media. Discuss any special limitations and advantages of these.

8.9. Briefly describe the equipment used for quenching.

8.10. What is *box* or *process annealing?*

8.11. How is full annealing carried out? What are its objectives?

8.12. How is normalizing carried out? What does normalizing accomplish?

8.13. How is spheroidizing carried out? What effect does spheroidizing have on steel?

8.14. How is tempering carried out? List the principal objectives of tempering.

8.15. Discuss the origin of residual stresses in quenched steels.

8.16. Why is it necessary to stabilize the dimensions of quenched steels? What is *retained austenite?* What factors favor a high percentage of retained austenite?

8.17. Upon what changes in microconstituents will the net dimensional change depend when a quenched steel is tempered?

8.18. What is the relationship between time and temperature of tempering? What temperature range during tempering results in stabilization of austenite? What is *blue brittleness* and under what conditions is it produced? What is *temper brittleness* and under what conditions is it produced?

8.19. Discuss the effects of alloying elements on behavior during tempering.

8.20. How do the properties of *quenched and tempered* steels compare with those of *normalized* steels?

8.21. (a) Given below are the R_c readings for SAE-AISI 4140 steel tempered for 2 hours at the temperatures shown:

Temperature °F	400	600	800	1000	1200
R_c Hardness	54.2	48.5	44.3	36.0	28.0

Construct a master tempering curve.

(b) What temperature should be used to give a tempered hardness of R_c 46 for this steel if a half-hour tempering cycle is to be used? If a three-hour tempering cycle is to be used?

(c) A piece of the above steel was quenched and then tempered for one hour at 900°F, producing a hardness of R_c 41.2. It is desired to produce a hardness of R_c 35 in this steel. What tempering temperature will produce this hardness after about one additional hour of tempering? Ans. 1065°F.

8.22. What is *austempering* and what are its advantages?

8.23. What is *martempering* and what are its advantages?

8.24. What three media are used for carburizing? Describe three possible quenching cycles following carburizing and compare the advantages of each.

8.25. Compare cyaniding, carburizing, and nitriding.

8.26. How does temperature control permit use of essentially the same salt baths for carburizing, cyaniding, and nitriding?

8.27. Describe flame hardening. What are the essential features by which flame hardening differs from carburizing, cyaniding, and nitriding?

8.27. Describe induction hardening. To what process of surface hardening does it most closely compare? What important advantages and disadvantages does induction hardening have with respect to flame hardening?

Bibliography

8.1. Bain, E. C., *The Alloying Elements in Steel.* Cleveland: ASM, 1948.

8.2. Cohen, M., "Retained Austenite," *Trans. ASM,* **41** (1949).

8.3. Vaughan, C. H., "A Survey of the Types of Furnace Atmospheres," *Steel Processing and Conversion,* February 1957.

8.4. Peck, C. E., "Controlled Atmospheres," *Steel Processing and Conversion,* April 1957.

8.5. Werner, F. E., B. L. Averbach, and M. Cohen, "The Tempering of Iron-Carbon Martensite Crystals," *Trans. ASM,* **49** (1957).

8.6. Lement, B. S., B. L. Averbach, and M. Cohen, "Microstructural Changes on Tempering Iron-Carbon Alloys," *Trans. ASM,* **47** (1955).

8.7. Nehrenberg, A. E., "Master Curves Simplify Tempering," *Steel,* **127** (October 23, 1957).

8.8. Grange, R. A., and R. W. Baughman, "Hardness of Tempered Martensite in Carbon and Low-Alloy Steels," *Trans. ASM,* **48** (1956).

CHAPTER 9

Iron and Its Alloys

9.1. Introduction

This chapter is divided into two major parts. The first portion presents a discussion of the behavior and effects of the alloying elements in steel. The second portion describes the nature of the common types of ferrous alloys. Some of the effects of alloying elements can be explained on the basis of how the elements are distributed in steel. Also of significance is the behavior of the alloying elements in binary alloys. These and other relationships are indicated below.

BEHAVIOR AND EFFECTS OF ALLOYING ELEMENTS IN STEEL

9.2. Distribution of Alloying Elements in Unhardened Steels

The alloying elements are found in one or more of the five following phases in annealed steels. (1) Most of the common alloying elements are soluble to a certain extent in *ferrite*, the α-*phase*. With most elements, of which aluminum, copper, nickel, phosphorus, and silicon are examples, substitutional solid solution occurs. Some elements, such as carbon, nitrogen, and hydrogen, have small enough atomic radii to permit interstitial solid solution. (2) The alloying elements may be present in cementite or similar *carbide phases*. Titanium, vanadium, molybdenum, and tungsten are frequently found in the carbide phase. (3) *Nonmetallic phases* are sometimes formed, as typified by aluminum oxide and silicon dioxide. (4) The alloying elements sometimes combine with iron and with each other to form an *intermetallic phase* such as may be expressed by the formulas, $FeCr$, FeW, or Fe_3Mo_2. (5) Finally, the alloying element may be present in the *free* or *uncombined* form. Lead, in the free-machining steels, and copper, when more than 0.75 per cent is present, are found as almost pure elements. Under conditions where austenite exists, in addition to the above mentioned phases, the alloying elements may also be found in the γ phase. For most steels, austenite exists in appreciable amounts only at elevated temperatures.

When an element occurs in more than one phase in the same piece of steel (a fairly common occurrence), the proportion existing in any one phase depends upon the composition and previous history of the steel. The distribution is affected by the nature and quantities of the other elements present. Thus the relative tendencies of two elements toward carbide formation, and the total carbon available for this purpose, may determine whether they are both in the carbide phase, or whether one is partly in the carbide and partly in some other phase. Furthermore, since the distribution of the elements depends upon diffusion in the solid state, significant variations in their distribution may occur as a result of previous history. Thus for all practical purposes it is impossible to predict with precision how the alloying elements will be distributed in steel. However, certain general tendencies have been observed in annealed steels, and these are set forth in the table below:

Table 9.1
Distribution of Alloying Elements in Annealed Steels

	Dissolved in Ferrite	Combined in Carbide	In Nonmetallic Inclusions	Special Intermetallic Compounds	In Elemental State
Nickel	Ni*			Ni·Si (?)	
Silicon	Si*		$SiO_2 \cdot M_xO_y$		
Aluminum	Al		Al_2O_3	Al_xN_y	
Zirconium	Zr		ZrO	Zr_xN_y	
Manganese	Mn ⟷ Mn		MnS, MnFeO, MnO·SiO₂		
Chromium	Cr ⟷ Cr		Cr_xO_y		
Tungsten	W ⟷ W				
Molybdenum	Mo ⟷ Mo				
Vanadium	V ⟷ V		V_xO_y	V_xN_y	
Titanium	Ti ⟷ Ti		Ti_xO_y	Ti_xN_y, $Ti_xN_yC_z$	
Phosphorus	P				
Sulfur	S (?)		MnFeS, ZrS		
Copper	Cu (<0.75%)				Cu(>0.75%)
Lead					Pb (?)

* Nickel and silicon are strong graphitizers, i.e., they promote the reaction $Fe_3C \rightarrow 3Fe + C$. Table reproduced by permission from E. C. Bain, *Alloying Elements in Steel* (Cleveland: American Society for Metals, 1948), p. 63.

Effects of alloying elements present in ferrite. It is apparent from Table 9.1 that the alloying elements are, for the most part, soluble in ferrite. The effectiveness of the elements in causing solid solution hardening of ferrite has been studied. As can be seen by reference to Fig. 9.1, phosphorus, silicon, and titanium are among the most potent of the ferrite strengtheners. The inclusion of these elements in the low-alloy, high-strength structural steel compositions has resulted in an improvement in properties. See section 9.8.

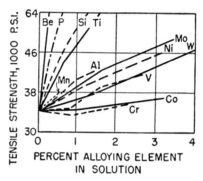

Fig. 9.1. The effect of various alloying elements as ferrite strengtheners. [After C. E. Lacy and M. Gensamer, *Trans. ASM*, **32**, p. 88. American Society for Metals, Cleveland, 1944.]

Effects of alloying elements present as carbides. In unhardened steels, the beneficial effect of alloying elements which might be found in a carbide phase is a consideration of little practical significance. Most steels containing sufficient carbon and alloy to form a carbide phase are used in the hardened rather than the unhardened condition so as to obtain the maximum benefit from the elements present. There is one instance where the presence of carbides has an indirect adverse effect on properties of steel. In some slowly cooled stainless steels the presence of more than 0.02 per cent carbon causes precipitation of chromium carbide and loss of corrosion resistance, as explained in section 9.11.

Effects of alloying elements in nonmetallic inclusions. Alloying elements found in the nonmetallic inclusions of iron and unhardened steel exert some important influences on properties. For instance, in wrought iron the stringers of slag, which are essentially silicates, serve to improve corrosion resistance and machinability. However, strength properties (measured transverse to the direction of the slag stringers) are greatly lowered.   The effect of sulfur, which forms a sulfide network, in causing hot shortness of steels, has been mentioned in section 5.5.   When sufficient manganese is present, the sulfide takes the form of isolated pools or stringers (after rolling) which improve machinability.   Aluminum oxide, which results from deoxidizing steel with aluminum, is a very hard substance which has an abrasive effect on cutting tools.

Effects of intermetallic compounds.   The elements silicon and nitrogen form what are classed as intermetallic compounds when they react with the metallic elements found in steel.   As far as the unhardened steels are concerned, the most important intermetallic compound is the Al_xN_y compound formed when aluminum-bearing steels are nitrided.   It will be recalled that the nitride particles produce an inherent surface hardness and wear resistance.   No heat treating or hardening operation similar to that required for carburized steels is used or needed.

Effect of free-metal particles.   The only important contribution of free-metal particles to the properties of unhardened steel is the improvement in machinability which results from the presence of lead.

9.3.   Distribution of Alloying Elements in Hardened Steels

In the case of steels *being heated for hardening* (as contrasted to the slowly cooled steels), the alloying elements are most likely to be found in the γ phase, carbides, or nonmetallic inclusions.   The *alloying elements in solution in austenite* render the steel more hardenable for any given cooling rate, as pointed out in the preceding chapter.   *Insoluble or persistent carbides* in hardened steel increase resistance to softening during tempering or during use at elevated temperature; this advantage has already been mentioned.

Effects of carbides.   In addition to improving high-temperature strength, carbides exert three other influences worthy of mention. Consider *first* a carbide which resists solution during heating.   If the over-all carbon content is low, the carbon content of the austenite may be so depleted as to produce a martensitic structure of inferior hardness.   (The hardness of martensite is largely determined by the carbon content.   See Fig. 9.2.)   This effect is most significant in steels containing chromium and titanium in combination. Very stable carbides have been observed to form in these steels. A *second* effect of persistent carbide particles is the part they play in preventing formation of large grains during the heating of steel for hardening. Apparently, the fine dispersion of carbide particles nucleates a large number of austenite grains at the $\alpha + Fe_3C \longrightarrow \gamma$ transformation temperature, and a small grain size results. The improved properties obtained in fine-grained steels upon hardening have already been pointed out. Fine-grained steels, however, have the disadvantage of decreased hardenability.

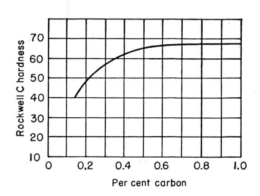

Fig. 9.2. **Hardness versus carbon content for fresh martensite.**

Nonmetallic inclusions, particularly titanium dioxide and aluminum oxide, behave in a manner similar to the carbides in preventing formation of large austenite grains during heating. *Third,* alloy steels containing carbide-forming elements exhibit greater toughness than carbon steels when quenched and tempered to the same hardness.

The purpose and function of alloys and carbon in hardenable steel. Fresh martensite containing 0.3 per cent carbon has a hardness of R_c 55. Hardness increases with increasing carbon up to about R_c 66 at 0.6 per cent carbon. This can be seen in Fig. 9.2. Steel to be heat treated usually contains at least 0.3 per cent carbon. If, in addition, it contains alloying elements totaling more than about 1 per cent, it almost certainly will be hardened by heat treatment. (Important exceptions are found in certain varieties of special high-alloy and stainless steel.) The amounts of the alloying elements are a major factor in determining how hard the steel can be made by a given heat treatment. The effect of alloying elements (and carbon) content in slowing down the ($\gamma \longrightarrow \alpha + Fe_3C$) transformation was pointed out in Chapter 7. The relationship between the retardation of transformation (indicated by the quench required for hardening) and how this is controlled by alloying additions is illustrated by considering several types of tool steels.

Table 9.2

Percentage Compositions of Typical Steels Intended for Hardening *

	C	Mn	Si	V	Cr	W	Mo
Water-hardening:							
1. Shallow-hardening plain carbon	0.95	0.25	0.20	0.20	....	....	....
2. Medium-hardening plain carbon	1.05	0.25	0.20	....	....	....	....
3. Deep-hardening plain carbon	1.10	0.30	0.50	....	0.25	....	....
4. Oil-hardening	0.90	1.25	0.25	....	0.50	0.50	....
5. Air-hardening	1.50	0.30	0.45	0.20	11.50	....	0.80
6. High-speed	0.73	0.30	0.30	1.0	4.0	18.00	....

* From *Tool Steel for the Non-Metallurgist*, Crucible Steel Company of America, New York.

Steel no. 1 in Table 9.2 contains such limited quantities of alloying elements that water quenching develops only a shallow hard case around a tough, unhardened core. Vanadium, which is a strong carbide former, has been added to prevent grain coarsening. In steel no. 2, vanadium is omitted and some grain growth occurs; this improves hardenability somewhat. Hardenability is further improved in steel no. 3 by an increase in the quantity of silicon and introduction of another element, chromium. By further increasing the quantity and variety of alloying elements, it is possible to secure equivalent hardness in a quench milder than water, as in the oil-hardening steel (no. 4). A continuation of the trend is indicated in steel no. 5. The advantages of using a milder quench are discussed in section 9.9. In the last steel listed, and to a certain extent in no. 5, appreciable hardness and wear resistance are due to persistent carbides in the structure. These carbides are stable at red heat, making possible the high-speed operation of cutting tools made of this material. It will be noted that the analysis for steel no. 6 shows large quantities of the strong carbide formers. Of course the steels listed represent only a few of the many possibilities. The SAE-AISI steels represent a large class of steels which includes many of the carbon steels and alloy steels. A study of these shows that with increasing alloy content, hardenability increases.

The multiplying effect. An important consideration is the multiplying effect exerted by the alloying elements on hardenability. Grossmann has determined that for a total alloy content, let us say, of X per cent, hardenability is greater if the X per cent represents several elements, rather than if it is made up entirely of one element. That is to say, 0.5 per cent each of chromium and nickel is more effective than 1 per cent of chromium alone. The effect of alloying elements is multiplicative rather than additive. This should be kept in mind. Another notable development is the discovery that when small amounts of boron (approximately 0.003 per cent) are present in steel, the usual alloy additions are rendered more effective in achieving hardenability. The use of boron makes possible the application of leaner alloys, and effects appreciable savings in alloy additions.

It is appropriate to mention at this time that specific alloying elements are used to achieve improvement in certain properties in addition to enhancing hardenability. While improved hardenability is the primary purpose of most additions, it is not always the only aim.

9.4. Austenite and Ferrite Stabilizers

A study of the binary alloys of iron indicates that the alloying elements may be divided into two major classes. Some of the elements behave as *austenite stabilizers,* that is, they cause a general expansion of the temperature range over which austenite exists. With increasing amounts of austenite stabilizers, the A_4 temperature ($\gamma \longrightarrow \delta$ transformation) is raised, while A_3 ($\gamma \longrightarrow \alpha$ transformation) is lowered. If sufficient amounts of the proper element are present, the A_3 temperature can be depressed below room temperature. In this case there will be no $\gamma \longrightarrow \alpha$ transformation. The second major classification of alloying elements includes those which reduce the temperature range over which austenite is stable. These elements are known as *ferrite stabilizers.* With increasing percentages of these alloys, the A_4 temperature is lowered and A_3 is raised in most cases. Both classes of alloying elements may be further subdivided, depending upon whether or not intermetallic compounds can exist in equilibrium with the α and δ phases. The classification just described is shown in Fig. 9.3. It is evident from this illustration that many, but not all, of the ferrite stabilizers are strong carbide formers.

The maximum solubility of the ferrite stabilizers in austenite is of great importance. The alloy content corresponding to the end of the $\gamma + \alpha$ phase is also of significance. It must be remembered that the phase diagrams represent binary alloys, and that they and the

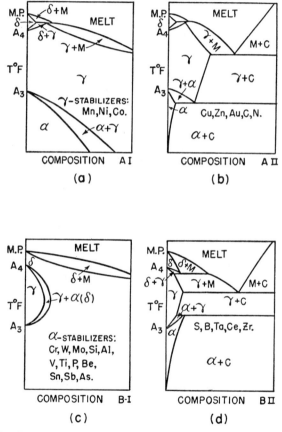

Fig. 9.3. **Types of binary iron-alloy phase diagrams.** The type-A diagram is characterized by a broadening of the γ-field, caused by a depression of the $\gamma - \alpha$ transformation temperature and elevation of the $\delta - \gamma$ transformation temperature. Elements which do this are known as *austenite stabilizers* and are characterized by (a) and (b). In the type-B diagram the ferrite field is stabilized, as indicated by (c) and (d). Ferrite stabilization is accomplished by elevation of the $\gamma - \alpha$ transformation temperature and depression of the $\delta - \gamma$ transformation. [After E. C. Bain, *Alloying Elements in Steel*, p. 9. American Society for Metals, Cleveland, 1948.]

limits of solubility are modified by the presence of carbon. This is shown in Table 9.4. If sufficient ferrite stabilizer is present to bring the alloy beyond the boundary of the γ loop, it is impossible to harden the alloy by quenching. For a few binary alloys, the approximate limits for 100 per cent austenite are as follows: Cr, 13%; W, 6%; Mo, 3%; Si, 2%; Al, 1%; V, 1%; Ti, 1%; Zr, 1%.

In the case of the austenite stabilizers, the significant composition is that which makes possible retention of γ at room temperature. The mechanism by which this is accomplished involves a depression of the γ transformation temperature to a point where transformation becomes very sluggish. Alloys containing more than about 12 per cent manganese or 20 per cent nickel are examples of this. Hardening by quenching then becomes an impossibility because no transformation occurs. Carbon and other elements, when present as a third component, modify both the binary diagrams and the alloy content required to stabilize austenite at room temperature.

It has been found that the alloy additions become more effective in producing a steel amenable to heat treating when a combination of austenite and ferrite stabilizers is used. Thus there have been developed the nickel-chromium steels. In this connection it should be kept in mind that carbon acts as an austenite stabilizer.

Because binary alloys are almost never used in practice, binary diagrams are limited in application. They are, however, useful in indicating tendencies such as age hardening possibilities. Copper, nitrogen, and molybdenum are capable of forming age-hardenable alloys with iron. This can be confirmed by referring to their respective binary phase diagrams.

COMMON FERROUS ALLOYS

9.5. Wrought Iron

Wrought iron consists essentially of rather pure iron in which are imbedded stringers of siliceous slag. The amount of slag varies from 1 to 4 per cent by weight and 2 to 8 per cent by volume. The presence of slag stringers gives rise to at least two unique properties of wrought iron. Probably the best known quality of wrought iron is its resistance to *corrosion* by water. This is believed to result from the protection afforded by the slag. Corrosion proceeds until slag is encountered by the corroding medium, eventually resulting in an almost continuous coating of slag on the surface of the metal. This presents a fairly good barrier to further corrosive attack.

Wrought iron is also known for its good weldability. This in part is accounted for by the presence of slag and by a low carbon content. When welded, the slag acts as a self-contained flux which floats away iron oxide as fast as it is formed. Thus, good sound welds are obtainable by pressure and forge welding as well as by gas and electric arc welding. The low carbon content insures that martensite cannot form near the weld zone and hence the welds are free from embrittlement associated with hardening.

The static strength of wrought iron is generally lower than that of steel used for structural purposes. This is to be expected because of its low carbon content. Its ductility is as good as that of the low carbon steels, when measured by straining parallel to the slag stringers. Its endurance limit is low as compared to structural steel. It is incapable of heat treatment because of its low carbon content, although it can be carburized.

The character and properties of wrought iron are summarized in Table 9.3 near the end of this chapter.

Wrought iron finds application where corrosion is a problem. It is therefore used for pipes carrying potable and waste water, processing tanks, gratings, trash racks in sewage plants, deck house sheathing on ships, rudders, and similar applications.

9.6. Carbon Steel

By far the largest tonnage of steel produced annually is carbon steel. According to the American Iron and Steel Institute, steel is considered to be carbon steel "when no minimum content is specified or guaranteed for aluminum, chromium, columbium, molybdenum, nickel, titanium, tungsten, vanadium, or zirconium; when the minimum for copper does not exceed 0.40 per cent; or when the maximum content specified or guaranteed for any of the following elements does not exceed the percentages noted: manganese 1.65, silicon 0.60, copper 0.60." In less specific terms, carbon steels are those in which carbon plays the predominant role in the determination of properties. Carbon steels are sometimes called plain-carbon or straight-carbon steels. There are three classes of carbon steels: low-carbon, medium-carbon, and high-carbon steels.

Low-carbon steels are those in which the carbon content varies from 0.08 to 0.35 per cent carbon.   Low-carbon steel is probably produced in the largest tonnage of all steel products.   It is not used in applications requiring the formation of martensite, because of its low carbon content.   Even if the steel could be quenched to form martensite, the hardness of the martensite so formed would be inferior because of lack of carbon.

Most low-carbon steel has been consumed by the construction industry in recent years.   In fact, consumption by the construction industry from the years 1940 to 1953 averaged near 10 per cent of all the steel finished, and in the first three months of 1954 averaged 19.3 per cent of finished steel produced.   The structural members of buildings, bridges, locomotives, railroad cars, ships, and automobile frames are made of low-carbon steel.   When rolled into plates, it is used for ship's hulls, large pipes, storage tanks, pilings, and similar applications.   It is used in large tonnage as "tin," galvanized steel sheet, and automobile body steel.   Refrigerators, air conditioners, and similar home appliances are responsible for appreciable consumption of low-carbon steel sheet.   This class of steel is also used for fencing wire and in considerable tonnages as cold-finished and hot-finished bars.   Cold-finishing of bars improves their mechanical properties (tensile and yield strengths are raised by cold work), machinability (hot-worked low-carbon steel is too ductile or "gummy" for good machinability), and surface finish and accuracy of dimensions (hot working produces scaled and decarburized surfaces).   Bars are used for shafting and in automatic screw machines for small machine parts.

Medium-carbon steel is steel containing between 0.35 and 0.50 per cent carbon.   Steel containing this much carbon can be through-hardened by the formation of martensite, if the section size is small, perhaps up to $\frac{1}{2}$ inch.   Medium-carbon steel is used for forgings and high-strength steel castings.   Examples of forgings are turbine bucket wheels, shafts, pinions and main reduction gears, steering arms, railroad axles, and crankshafts.

High-carbon steels contain more than 0.50 per cent carbon.   Carbon contents as high as these almost insure that the steel will be heat-treated for improvement of properties.   High-carbon steel is used for forgings such as railroad wheels and wrenches.   Important hot-rolled products are railroad rails and some concrete reinforcing bars.   High-strength wire products such as piano wire, stitching wire, suspension bridge cables, and springs are made of high-carbon steel. Carbon steel tools are high-carbon products and are among the best general purpose tools. They are used for such applications as blanking dies, threading dies, tube-drawing dies, drills, reamers and taps, forming tools, hammers and sledges, chisels, shear blades, knives and planer tools, and razors. In general, lower carbon contents are used where impact and shock loading are encountered in usage. If maintenance of keen cutting edges is more important than impact resistance, higher carbon content steels are used. There are a number of limitations which must be respected in the use of high-carbon steels for tools. First, their high-temperature hardness and strength are poor, and therefore they are inferior to alloy tool steels for hot-forming or high-speed cutting operations. Second, the high-carbon steels tend to deform during hardening and this leads to distortion, warpage, and cracking of large and complex dies. Third, they are shallow-hardening and are hence at a disadvantage with respect to deeper-hardening steels.

9.7. Alloy Steels

Alloys of iron and carbon containing other intentionally added elements are known in this text as alloy steels. The alloying elements are added to provide special mechanical, physical, or chemical properties. In some cases addition of the alloying element improves mechanical properties, and no special hardening procedures are required; in other cases maximum benefit is derived only if the steel is hardened. Alloying elements may be added to improve corrosion resistance, high-temperature properties, electric and magnetic behavior, and for other purposes. The reasons for the use of alloying elements are made clear in the discussions of the major categories of alloy steels, i.e.: low-alloy high-strength structural steels, medium-alloy structural steels, tool and die steels, stainless steels, and special-purpose steels.

9.8. Low-alloy High-strength Structural Steels

These steels are closely related to low-carbon structural steels. They are not hardened to form martensite. Rather, their microstructure consists of a ferrite matrix in which there are colonies of pearlite.   As might be expected, these steels are soft (in comparison with hardened steels) and ductile.   They are high-strength steels if compared to the low-carbon structural steels with which they compete.

The low-alloy high-strength structural steels depend for their strength upon two mechanisms:

1. The effect of the alloying elements as ferrite strengtheners.
2. The effect of the alloying elements in displacing the T-T-T diagram toward the right.

The strength of plain carbon steels increases with increasing carbon content.   This is accompanied, unfortunately, by a loss of ductility and weldability.   Weldability is lost at higher carbon contents because the cooling rates following welding are fast enough to produce martensite.   A martensitic structure produces an unsuitable brittle weld.   In the low-alloy high-strength steels, strength is achieved by the use of alloying elements which dissolve in ferrite.   The solid solution hardening of the continuous phase results in an over-all strengthening of the alloy.   Phosphorus and silicon are two of the most useful elements for ferrite strengthening.   In addition to strengthening the ferrite, the alloys shift the T-T-T curve to the right.   As can be seen by reference to Fig. 9.4, a given rate of cooling produces a greater proportion of pearlite to ferrite, and also a finer pearlite, as the T-T-T diagram is displaced further to the right.   Both the increased quantity of pearlite and its greater fineness tend to produce a steel of greater strength than carbon steel.   Chromium, nickel, and molybdenum are added to shift the T-T-T curves to the right.

The low-alloy, high-strength structural steels have a higher ratio of yield strength to tensile strength [1] than the corresponding plain carbon steels.   Though these steels are somewhat more expensive than plain carbon steels, their higher strength/weight ratio makes an over-all saving possible for some structures.   When greater pay load is a consideration, the use of these steels is justified.   Since the structures are made of thinner sections than when plain carbon steels are used, corrosion presents a greater problem.   However, the use of copper as an alloying element is effective in retarding corrosion.   Steels used for riveted structures would probably have

---

[1] About 70 to 80 per cent as compared to about 60 to 70 per cent for hot-rolled plain carbon structural steels.

about twice the carbon content of steels which are to be welded. The higher carbon content improves the strength of an application where loss of weldability is not significant. A typical low-alloy

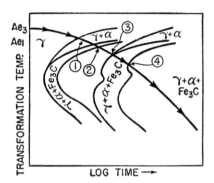

Fig. 9.4. Effect of alloying elements on *T-T-T* curve for a hypoeutectoid steel. A comparison of a plain carbon and an alloy steel shows how the alloy elements effect improvement in strength. For the plain carbon steel the portion of ferrite to pearlite is greater than for the alloy steel (see ① and ③). The pearlite in the plain carbon steel is softer and coarser than in the alloy steel (see ② and ④). These effects are in addition to the strengthening which results from solid solution of the alloys in ferrite. See Fig. 9.1.

high-strength structural steel composition is shown in Table 9.3 at the end of this chapter.

9.9. Medium-alloy Structural Steels

Hardenable alloys steels (excluding the hardenable stainless steels and tool and die steels), are called in this book medium-alloy structural steels. The most important function of the alloying elements in the medium-alloy structural steels is to increase hardenability. Steels falling in this category usually contain at least 0.3 per cent carbon. Listed in the order of decreasing effect on hardenability, these steels contain such alloying elements as V, Mo, Mn, Cr, Si, and Ni. There are other secondary effects already described, notable among which is the tendency of nickel to improve low-temperature toughness. Molybdenum and vanadium raise the grain-coarsening temperature and tend to produce a fine-grained tough steel.

The medium-alloy structural steels are typified by many of the steels whose specifications have been written by the SAE [2] and AISI.[3] Many of these steels, in addition to being used for automotive applications, are used for other machine components where hardenability is a requirement. The SAE-AISI system designates the steels by four and five number series as follows:

Manganese steels (1.75% Mn) .... 1 3 - -
Nickel steels, 3.5–5.0% Ni .... 2 - - -
Nickel-chromium steels .... 3 - - -
Molybdenum steels (may also contain Ni and Cr) ...... 4 - - -
Chromium steels (0.5–1.60% Cr) .... 5 - - - -
Chromium-vanadium steels .... 6 - - -
Nickel-chromium-molybdenum .... 8 - - -
                                                     9 3 - - to 9 8 - -

The last two digits of any number show the approximate carbon content in hundredths of a per cent. Although they are not alloy steels, there are also SAE-AISI designations for carbon and free-cutting carbon steels as follows:

Plain carbon steels .... 10 - -
Free cutting .... 11 - - to 12 - -

The SAE-AISI designations do not cover all the medium-alloy structural steels commercially available. Therefore the terms *medium-alloy structural steels* and *SAE-AISI steels* are not synonymous. Some SAE-AISI steels are used for tools and dies.

The medium-alloy structural steels usually are used in the quenched and tempered condition in order to derive maximum benefit from the carbon and alloying elements they contain. In some cases, austempering is used to produce a tougher steel than conventionally hardened steel of the same hardness.

The medium-alloy structural steels are used for such applications as splined shafts, gears, springs, bolts and nuts, ball-bearing balls and races, connecting rods, and clutches. The medium-alloy structural steels are used where carbon steels do not provide sufficient depth of hardening to satisfy requirements for such properties as strength and toughness. In some cases a water or iced brine quench of a carbon steel might provide the necessary depth of hardening, but the vigor of the quench would also produce cracking. Furthermore, complicated shapes, such as gears and splined shafts if quenched vigorously are likely to crack. Therefore, alloy steels

[2] Society of Automotive Engineers.
[3] American Iron and Steel Institute.

are preferred for complicated shapes because hardening can be achieved by a moderate quenching procedure.

9.10. Tool and Die Steels

Although tool and die steels represent only a small percentage of total steel production, they are nevertheless extremely important materials. It is necessary that suitable tool and die materials be available for the shaping and processing of all the materials of engineering.

There are five major classifications of tool steels and many more subclasses in each of the major categories. The five major classes are: (1) carbon tool steels (discussed in section 9.6), (2) nondeforming tool steels, (3) shock-resisting tool steels, (4) hot-work steels, (5) high-speed steels. The names of the various classes indicate some of the special properties of these steels. All tool steels should be hard, tough, and wear resistant although there is a variation in the degree to which these properties are needed. In addition, some tool steels are required to exhibit low distortion during hardening (nondeforming steels); others must show unusual toughness (shock-resisting steels), resistance to heat softening (hot-work and high-speed steels) and resistance to heat checking (hot-work steels). It is desirable that tool steels be as machinable and grindable as possible, and free from tendencies to decarburize during heat treatment. Since optimum values of all of these properties cannot be achieved simultaneously, the less important ones are sacrificed by varying the composition of the steel.

Carbon is the most important alloying element in tool as well as other steels. The carbon in hardened tool steels is present either in the martensite phase or as small isolated particles of complex carbides. A decrease in the carbon content results in an increase in toughness. However, the effect of the elements which react strongly with carbon to form carbides must be kept in mind. These elements do not dissolve readily in austenite, and hence martensite formed from such austenite may be low in carbon and may have inferior hardness (see Fig. 9.2). In tool and die steels subject to impact, the carbon content is kept low for reasons of toughness, and yet it must not drop so low that hardness suffers.

The **strong carbide formers** (Ti, V, Mo, W, and Cr), in addition to their tendency to deplete the carbon content of austenite and martensite, produce other changes in steel. *First,* they tend to produce a fine austenite grain size, because they are present as insoluble carbide particles at the temperatures used for hardening. Fine austenite grain sizes mean good toughness in the hardened steel. However, there is some loss of hardenability associated with fine austenite grain sizes. In general, the stronger the carbide former, the greater is the improvement in toughness. *Second,* the presence of carbide particles in the continuous martensite phase has been found to improve wear resistance of tools and dies. *Third,* along with the improved wear resistance, there is a loss of machinability. This is an important factor in some tools and dies. *Fourth,* the presence of carbide particles improves hot hardness. Hot hardness is important in high-speed cutting operations when the edge of the cutting tool is likely to become hot, and also in hot-working operations such as forging and extrusion. *Fifth,* the carbide formers resist softening during tempering. This means that the hardened steels can be tempered at higher temperatures and for longer times without adverse softening effects. In fact, some of the tool steels show secondary hardening, similar to age hardening, during tempering. Thus, greater toughness can be achieved before harmful softening is encountered. And *sixth,* any of the carbide-forming elements in solution in the austenite improve hardenability. Most of the tool and die steels are air or oil hardening.

Molybdenum deserves special mention along with **cobalt**: both tend to promote decarburization, or loss of carbon from the skin of the steel while it is being heated for hardening. Such a loss of carbon reduces hardness and wear resistance, and may reduce hardenability. It can be prevented by proper heat-treating techniques.

Cobalt excepted, all the alloying elements, if dissolved in austenite at the time of quenching, tend to improve hardenability. Why, then, is cobalt used in some tool steels? Cobalt performs a very special function in improving red hardness or hardness at red heat. Immediately after hardening the cobalt is found in the continuous martensite phase. Upon tempering, martensite becomes ferrite plus carbide and the cobalt is found in the ferrite phase. In this form it acts as a potent ferrite strengthener, known particularly for its ability to retain ferrite strength at high temperatures. However, cobalt also tends to impair toughness somewhat and hence is not used in steels subject to impact loading.

Silicon and **manganese** act to improve hardenability. They also tend to improve fatigue strength, when used together. Silicon also promotes embrittlement and *graphitization*. Graphitization is the opposite of carbide formation, in that carbides are decomposed into graphite and metallic elements. This tends to impair properties, but it can be offset by using sufficient quantities of strong carbide formers to counteract the graphitizing tendency.

Tool steel **applications** can be divided into a number of different categories: (1) Cutting tools for applications such as lathe tools, gear hobbers, millers, drills, and taps. Steels selected for these applications should have high hardness and wear resistance. If high-speed cuts are to be made, resistance to softening at high temperatures is important. The high-speed steels mentioned in the second paragraph of this article are used widely. (2) Shearing tools such as punches, blanking and trimming dies, and shears. These steels should compromise between wear resistance and toughness, since they must combat the effect of impact and abrasion. Some of the shock-resisting and hot-working steels fill these requirements. (3) Forming tools for hot- and cold-working operations. Among these are forging and cold-heading dies, die-casting dies and plastic molds. In the forging and cold-heading operations toughness is of great importance. Thermal stability and resistance to softening and checking at prolonged or intermittent high temperatures are more important for die casting and plastic molding. Machinability should also be considered if the die shape is complex. (4) Battering tools, including pneumatic hammers, chisels, and sledges. Toughness is the most important property to be considered in connection with battering tools. Finally, there are some tools for miscellaneous operations such as hot and cold drawing of wire and pipe, extrusion, rolling and roll forging. Each of these will present its own particular problems.

The **heat treatment** of tool steels frequently involves special problems not encountered in heat treatment of medium-alloy structural steels. One of these, decarburization, has been mentioned in connection with the use of Co and Mo as alloying elements. When very high temperatures are required ($2100°$–$2375°$F or $1150°$–$1300°$C for the high speed steels), preheating is recommended largely to prevent cracking. The time at maximum temperature must be carefully controlled in order to prevent excessive grain growth and loss of toughness. However, if too short a time is used sufficient solution of carbon and other alloying elements may not occur.

9.11. Corrosion- and Heat-Resistant Steels

A very important class of high-alloy steels are the corrosion- and heat-resisting materials. This includes the stainless steels and stainless irons, in which the principal function of the alloying additions is to produce corrosion resistance. The principal source of corrosion resistance is the element chromium. It has been found that a ratio of about 1 chromium atom to 7 iron atoms provides good protection against corrosion. On a weight basis this amounts to slightly more than 10 per cent chromium.

Stainless steels. Stainless steels are divided into three major classifications according to their microstructure: ferritic, martensitic, and austenitic. These structural differences, made possible by varying the chromium, nickel, and carbon content, are associated with significant differences in properties. The structures present in stainless steels are readily explained by consideration of binary diagrams and the modifying effects of alloying elements.

The **ferritic** and **martensitic stainless steels** usually contain no nickel. The corrosion resistance of these steels results solely from the presence of chromium. Their microstructures can be appreciated by considering Fig. 9.5, the equilibrium diagram for the iron-chromium system. According to this diagram, binary iron alloys containing more than about 15 per cent chromium are ferritic at all temperatures up to the solidus. The influence of carbon on these alloys is important. For instance, in the complete absence of carbon, the limit of solubility of chromium in austenite occurs at 12 per cent chromium. With only 0.2 per cent carbon the limit is extended to 14 per cent, and with 0.5 per cent carbon it goes out to about 20 per cent chromium. Thus, the presence of carbon tends to expand the size of the so-called γ-loop. When stainless steels containing sufficient carbon but not too much chromium (always less than 20 per cent) are heated to the γ region and cooled quickly enough, the austenite transforms to martensite. The microstructure frequently consists of hard chromium carbide particles (not dissolved during austenitizing) imbedded in a hard martensitic matrix. The martensitic stainless steels are used for cutlery, instruments, valves and similar applications. If the carbon content

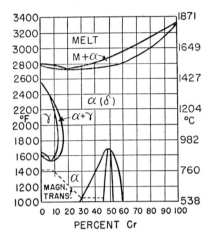

Fig. 9.5. The iron-chromium diagram. Iron-chromium alloys have phase diagrams similar to type B-I (see Fig. 9.3). The γ-loop and the nature of the ferrite-stable field is indicated. [After G. Sachs and K. R. Van Horn, *Practical Metallurgy*, p. 518. American Society for Metals, Cleveland, 1947.]

is low enough and there is sufficient chromium to get beyond the γ-loop the stainless steel has a ferritic structure. See Fig. 9.6. Such a structure cannot be hardened by formation of martensite. The ferritic stainless steels are easier to form and machine than the austenitic stainless steels and have equally good resistance to atmospheric corrosion. They are used for decorative applications

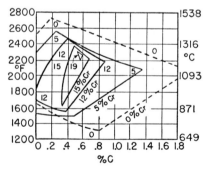

Fig. 9.6. The austenite region in chromium steels. With increasing carbon content the solubility of chromium in austenite increases (up to about 0.6 per cent carbon). With increasing chromium content, the eutectoid composition shifts toward a lower carbon content. [Adapted from *Metals Handbook*, p. 459. American Society for Metals, Cleveland, 1948.]

such as automobile trim and for chemical equipment. Weldability of the ferritic stainless steels is not good because of excessive grain growth and embrittlement of the weld zone.

The **austenitic stainless steels** are probably the most widely used of the three principal types. The principal alloy ingredients are chromium (a ferrite stabilizer) and nickel (an austenite stabilizer). The combined effects of the two alloying elements are indicated in Fig. 9.7. In the austenitic stainless steels the composition is adjusted so that when the alloy is heated to the proper temperature the steel becomes austenitic. For instance, if a steel containing 18 per cent chromium and 8 per cent nickel is heated to about 1800°F (983°C), it becomes austenitic. Upon cooling to room temperature in an air quench it remains austenitic as a result

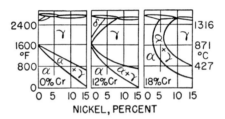

Fig. 9.7. The effect of chromium and nickel on phase changes in iron-nickel-chromium alloys. [Adapted from *Metals Handbook*, p. 421. American Society for Metals, Cleveland, 1948.]

of the very sluggish transformation of austenite to ferrite caused by the presence of nickel. The austenitic stainless steels differ from the ferritic and martensitic stainless materials in that they are nonmagnetic. Austenitic stainless steel work hardens easily and is difficult to machine. The austenitic grades are usually considered superior to the ferritic and martensitic varieties with respect to corrosion resistance, high-temperature strength, and scaling resistance. Successful welding of austenitic stainless steels is readily accomplished if certain precautions are observed. The difficulties encountered are the result of reactions between carbon and chromium in the steel. If there is more than 0.08 per cent carbon, appreciable amounts of a chromium carbide may precipitate at the austenite grain boundaries. Beyond 0.12 per cent carbon, the potential quantity of carbide which may precipitate is large enough to produce a serious tendency toward intergranular corrosion. Attack occurs because the chromium originally in solution at the austenite grain boundaries has been precipitated as a carbide. In the precipitated form the chromium no longer provides protection against corrosion. If the steel is quickly cooled from the welding temperature during processing, the carbide is retained in supersaturated solution and corrosion resistance remains good. If, during subsequent processing, the steel is slowly cooled through the temperature range between 1500°F (815°C) and 600°F (315°C), the carbide can precipitate and corrosion resistance may thus be impaired. There are several solutions to the problem. (1) Good properties can be restored by reheating to at least 1750°F, followed by a quench. (2) The carbon content of the steel can be reduced to a value below 0.08 per cent. (Low-carbon 18-8 is available at slightly higher cost.) (3) Small amounts of alloying elements having stronger carbide-forming tendencies than chromium can be added to the steel. Columbium, titanium, and molybdenum are used for this purpose. Such elements combine with and retain the carbon, minimizing the possibility that any uncombined carbon remains to reduce the amount of chromium in solid solution.

Manganese austenitic stainless steels. Manganese and nitrogen are both austenite stabilizers used as partial replacements for the nickel found in 18 per cent chromium—8 per cent nickel stainless steels. About half the nickel can be replaced by an equal amount of manganese and 0.3–0.7 per cent nitrogen. Complete replacement is impossible because of hot-working difficulties. The manganese stainless steels have essentially the same fabricating and service properties as the chromium-nickel grades, and at the same time are about 2–3 per cent cheaper. In time of war, it is expected that chromium-nickel steels will be much less available than manganese stainless.

Precipitation hardenable stainless steels. New classes of stainless are available which rely upon precipitation hardening for development of optimum properties. By varying the ratio of chromium to nickel, the steels are made either martensitic, semi-austenitic, or austenitic. Lowering the chromium/nickel ratio tends to stabilize the austenitic condition; raising it promotes transformation to martensite. Hardening is accomplished by precipitation of titanium or copper from martensitic varieties, by precipitation of aluminum from the semi-austenitic types and by precipitation of carbides from the austenitic stainless steels.

Table 9.3. Approximate Compositions and Properties of Typical Ferrous Alloys

COMPOSITIONS (per cent)

NAME	C	Mn	P	S	Si	Cr	Ni	Other
Wrought iron	<0.1	<0.1	<0.16	<0.04	0.15	......	......	
Carbon steel, SAE 1020	0.18/0.23	0.30/0.60	<0.04	<0.05	<0.10	......	......	
Low-alloy high-strength	0.09	0.38	0.09	0.033	0.48	0.84	0.28	0.41 Cu
Carbon steel, SAE 1030	0.28/0.34	0.60/0.90	<0.04	<0.05	0.15	......	......	
Carbon steel, SAE 1045	0.43/0.50	0.60/0.90	<0.04	<0.05	0.15	......	......	
Med. alloy steel, SAE 4345	0.44/0.49	0.60/0.80	<0.04	<0.04	0.20/0.35	0.70/0.90	1.65/2.00	0.20/0.30 Mo
White cast iron	2.9	0.6	0.15	0.15	0.90	......	......	
Malleable cast iron	2.25	<0.55	<0.18	<0.20	1.15	......	......	
Gray cast iron ①	3.6	0.55	0.75	0.06	2.06	......	......	
Gray cast iron ②	2.9	0.51	0.43	0.10	2.0	......	......	
Gray cast iron ③	2.8	0.50	0.03	0.06	2.4	0.09	0.50	
Nodular cast iron	3.5	0.15	0.025	0.015	2.6	......	......	0.05 Mg
Austenitic stainless	0.08/0.20	<2.0	<0.045	<0.030	<1.0	17.0/19.0	8.0/10.0	
Martensitic stainless	<0.15	<1.0	<0.040	<0.030	<1.0	12.5	......	
Ferritic stainless	<0.12	<1.0	<0.040	<0.030	<1.0	16	......	

① Common gray cast iron. ② High-strength gray cast iron. ③ Alloy gray cast iron.

286

Table 9.3 (Cont'd) Approximate Compositions and Properties of Typical Ferrous Alloys

PROPERTIES

NAME	Tens. Str., 1000's psi	Yld. Str., 1000's psi	% Elong., 2 inches	End. Lim., 1000's psi	Impact Str., Charpy, *Izod*	Hardness Rockwell, *Brinell*	COMMENTS
Wrought iron	47	26	22 ④	23	**17.5**	*105*	Tensile properties are longitudinal. Good corrosion resistance.
Carbon steel, SAE 1020	60	40	35	30	*55*	**53B-78B**	Properties for annealed steel.
Low-alloy high-strength	70	50	22	42	**40**	**78B**	Properties for hot-rolled steel. Corrosion resistance about five times better than for SAE 1030. Y.S./T.S. higher than for SAE 1030.
Carbon steel, SAE 1030	66	44	26	31	. . . . .	**75B**	Properties for hot-rolled steel.
Carbon steel, SAE 1045	90	55	23	45	*20*	**17C**	Properties for hot-rolled steel.
Carbon steel, SAE 1045	175	150	14	78	. . . . .	**37C**	Properties after water quenching and tempering at 800°F (427°C).
Med. alloy steel, SAE 4345	205	185	12	82	. . . . .	**46C**	Properties after water quenching and tempering at 800°F (427°C).
White cast iron	. . . . .	. . . . .	. . . . .	. . . . .	. . . . .	*425*	
Malleable cast iron	57	37	22	31	**16.5**	*128*	
Gray cast iron①	22	. . . . .	0	11	*3.6*	*163*	91,000 psi compressive strength.
Gray cast iron②	41	. . . . .	0	20	*3.9*	*215*	119,000 psi compressive strength.
Gray cast iron③	57	. . . . .	. . . . .	25	*8.2*	*236*	136,000 psi compressive strength.
Nodular cast iron	80	55	10	. . . . .	. . . . .	*190*	Innoculation increases Si by 1.5% and decreases S by 0.085%.
Austenitic stainless	80	35	60	. . . . .	*110*	**135, 75B**	Properties for annealed AISI Type 302. Scale resistant to 1450°F (789°C).
Martensitic stainless	200	180	15	. . . . .	*25*	**375, 40C**	Properties for heat-treated AISI Type 410. Scale resistant to 1400°F (760°C).
Ferritic stainless	70	40	30	. . . . .	*45*	**145, 79B**	Properties for annealed AISI Type 430. Scale resistant to 1600°F (871°C).

① Common gray cast iron.   ② High-strength gray cast iron.   ③ Alloy gray cast iron.   ④ Elongation for wrought iron measured on 8 in. specimen.

Table 9.4

Specific Effects of Alloying Elements in Steel

Element	Solid Solubility In Gamma Iron	Solid Solubility In Alpha Iron	Influence on Ferrite	Influence on Austenite (Hardenability)	Influence Exerted Through Carbide Carbide-Forming Tendency	Influence Exerted Through Carbide Action During Tempering	Principal Functions
Aluminum Al	1.1% (Increased by C)	36%	Hardens considerably by solid solution	Increases hardenability mildly, if dissolved in austenite	Negative (graphitizes)	......	1 Deoxides efficiently 2 Restricts grain growth (by forming dispersed oxides or nitrides) 3 Alloying element in nitriding steel 4 Improves scaling resistance
Chromium Cr	12.8% (20% with 0.5% C)	Unlimited	Hardens slightly; Increases corrosion resistance	Increases hardenability moderately	Greater than Mn; less than W	Mildly resists softening	1 Increases resistance to corrosion and oxidation 2 Increases hardenability 3 Adds some strength at high temperatures 4 Resists abrasion and wear (with high carbon)
Cobalt Co	Unlimited	75%	Hardens considerably by solid solution	Decreases hardenability as dissolved	Similar to Fe	Sustains hardness by solid solution	1 Contributes to red hardness by hardening ferrite 2 Tends to cause decarburization
Manganese Mn	Unlimited	3%	Hardens markedly; reduces plasticity somewhat	Increases hardenability moderately	Greater than Fe; less than Cr	Very little, in usual percentages	1 Counteracts brittleness from the sulfur 2 Increases hardenability inexpensively
Molybdenum Mo	3% ± (8% with 0.3% C)	37.5% (Less with lowered temperature)	Provides age-hardening system in high Mo-Fe alloys	Increases hardenability strongly (Mo > Cr)	Strong; greater than Cr	Opposes softening, by secondary hardening	1 Raises grain-coarsening temperature of austenite 2 Deepens hardening 3 Counteracts tendency toward temper brittleness 4 Raises hot and creep strength, red hardness 5 Enhances corrosion resistance in stainless steel 6 Forms abrasion-resisting particles 7 Tends to cause decarburization

Table 9.4 (Cont'd)

Specific Effects of Alloying Elements in Steel

Element	Solid Solubility		Influence on Ferrite	Influence on Austenite (Hardenability)	Influence Exerted Through Carbide		Principal Functions
	In Gamma Iron	In Alpha Iron			Carbide-Forming Tendency	Action During Tempering	
Nickel Ni	Unlimited	10% (Irrespective of carbon content)	Strengthens and toughens by solid solution	Increases hardenability mildly, but tends to retain austenite with higher carbon	Negative (graphitizes)	Very little in small percentages	1 Strengthens unquenched or annealed steels 2 Toughens pearlitic-ferritic steels (especially at low temperature) 3 Renders high-chromium iron alloys austenitic
Phosphorus P	0.5%	2.8% (Irrespective of carbon content)	Hardens strongly by solid solution	Increases hardenability	Nil	......	1 Strengthens low-carbon steel 2 Increases resistance to corrosion 3 Improves machinability in free-cutting steels
Silicon Si	2% ± (9% with 0.35% C)	18.5% (Not much changed by carbon)	Hardens with loss in plasticity (Mn < Si < P)	Increases hardenability moderately	Negative (graphitizes)	Sustains hardness by solid solution	1 Used as general-purpose deoxidizer 2 Alloying element for electrical and magnetic sheet 3 Improves oxidation resistance 4 Increases hardenability of steels carrying nongraphitizing elements 5 Strengthens low-alloy steels 6 Graphitizer
Titanium Ti	0.75% (1% ± with 0.20% C)	6% ± (Less with lowered temperature)	Provides age-hardening system in high Ti-Fe alloys	Probably increases hardenability very strongly as dissolved. The carbide effects reduce hardenability	Greatest known (2% Ti renders 0.50% carbon steel unhardenable)	Persistent carbides probably unaffected. Some secondary hardening	1 Fixes carbon in inert particles (a) Reduces martensitic hardness and hardenability in medium-chromium steels (b) Prevents formation of austenite in high-chromium steels (c) Prevents localized depletion of chromium in stainless steel during long heating
Tungsten W	6% (11% with 0.25% C)	33% (Less with lowered temperature)	Provides age-hardening system in high W-Fe alloys	Increases hardenability strongly in small amounts	Strong	Opposes softening by secondary hardening	1 Forms hard, abrasion-resistant particles in tool steels 2 Promotes hardness and strength at elevated temperature
Vanadium V	1% (4% with 0.20% C)	Unlimited	Hardens moderately by solid solution	Increases hardenability very strongly, as dissolved	Very strong (V < Ti or Cb)	Maximum for secondary hardening	1 Elevates coarsening temperature of austenite (promotes fine grain) 2 Increases hardenability (when dissolved) 3 Resists softening during tempering and causes marked secondary hardening

From *Metals Handbook*, American Society for Metals, Cleveland, 1948, p. 457.

9.12. Special Purpose Steels

A number of steel compositions have been developed to perform special functions. Important among these are the alloys used for **high-temperature service.** In order to be useful at elevated temperatures, alloys should possess good creep properties and resistance to oxidation. They should not undergo crystallographic changes, such as precipitation of embrittling phases, after long exposure to operating conditions. In some instances the stability of protective scale coverings in the face of thermal shock is important. The stainless steels, particularly the austenitic stainless steels, perform well at elevated temperatures. They give better resistance to scaling if silicon or aluminum is added as an alloying element. The best performance at high temperature is afforded not by steels but by alloys in which such elements as chromium, nickel, cobalt, molybdenum, and iron are present, with no one element present in amounts greater than 50 per cent. These alloys can hardly be called steels.

Another special purpose steel alloy is **Hadfield's steel.** This is an alloy known for its pronounced work-hardening characteristics, imparting good abrasion and wear resistance under some conditions. It contains about 1 per cent carbon and 12 per cent manganese. This composition produces an austenitic steel at room temperature. It is used for power shovel buckets, railroad switch frogs, rock crusher jaws and similar applications where service conditions result in work hardening and hence an improvement in properties.

Magnetic alloys of iron are of two types: (1) those in which magnetism is readily induced but in which the magnetism is temporary, and (2) those in which magnetism remains permanently. The first kind of magnetic material is used in a-c equipment and machinery. The most popular iron alloy of this type is one containing about 4 per cent silicon. Pure iron itself has desirable magnetic properties but its resistivity is so low that eddy current losses are high. Silicon is used because it increases the electrical resistance most effectively. Aluminum is also effective in this respect but its use involves processing difficulties. Considerable success has been achieved in controlling the orientation of the grains in silicon iron so as to obtain the best magnetic performance. This is an application of the knowledge of anisotropic properties (see section 1.5). There are many other iron alloys having special magnetic characteristics. Steel permanent magnets are high-carbon alloys containing such alloying elements as chromium, tungsten, molybdenum, and cobalt. They are first hardened and then permanently magnetized. They are not tempered after hardening because this destroys the magnetic properties. In addition to ferrous magnetic alloys there are in use today a number of magnetic alloys containing little or no iron.

Alloys of iron and nickel are also known for low coefficients of thermal expansion. These are useful in such applications as glass-metal seals, standards of length, and chronometer springs. One alloy (64Fe-36Ni) tends to become stiffer with increasing temperature. Since most metals become less stiff as the temperature rises, bimetal springs in which one component is the iron-nickel alloy retain constant elastic properties over a range of temperatures. The loss of stiffness in one metal is compensated by the gain in stiffness of the iron-nickel alloy. Still another alloy (54Fe-36Ni-10Cr) has a constant modulus of elasticity over a range of temperatures. This has been used for chronometer springs and bourdon tubes.

9.13. Summary

Properties of the common ferrous alloys are summarized in Table 9.3, including the *cast irons*, which were discussed in sections 7.9–7.11. A general summary of the mode of distribution and principal effects of the alloying elements in steel is given in Table 9.4 at the end of this chapter.

Questions

9.1. (a) In what five phases are alloying elements found in unhardened steel?

(b) What determines the distribution of the alloying elements in the phases of question 9.1(a)? Illustrate with an example.

(c) List the carbide formers in the order of increasing tendency to form carbides.

(d) What is the only important contribution of free-metal particles to properties of steel?

(e) Give an instance in which a metal existing as an intermetallic compound has an important effect on properties.

(f) Give an instance in which a metal existing as a nonmetallic inclusion has an important effect on properties.

9.2. (a) What effects do the presence of carbide formers have on steel which is intended for hardening or high-temperature use?

(b) What is the principal reason for the use of carbon and other alloying elements in steels?

(c) Explain what is meant by the *multiplying effect* of the alloying elements.

9.3. (a) Define *austenite* and *ferrite stabilizers.*

(b) Why is the maximum solubility of ferrite stabilizers in austenite of importance?

(c) In what way do austenite stabilizers render steel nonhardenable?

(d) What principles are illustrated by the good hardenability of the nickel-chromium steels as compared to alloy steels containing nickel or chromium alone?

9.4. For what purposes are the following used:

(a) Low-carbon steel?   (b) Medium-carbon steel?   (c) High-carbon steel?

(d) What are some disadvantages of high-carbon steels used for tools as compared to alloy steels used for the same applications?

9.5. (a) What mechanisms render the presence of alloying elements effective in improving the properties of low-alloy, high-strength structural steels?

(b) Compare the weldability of low-alloy, high-strength structural steels with the weldability of ordinary structural steels.

9.6. (a) What alloying elements are likely to be found in medium-alloy structural steels and what functions do they perform?

(b) For what applications are medium-alloy structural steels used?

9.7. (a) What are the five major classes of tool and die steels and what differences exist among them?

(b) What is the relationship between carbon content and toughness in tool and die steels?

(c) What functions are performed by the strong carbide formers in tool and die steels?

(d) Name two elements likely to promote decarburization of tool and die steels.

(e) What are the effects of cobalt, silicon, and manganese in tool and die steels?

(f) Name some applications of tool and die steels.

9.8. (a) Distinguish among the ferritic, martensitic, and austenitic steels.

(b) Describe the difficulties of welding austenitic stainless steels and steps used to overcome them.

(c) What are the manganese austenitic stainless steels and what special virtue do they possess?

(d) Describe the three classes of precipitation-hardening stainless steels.

9.9. What are the special properties which are desired in some of the special purpose steels?

Bibliography

9.1. Bain, E. C., *The Alloying Elements in Steel.* Cleveland: American Society for Metals, 1939.

9.2. *Standard Steel Analyses.* Pittsburgh: United States Steel Co., published annually.

9.3. *Nickel Alloy Steels,* 2nd Ed. New York: The International Nickel Co., Inc., 1949.

9.4. Woldman, N. E., and R. J. Metzler, *Engineering Alloys,* 2nd Ed. Cleveland: American Society for Metals, 1945.

9.5. Samans, C. H., *Engineering Metals and Their Alloys.* New York: The Macmillan Co., 1949.

9.6. Emmons, J. V., *The Mo-W High-Speed Steels,* 7th Ed. Cleveland: The Cleveland Twist Drill Co., 1947.

9.7. *Tool Steel for the Nonmetallurgist,* Crucible Steel Co. of America (pamphlet).

9.8. *The Tool Steel Trouble Shooter.* Bethlehem, Pa.: Bethlehem Steel Co., 1952.

9.9. Vennerholm, G., H. N. Bogart, and R. B. Melmoth, "Nodular Cast Iron," *SAE Journal,* **4-3** (1950), pp. 422–435.

9.10. *Republic Alloy Steels.* Cleveland: Republic Steel Corporation, 1949.

9.11. *Metals Handbook,* 1948 Ed. Cleveland: American Society for Metals.

9.12. *Metal Progress,* **66-1A** (July 15, 1954), Supplement to *Metals Handbook,* 1948 Ed. Cleveland: American Society for Metals.

9.13. *Metal Progress,* **68-2A** (August 15, 1954), Supplement to *Metals Handbook,* 1948 Ed. Cleveland: American Society for Metals.

9.14. Roach, D. B., and A. M. Hall, "The New Stainless Steels," *Materials and Methods,* **43–4** (April 1956).

9.15. Lula, R. A., and W. G. Renshaw, "Corrosion Resistance and Mechanical Properties of Cr-Ni-Mn Stainless Steels," *Metal Progress,* **69-2** (February 1956).

CHAPTER 10

The Light Metals

10.1. Nonferrous Metals and Alloys

The next three chapters consider some of the nonferrous metals and alloys. This chapter is devoted to the light metals, while following chapters treat copper and the copper-base alloys, zinc, the white metals, the bearing metals, and others. The same general scheme is followed in discussing the more important of the nonferrous metals, although the same emphasis is not placed on the same features in each discussion. Service properties, fabricating possibilities as determined by physical characteristics, and metallurgical aspects of the metals and alloys are treated in the order listed. This is followed by a very brief mention of uses, to fit the particular metals into the over-all picture.

10.2. Definition of Light Metals

The light metals are often considered to include magnesium, beryllium, aluminum, and titanium.[1] The metals are listed in the order of increasing specific gravities which are, respectively: 1.74, 1.82, 2.699, and 4.54. This is not the order of their importance, however, which might place aluminum first, followed by magnesium, with beryllium and titanium competing for third place.

ALUMINUM

10.3. Service Properties

The applications for which aluminum is useful depend to a large extent on *mechanical* and *physical properties* such as yield strength,

---

[1] In this chapter the words "magnesium," "aluminum," etc., are used to indicate either the metal itself or an alloy in which the particular metal is the major component. If the pure metal alone is referred to, it is so specified.

tensile strength ductility, stiffness, density, and electric conductivity. Commercially pure, annealed aluminum has a yield strength [2] of only 5000 psi, and a tensile strength of 13,000 psi with 45 per cent elongation.[3] By cold working alone, the yield strength may be increased over 4 times to 22,000 psi, with an accompanying drop in ductility to 15 per cent. Tensile strength, which is not as important as yield strength for most applications, rises to 24,000 psi. By a combination of alloying, hot working, and heat treating, the yield strength can be more than tripled again to reach a value of 73,000 psi, which is more than 14 times that of the pure, annealed metal. This particular alloy (known as 7075-T6) has an elongation of 11 per cent, with an ultimate strength of 83,000 psi. The modulus of elasticity of aluminum, which is dependent upon alloy content, fluctuates within about 15 per cent of 10.6×10^6 psi. This means that aluminum is only about one-third as stiff as steel, or in other words, under equal stresses below the proportional limit, aluminum deforms about three times as much as steel. The disadvantage of the low strength and stiffness of aluminum as compared to steel is largely offset where weight is a consideration. Thus the specific gravity of aluminum, which is about 2.7, is of extreme importance. A comparison of the ratio of strength to specific gravity (known as the strength/weight ratio or specific strength) yields some significant figures. For instance, several typical aluminum alloys have yield strengths of about 45,000 psi. A typical low-alloy high-strength structural steel might have a yield strength of 70,000 psi. For aluminum this gives a strength/weight ratio of 45,000/2.7, or 16,700. For steel, the corresponding ratio is 70,000/7.8, or 9000, a considerably lower figure. (The advantage may be reversed if the ratio of fatigue strength to weight is calculated or if comparisons with ultra-high-strength steels are made.) Thus, where weight is a consideration, aluminum sometimes compares more than favorably with steels. When computing the rigidity of structures the effect of bulk must be considered. For instance, the deflection of a beam under load is inversely related to the cross-sectional area of the beam. Comparing steel and aluminum again, aluminum beams require greater cross sections than steel beams, when both are designed for equal load-carrying

[2] Data on aluminum are from *Alcoa Aluminum Handbook*, Aluminum Company of America, Pittsburgh, 1956.

[3] Elongation, unless otherwise noted, refers to the elongation over a 2-in. gage length in a conventional tensile specimen.

capacities.   The larger cross section of the aluminum member acts to offset the higher modulus of elasticity of steel, and the rigidity of the aluminum structure may approach that of the steel structure.

Consider two beams of rectangular cross section, one made of aluminum and the other made of steel.   Both are carrying the same loads as cantilevers.   The deflection at the unsupported end of the beam, δ, may be calculated from

$$\delta = \frac{PL^3}{3EI}$$

where:

    $\delta =$ deflection, inches
    $P =$ load, pounds (identical in both cases)
    $E =$ modulus of elasticity, psi
    $L =$ length, inches (identical in both cases)
    $I =$ moment of inertia, which for a rectangular cross section $=$
       $BH^3/12$, where $B =$ width, inches (assumed identical in both
       cases), and $H =$ depth, inches.

Combining all constants into a single term, we have

$$\delta = K/EH^3$$

Assuming the yield strength of aluminum to be one-half that of steel, the depth of the aluminum beam should be 1.4 times that of the steel beam, where both have the same width and are designed to equivalent yield loads.   Since the modulus of elasticity of aluminum is one-third that of steel, the deflection of the aluminum beam is $1.1\delta_{st}$, where $\delta_{st} =$ the deflection of the steel beam.   This, of course, represents an idealized case, but in actual practice the same principles are involved.   If designed to the same weight, the aluminum beam would be considerably more rigid than the steel beam.

The fairly *low modulus of elasticity* of aluminum must be considered when aluminum is deformed, as it causes an appreciable amount of "springback" when the deforming load is removed. Compensation for this is accomplished by deformation slightly past the required shape.   The *wear resistance* of aluminum, as might be suspected from its low yield strength and hardness values, is not good. Means of improving the surface hardness of aluminum would broaden its applications.

The *fatigue strength* of aluminum is not high.   For fully annealed wrought aluminum, the endurance limit may equal or slightly exceed the yield strength. Since the yield strength of fully annealed materials is low, the fatigue strength is also poor. For alloys which have been hardened by heat treating or cold working, the fatigue strength does not exceed 23,000 psi and may be as low as $\frac{1}{3}$ the yield strength.

The *creep strength* of aluminum generally limits its use in the stressed condition to fairly low temperatures. This is in keeping with the general tendency for metals having low melting points to have low strength at elevated temperatures. For instance, one alloy (2018-T61) having a yield strength of 46,000 psi at room temperature has a yield strength of only 13,000 psi at 400°F (220°C). This alloy is typical in that it shows a sharp decrease in yield strength between 300°F (149°C) and 400°F (220°C), the change being from 40,000 psi to 13,000 psi. Many other alloys show a similar drop over the same temperature range. Thus, occasionally 350°F (177°C) is recommended as a maximum service temperature. Of course, the actual maximum service temperature depends upon stress, anticipated life, and permissible deformation (unless rupture occurs without appreciable deformation, under the conditions of use). Alloys have been developed to give satisfactory service in internal combustion engines, and much aluminum is consumed annually for this application. Powder metallurgy aluminum products, which are a mixture of pure aluminum and aluminum oxide show promise of good long-time service at temperatures near 600°F (316°C) and short-time service at temperatures near 900°F (482°C). The manufacture and nature of these products are discussed in section 14.19.

The *corrosion resistance* of aluminum is good against many types of attack which are harmful to other metals. This is probably due to the formation of a very adherent passive oxide layer on the surface. Aluminum alloys, though high in the activity series, resist attack by concentrated nitric acid, the organic acids, and even sulfuric acid at a concentration of nearly 100 per cent. They are, on the other hand, readily attacked by the halogen acids and by strong alkalies. The oxide of aluminum is amphoteric, i.e., it can behave as either a basic or acidic oxide. It reacts as an acidic oxide with alkaline materials to form soluble salts, thereby exposing fresh metal to attack. The aluminum alloys generally show good resistance to attack by the atmosphere, including salt spray. Some alloys, of course, are superior to others in their corrosion resistance to specific kinds of attack, and they should be selected on this basis.

The *electric conductivity* of high-purity aluminum is better than that of copper, when conductors of equal mass are compared. On the basis of equal volumes, the conductivity of electric conductor grade (EC-O, 99.45 minimum per cent aluminum) aluminum is 62 per cent of that of standard copper. On the basis of equal masses, aluminum conducts slightly more than twice as much current as copper under the same conditions.

The *heat conductivity* of aluminum is also quite high, as is usually the case with metals exhibiting good electric conductivity. Aluminum also has *excellent ability to reflect light*. Electrolytic polishing, followed by anodizing to produce a protective oxide finish, results in surfaces which reflect more than 80 per cent of the incident light. Figures as high as 97 per cent reflection have been reported depending upon metal purity, surface finish, and wavelength of the light striking the surface.

Another interesting feature of some alloys of aluminum is the lack of embrittlement at temperatures as low as −320°F (−199°C). At a temperature of −100°F (−79°C) some wrought alloys elongate 29 per cent, whereas the room temperature value is only 22 per cent. Even the cast alloys show a slight improvement in their limited ductility. This is not true of steel, and is a definite advantage of aluminum.

10.4. Fabrication of Aluminum

Of the fabricating methods available (see Chapters 13–18, inclusive), aluminum lends itself readily to casting, mechanical working, joining, machining, and finishing.

Casting. Aluminum is successfully cast in sand molds, and, because of its low melting point, also in permanent molds and die-casting machines. Some centrifugal casting is also done. The permanent mold and die castings faithfully reproduce intricate designs with good tolerances and surface finish. Pure aluminum has good pouring characteristics, but the skin of oxide forming on the exposed surfaces of the molten metal has a high surface tension and may require some special techniques, as described in Chapter 13. Turbulence and breaks in the stream of metal should be avoided during pouring, since both cause entrapment of dross or oxide particles. These, having a specific gravity not greatly different from that of aluminum, do not readily rise and separate themselves from the body of the casting.   Porosity in aluminum castings is largely the result of hydrogen absorbed when the molten metal reacts with moisture in the atmosphere.   This can be controlled by proper foundry techniques and equipment.   Shrinkage in aluminum castings amounts to about $\frac{5}{32}$ inch per foot, or about 1.3 per cent, but compensation is made for this when patterns and molds are designed, and it presents no major problem.   The aluminum alloys which have been developed for particular products and casting processes are generally considered to exhibit good casting characteristics.

Mechanical working.   Aluminum is worked both hot and cold. Most of the common structural shapes, including plate, rod, bar, and wire may be hot rolled.   Hammer, press, and drop forging of aluminum is also carried out successfully, though the power requirements are sometimes higher than for steel.   Extrusion is another hot-working process used for and particularly well suited to fabrication of aluminum.   A wide variety of either simple or complicated cross sections is possible.   Cold working is readily accomplished by most of the common methods, such as rolling of plate, sheet, and foil, drawing of rod, bar, and wire, reducing of tubing, deep drawing, etc.   Aluminum is also particularly adapted to forming by spinning, and by impact extrusion.

Joining.   Aluminum is joined by riveting, welding, and brazing. An interesting metallurgical feature of *riveting* is the use of rivets made of an age-hardenable aluminum alloy.   Rivets of this type may be solution heat-treated, quenched, and maintained in a refrigerated condition until driven.   At the end of a period of time, which varies from four days to two weeks, age hardening takes place, and the rivets develop their maximum strength.   Another ingenious fastener is the rivet having an explosive end.   This rivet, placed in a hole through the pieces to be joined, is heated by a small gun, which causes the explosive to detonate and expand the metal surrounding it.   This method of joining is particularly applicable to inacessible joints.   Aluminum is successfully *welded* by resistance methods (spot, seam, and flash welding) and by arc welding.   *Gas welding* is used to a limited extent where greater soundness is required than can be obtained by arc welding.   Because of aluminum's high coefficient of thermal expansion and high heat conductivity, and because the heat is not as concentrated as in arc welding, gas welding is slower, more expensive, and results in greater distortion during welding. *Arc welding* is carried out using metal arc, tungsten arc, carbon arc, or atomic hydrogen. *Metal-arc* welding of aluminum produces strong joints, but requires more skill than the welding of steel by similar methods. *Inert-gas shielded-arc* welding, with tungsten electrodes and argon as a shielding medium, is frequently used and is the only fusion process in which the need for fluxes and cleanup is eliminated. It also has been adapted to automatic methods with great success. *Carbon-arc* welding has been used as a manual as well as an automatic method. It results in a weld whose soundness approaches that achieved by gas welding. *Brazing* is sometimes used, having the advantage of being more economical than gas or arc welding in many applications. It is also applicable to components too thin for welding. Torch, dip, and furnace brazing are all used with success.

Machining and finishing. Excellent machinability is a well-known characteristic of most aluminum alloys. Some aluminum alloys have a machinability rating 20 times that of free-machining Bessemer stock. Many of the alloys show free-machining characistics and are successfully cut with tools having a small rake angle so as to produce discontinuous chips and a good finish. Larger rake angles and tools modified so as to break or accommodate long, continuous chips (see Chapter 18) are used where necessary. Because of the high thermal expansion of aluminum, overheating during machining may cause distortion. This can be avoided by the use of sharp, correctly designed tools, proper adjustment of feed and cut, and correct use of lubricants. Aluminum is usually cut at higher speeds than most metals, and because of this the work must be rigidly held and vibration prevented.

Aluminum can accept most of the mechanical finishes described in Chapter 18. A very high finish, used for reflecting surfaces, is achieved by electropolishing. Bright dipping is also used to produce surfaces of high luster.

Anodized coatings are applied to aluminum surfaces for special applications. The process consists of making the part to be coated the anode in a bath containing acids such as sulphuric, chromic, oxalic, sulfamic, or boric acid. Electrolysis liberates oxygen at the anode, forming aluminum oxide on the surface. In *colored anodic coatings*, the oxide layer is a mordant for dyes and takes a wide variety of colors. After dyeing, the colors are sealed by immersion in nickel or cobalt acetate solutions which precipitate the hydroxides of these metallic ions. The most stable colors are mineral colors formed by reaction of the anodizing bath with the alloying elements of the particular alloy. Thus, silicon-bearing alloys produce a gray or brownish color. Mineral pigments are also used to color the coatings, and the coatings so colored tend, in general, to be more stable than dyed coatings. *Hard anodic coatings* are 0.0001 to 0.005 in. thick. Sealing is accomplished by immersion in steam or hot water, thus converting the aluminum oxide to a hydrate. This causes an increase in the volume of the coating and provides a more impervious film. *Insulating anodic coatings* are produced in special boric acid electrolytes. Such surfaces are used on foil from which capacitors are made. The coating is about 0.006 in. thick and has a breakdown voltage between 600 and 4000 volts. *Corrosion-resistant* anodic coatings are about 0.004 in. thick. They preserve initial appearance, preventing streaking and nonuniform weathering of architectural trim.

Electroplating is applied in a limited extent to aluminum. Usually the part to be plated is given a coating of zinc, onto which the final plated layer is deposited. When a metal below aluminum in the chemical activity series is plated onto aluminum, the layer of plated metal must be continuous, to prevent attack of the basis metal by galvanic action.

10.5. Metallurgical Aspects

Aluminum is used as both a major and minor component of alloys. The properties of many alloys are improved by heat treating.

Crystal structure. Aluminum is the *only* one of the light metals which has a face-centered cubic structure. It is like most of the face-centered cubic metals in that it lends itself readily to being shaped and worked.

Effects of alloying elements in aluminum. The effects of the alloying elements in aluminum alloys are quite complex. In the casting grades, some of the alloying elements are added to provide better casting characteristics, while others are added to improve mechanical properties. In wrought alloys, better forming characteristics and superior mechanical and physical properties are the usual goals. It should be pointed out that even though different alloys may have the same tensile strength, their other mechanical properties may vary widely. Particular additions may be made to improve certain properties or a combination of them. Some of the more important effects of the alloying elements in aluminum are noted below.

Copper. The addition of copper to aluminum alloys results in one of the best known age- and precipitation-hardening systems. This is probably the principal reason for using copper as an alloying element. It also raises the strength of aluminum at high temperatures, and hence the alloy may be used for piston castings. Compositions containing copper are also among the most machinable of the aluminum alloys. In both wrought and cast products copper increases the susceptibility to intergranular corrosion. In slowly cooled alloys the copper-rich constituent ($CuAl_2$) precipitates as a massive interdendritic phase. In this form, the alloy is very susceptible to corrosive attack. In chilled castings and properly heat-treated alloys, the copper constituent is finely divided and the aluminum solid solution (α) is more nearly continuous. This improves corrosion resistance and also mechanical properties. The least corrosion-resistant of all aluminum alloys are those bearing copper.

Silicon. Among the most important contributions of silicon to aluminum alloys is the improvement which results in casting characteristics. This manifests itself in (1) shrinkage being reduced to one-half the value for pure aluminum, (2) improvement in gas-tightness of castings, and (3) greatly improved fluidity, which is important in producing thin sections in die and permanent mold castings. Silicon produces some age-hardening tendencies, but these are much less pronounced than those of copper. Addition of silicon also results in improvement of corrosion resistance, and this effect may be amplified by the addition of smaller quantities of magnesium. Silicon, when combined with small quantities of magnesium (to form magnesium silicide, Mg_2Si) results in an age-hardenable alloy. (Magnesium silicide has a maximum solubility of 1.85 per cent in α at 1102°F or 594°C.) Addition of silicon causes a drop in machinability largely because of the abrasive nature of the silicon-rich particles in the eutectic. The machinability of silicon-bearing alloys may be improved by chill casting or by addition of small amounts of sodium (the latter is difficult to control). Both of these procedures produce smaller and more uniformly distributed particles of precipitate. Strength and ductility as well as machinability are thereby improved. However, silicon decreases workability of aluminum alloys.

Magnesium. The use of magnesium is justified by the promotion of corrosion resistance. By itself, magnesium is better than silicon in this respect. In combination with silicon it improves the corrosion resistance developed by silicon, and also forms an age-hardenable alloy. It does not impair the ductility of the alloys, as do some other additions. In fact, some castings containing magnesium show remarkable ductility. It imparts good machinability to castings. However, magnesium is a very reactive metal (which is probably related to the protection it affords against corrosion), and alloys containing it require some special care in handling. It tends to cause intergranular oxidation during heat treatment and may lead to burned castings. High-magnesium alloys are handled more like magnesium-base than aluminum-base alloys.

Manganese. Corrosion resistance is improved by the use of manganese, which is added along with magnesium for strengthening purposes in wrought alloys.

Nickel. The addition of nickel either produces an age-hardening system or assists copper in this respect.

Zinc. The highest strength alloy of aluminum is one containing 5 to 6 per cent of zinc with smaller amounts of magnesium and copper. Small amounts of chromium are added to these alloys to improve corrosion resistance.

Lead and bismuth are added to impart free-machining characteristics to wrought alloys. They act as chip breakers.

Iron has a slight hardening effect. In the cast alloys the presence of iron in excess of specified amounts causes an undesirable increase in solidification shrinkage. If present in less than specified amounts in the die-casting alloys, rapid corrosion of the dies is caused by their reaction with the molten alloy.

10.6. Aluminum Alloy Designations

Wrought aluminum alloys are designated by four digits, such as 2024. The first digit indicates the alloy type, as shown in Table 10.1. The second digit shows the modification of the basic alloy. The last two digits indicate the purity of the aluminum or the specific alloy involved.

Table 10.1

Designation of Wrought Aluminum Alloys

Type of Alloy	Number
Aluminum, 99.00% minimum or greater	1 - - -
Copper	2 - - -
Manganese	3 - - -
Silicon	4 - - -
Magnesium	5 - - -
Magnesium and silicon	6 - - -
Zinc	7 - - -
Other element	8 - - -

The cast alloys, with the exception of one designated as 43 alloy, are all identified by three-digit numbers.

The three- and four-digit series are followed by a dash and temper designations. The letters used for temper designations are O, F, T, and H. The letters T and H are followed by numbers to describe more fully the alloy history. The letter O is applied only to wrought alloys and shows that the alloy has been annealed and is in the dead soft condition. The letter F when used in connection with wrought alloys indicates the as-fabricated condition. If applied to cast alloys, F shows the alloy to be in the as-cast condition. The significance of the T designations is shown below:

-T2 Applies only to cast alloys, indicating the annealed condition.

-T3 Solution heat treated and strain hardened. The amount of strain hardening is indicated by a second digit, as in 2024-T36.

-T4 Solution heat treated followed by aging until stable.

-T5 Precipitation hardened after cooling rapidly from the fabricating temperatures.

-T6 Solution heat treated followed by precipitation hardening.

-T7 Solution heat treated and stabilized to control growth and distortion.

-T8 Solution heat treated, strain hardened, and aged.

-T9 Solution heat treated, aged, and strain hardened.

Additional digits indicate variations of the basic procedures listed above.

The H designations apply only to wrought alloys, as follows:

-H1 Strain hardened by cold working to final dimensions. Digits following the 1 run from 2 to 9, 9 indicating extra hard, 8 full hard, and so forth.

-H2 Strain hardened and then partially annealed. The second digits have the same significance as for the -H1 tempers.

-H3 Strain hardened and stabilized.

10.7. Uses of Aluminum

To list all the uses of aluminum would be a considerable task. However, an appreciation of its applicability can be gained by considering a few of its uses and the reasons therefore.   Whenever any metal is finally selected for a particular use, the decision probably has been based upon consideration of:

1. Service characteristics, i.e., physical, chemical, and mechanical properties and the assurance that they will meet the demands of service.
2. Fabricating characteristics, i.e., how easily the metal may be put into a usable form.
3. Cost, which is of course closely related to item (2).   In addition, cost is connected with supply and demand through their effects on price.

It is beyond the scope of this text to discuss costs in detail.   Economic factors and advances in technology might quickly render cost figures obsolete.   Therefore, in the discussion which follows, only the first two factors are considered in their relationship to uses for aluminum.   It would be well to remember that similar principles apply to the selection of any metal for any particular purpose.

Light-weight pistons, because of their lower inertia, result in greater efficiency of fuel consumption in internal combustion engines.   Thus alloys of aluminum, which are inherently light, have found wide applications.   The best alloys of this type may contain copper for greater strength at elevated temperatures, or other elements which reduce the coefficient of thermal expansion. The advantage of light-weight pistons in aircraft engines is obvious.

Aircraft cylinder heads, with their thin fins, are made of aluminum alloys.   While weight saving is a consideration, another factor favoring aluminum is its good castability, which insures a completely filled mold and a gastight casting.   In addition, the high heat conductivity of aluminum is extremely important in this application, as is corrosion resistance.   Similar applications are found in economizers and heat exchangers.

Light weight, high strength/weight ratio, ability to be joined readily by riveting and welding, and good corrosion resistance make aluminum ideal for train, truck, and aircraft construction.   Pay loads are increased, fabrication is facilitated, and maintenance costs are reduced by use of aluminum in this case.

The corrosion products of aluminum, when it undergoes mild corrosive attack, are colorless and tasteless. This has led to the use of aluminum in textile machinery where contamination of dyes must be avoided. It also has resulted in wide adaptation of aluminum to the food processing industry, where both appearance and taste are important. Furthermore, where heating is involved as in food processing, the high heat conductivity of aluminum is another advantage. Aluminum alloys have for this reason and because of their good workability found wide favor in the manufacture of large and small cooking utensils. The facility with which aluminum is spun has promoted its application to shapes not readily made by cupping or deep drawing.

Aluminum is used for making tubes, such as toothpaste tubes, because it is readily extruded by impact, has good corrosion resistance, and yields tasteless and nontoxic corrosion products.

Architectural trim, both inside and outside, is made of aluminum. Entering into the picture here are the variety of cross sections which can be made easily by extruding. In addition, corrosion resistance, and excellent appearance of dyed anodized coatings are definite advantages in this instance.

The very high reflectivity of aluminum when electrolytically finished, coupled with ease of spinning, has suited it for use in lighting reflectors.

Not only does aluminum reflect light, but also heat; for this reason, thin foil is used for industrial and home insulation. It is also used as a cooking wrap for uniform heating and to prevent loss of moisture from food.

The high electric conductivity of aluminum has resulted in its use in transmission lines and electric motors. In the latter application, the aluminum conductors are die cast into place, rather than being wound as in designs where copper is used.

Good machinability accounts for many applications of aluminum, including its wide use in automatic screw machines.

Though the uses listed above do not represent the entire field, they serve to illustrate the versatility of aluminum. In fact, aluminum is probably the strongest competitor of ferrous materials as the most useful engineering metal.

MAGNESIUM

10.8. Service Properties: Strength, Ductility, and Modulus of Elasticity

Magnesium, like aluminum, exhibits high strength/weight ratios and good stiffness in structures made from it. Commercially pure, annealed magnesium has a yield strength of 14,000 psi [2] (almost three times that of pure and annealed aluminum), a tensile strength of 27,000 psi (about double that of aluminum), with about 11 per cent elongation (about one-third that of aluminum). By cold working, the yield strength is raised to 27,000 psi, tensile strength goes to 37,000 psi, and elongation drops to 9 per cent. Except for ductility, these properties are superior to those for pure aluminum. Magnesium is not as responsive as is aluminum to improvement in properties by alloying and heat treating. For instance, the strongest wrought, heat-treated magnesium alloy (AZ80X) has a yield strength of 40,000 psi (about 32,000 psi less than the best aluminum alloy), an ultimate strength of 53,000 psi (about 30,000 psi less than for aluminum), with an elongation of only 7 per cent (appreciably less than for aluminum). While the properties of magnesium are greatly improved by various hardening techniques, the response is not nearly as great as for aluminum. Magnesium, therefore, usually is considered to be a weaker metal, and one which has lower ductility than aluminum. The modulus of elasticity of magnesium is about 6.5×10^6 psi, and strangely enough this may be lowered by cyclic working to about 4.0×10^6 psi. Nevertheless, the low value of E is offset by the greater bulk required for magnesium structures designed to the same strength as steel. Thus magnesium structures may be more rigid than those of aluminum or steel designed to the same strength. A magnesium beam of the same weight as an alloy steel beam has been calculated to be 1860 times as rigid as the steel beam in resistance to bending.[3]

The *wear resistance* of magnesium alloys is very low. This is indicated by low values for both yield strength and hardness. The

[2] Data in the section on magnesium are from the *Metals Handbook*, American Society for Metals, Cleveland, 1948.

[3] *Designing with Magnesium*, American Magnesium Corporation (subsidiary of the Aluminum Company of America), Cleveland, 1945, p. 35.

wear resistance of magnesium structural parts occasionally is improved by the use of inserts or overlays of hard materials at the points of wear.

The *fatigue strength* of magnesium is low. Although for some heat-treated castings the endurance limit is within 10 per cent of the yield strength, a more generally applicable figure places it between one-third and one-half the yield strength. The best magnesium alloys, with respect to fatigue strength, show endurance limits of about 18,000 psi. This is not quite as good as the best of the aluminum alloys.

The *creep strength* of magnesium is not good. This might be suspected from its low melting point 650°C (1202°F) and a rapid decrease in yield and tensile strengths between room temperature and 600°F (315°C). The magnesium alloys are not recommended for long-time use at temperatures over 500°F (260°C). The maximum temperature for short-time exposure is 700°F (371°C).

The *corrosion resistance* of many magnesium alloys is poor. Magnesium is just above aluminum in the chemical activity series, and unfortunately does not form a passive layer. Magnesium usually suffers uniform attack and is more quickly attacked when in contact with water than when dry. It is particularly susceptible to attack by salt water and most inorganic acids and their salts. Magnesium is fairly resistant to dry inland atmospheres, but structures must be designed to avoid accumulation of water. Very closely controlling the impurities in magnesium has produced alloys of much improved resistance to corrosive attack by marine atmospheres.

10.9. Fabrication of Magnesium

Magnesium is fabricated by casting, mechanical working, joining, and machining and finishing.

Casting. The casting of magnesium is in many respects similar to the casting of aluminum. Sand, permanent mold, and die-casting methods are applicable. Shrinkage is slightly higher than for aluminum, amounting to $\frac{11}{64}$ inch per foot, or about 1.43 per cent. Oxide entrapment must be avoided by careful pouring practice, because of the sluggishness of gravity separation of oxides from the melt. Gas porosity may be caused by hydrogen picked up from the reaction of the hot metal with water vapor. Because of the very reactive nature of magnesium, iron scale is carefully removed from the melting furnaces, where it forms on the surfaces of the melting pots. An accumulation of iron scale reacts violently with any hot magnesium which may be spilled on it; the reaction is similar to the thermit reaction. Under some conditions magnesium is melted under an atmosphere of sulfur dioxide, to which it is inert. This prevents burning, which tends to occur by reaction with the oxygen of the air. Magnesium cannot be cast in ordinary green sand molds because of its tendency when molten to react with the water which is present. If chemical inhibitors are mixed with the sand this difficulty may be overcome.

Mechanical working. Because of its low ductility at room temperature, magnesium is not widely cold worked. Sheet and strip are given their final reductions cold, but the amount of cold reduction between each anneal is kept low. Magnesium is successfully hot worked by forging, rolling, drawing, bending, and spinning. Considerable ingenuity is employed in adapting to elevated temperatures those operations which are performed at room temperature for most metals. Spinning, bending, and drawing are examples. Magnesium can be extended to produce rods, bars, and shapes of odd cross section.

Because of its lower modulus of elasticity, magnesium shows even more springback than aluminum. In deforming magnesium it must be bent to more than final shape, so that when the deforming load is removed, it will assume the desired contour.

Joining. Inert-gas shielded-arc welding, gas welding, and riveting are the most commonly used methods for joining magnesium. Some spot, seam, and flash welding is also used. Inert-gas shielded-arc welding produces the highest strength welds, and since a flux is not required, cleanup is no problem. Furthermore, distortion is reduced because of a more concentrated heat source, making possible the joining of thicker pieces than gas welding. However, a postwelding stress relief anneal is recommended. Residual stresses have been reported to be as great as 15,000 psi in the neighborhood of the weld. Gas welding requires the use of a flux, and since the fluxes used are quite corrosive, a thorough cleanup is required. Spot and seam welding can be used on magnesium structures where service stresses are to be low, or if high, at least free from excessive vibration.

Machining and finishing. The machinability of magnesium is unsurpassed by that of any other common metal. Machining characteristics are similar, but superior, to those of aluminum. Type I chips are commonly formed (see Chapter 18). High speeds and heavy feeds are used, but these require tools designed to accommodate the rapidly produced volume of chips. Smooth tool faces are necessary to prevent excessive friction, and thus minimize overheating and any tendency for the chips to foul tool and work. Milling cutters for magnesium have fewer teeth than cutters for less machinable metals, so that they can accommodate the chips from high-speed operations. A very fine finish is obtained on magnesium, one frequently good enough to obviate finish grinding. Power consumption for machining is very low. Magnesium alloys are also well suited to automatic screw machines. Because of the high chemical reactivity of magnesium there is some danger that the turnings will catch fire. Therefore accumulations of magnesium particles should be removed periodically and placed in covered cans. Smothering with dry sand is recommended for control of magnesium fires. Grinding is carried out wet in a well-ventilated system. Fine magnesium particles liberate hydrogen from water creating an explosion hazard unless precautions are observed.

Magnesium may be finished by scratchbrushing, grinding, polishing, or buffing, but often a machined finish is adequate. Various pickling baths are used, sometimes before painting; these have as their primary object improvement of corrosion resistance.

10.10. Metallurgical Aspects

Magnesium is used as either the major or the minor component of alloys. Some improvements results from heat treating many of the alloys, but the improvement is not as marked as in the case of the aluminum alloys.

Crystal structure. Magnesium has a hexagonal close-packed crystal structure, and like many metals having this structure, exhibits poor ductility. Thus magnesium is difficult to form while cold. By heating, additional slip planes are brought into play, and the ductility is improved.

Aluminum is the principal alloy addition in magnesium alloys. It produces a precipitation-hardenable alloy in which the precipitate strongly resembles the pearlitic structures found in steel. Precipitation-hardenable alloys contain more than about 7 per cent aluminum. Aluminum remaining in solid solution exerts a slight hardening effect.

Zinc is another element frequently found in magnesium alloys. It functions as a solid solution hardener, and also improves corrosion resistance.

Manganese when present in small controlled amounts improves resistance to corrosive attack by salt water. In larger amounts manganese improves hot formability for forging and extrusion.

Zirconium, thorium, and the *rare earths* are used as alloy additions to improve elevated temperature properties.

Silicon, usually present as an undesirable impurity which reduces ductility, may be added to the die-casting alloys to improve casting characteristics. *Nickel, copper,* and *iron* all decrease corrosion resistance and are hence kept as low as possible.

When magnesium alloys are solution heat treated the temperatures [750°–800°F (400°–430°C), depending upon the alloy] are high enough to cause appreciable softening of the metal. Since the time varies between 10 and 20 hours, creep and distortion may set in. Therefore large castings should be supported, and small castings should not be piled too high unless support is provided.

Small percentages of magnesium are added to aluminum to make aluminum-base alloys; this is the principal application of magnesium as an alloying element. Smaller amounts of magnesium play an important part in the zinc-base die-casting alloys, where they serve to improve corrosion resistance.

10.11. Uses of Magnesium

The uses for which magnesium is best suited depend to a large extent upon its high strength/weight ratio, good casting characteristics, and excellent machinability. It is not more widely applied because of the low corrosion resistance of most of its alloys to salt water and marine atmospheres, because of cold-forming difficulties, and low hardness and wear resistance.

Thus magnesium has been used for aircraft engine parts, housings for automotive accessories, wheels, gas tanks, and some structural members.

It is also used in the manufacture of portable tools and machinery where lightness is important. Magnesium is used for the moving parts of many machines where inertia is to be reduced to a minimum, e.g., for pieces subject to reciprocating or intermittent movement. It has found fairly wide use in the form of spools for textile mills, where the high strength/weight ratio permits use of lighter, more easily handled spools.

Because of its highly reactive nature, magnesium is used to deoxidize molten copper, nickel, and silver, and their alloys. It is granulated or powdered and used in flares, incendiary bombs, and pyrotechnics. One method of producing titanium, another light metal, depends upon the reduction of titanium tetrachloride by magnesium, in accordance with the equation:

$$TiCl_4 + 2Mg \longrightarrow 2MgCl_2 + Ti$$

BERYLLIUM

10.12. Properties

Beryllium is an extremely reactive metal, and because of this, its extraction from ores is difficult. It is slightly heavier than magnesium, having a specific gravity of 1.82. However, beryllium in the pure, annealed condition is stronger than magnesium; it has a yield strength of 26,400 psi.[4] Beryllium has the highest strength/weight ratio of any known metal. It has a modulus of elasticity of 36.8×10^6, which is higher than that of steel. It has almost no ductility, which is typical of many of the hexagonal close-packed metals. Melting practice calls for exclusion of oxygen atmospheres, and casting is often carried out under a vacuum. Beryllium is successfully hot extruded.

10.13. Uses

Fabricating difficulties and high cost limit the use of beryllium. It is used in the pure state as a neutron moderator in atomic energy plants. It is alloyed with copper (2 per cent beryllium) to produce beryllium-copper, which in the age-hardened condition has high values for yield strength, proportional limit, and modulus of elasticity. This material is useful for springs which require good corrosion resistance and electric conductivity. Beryllium-copper is also nonmagnetic, is easily formed in the annealed condi-

[4] Data on beryllium are from the *Metals Handbook*, American Society for Metals, Cleveland, 1948.

tion, and has good fatigue strength. The nonsparking character of beryllium-copper tools has made them particularly useful for work around combustible or explosive substances.

Beryllium has given indications of being a potent ferrite hardener, but its cost make its use in this connection prohibitive.

TITANIUM

10.14. Service Properties

High-purity annealed titanium has a yield strength of about 17,-500 psi. Cold reduction of the annealed metal 50 per cent raises the yield strength to 87,000 psi, and causes the elongation to drop from 55 per cent to about 11 per cent. Commercially pure titanium, made by remelting titanium sponge (obtained by reduction of $TiCl_4$ with Mg, see section 10.11), has a yield strength near 50,000 psi. Cold working of commercially pure grades of titanium raises the yield strength to 110,000–120,000 psi with a simultaneously drop in elongation to 5–10 per cent. Titanium is certainly the strongest of the light metals, beryllium excluded. Its modulus of elasticity varies slightly depending upon previous history and composition. High purity, annealed titanium has a modulus of elasticity of 11.2×10^6 psi, but this is raised to $15.0–16.0 \times 10^6$ psi by mechanical working and the introduction of carbon in the commercially pure metal. In other alloys the modulus of elasticity goes as high as 18.0×10^6 psi. Thus, titanium is stiffer than either aluminum or magnesium, but not as stiff as beryllium. Although its specific gravity of 4.5 is greater than the values for the other light metals, titanium is only slightly more than half as dense as steel.

The *wear* and *abrasion resistance* of titanium are good. *Fatigue strength* is much higher than for aluminum and for magnesium alloys. The *creep strength* of titanium is good for service in the temperature range between 300–800°F (149–427°C). The alloy containing 8 per cent manganese, balance titanium undergoes only one per cent elongation after 1000 hours at 800°F (427°C) under a stress of 13,000 psi. The *corrosion resistance* is about the same as that of stainless steel. Titanium has excellent resistance to nitric and other strongly oxidizing acids, but poor resistance to halogen acids, sulfuric acid and phosphoric acid. It also strongly resists attack by hydroxides and salt solutions. The formation of a protective passive film must account for its corrosion resistance, because titanium is a highly reactive element.

Electric and thermal conductivity and specific heat are low.

10.15. Fabrication of Titanium

Melting of titanium sponge prior to casting entails difficulties, because titanium is very reactive at its melting temperature, 3300°F (1820°C). Heat is supplied for melting by an electric arc. Electrodes for arc furnaces usually are made from titanium. Melts made in water-cooled copper crucibles using titanium electrodes yield the highest purity metal. An argon atmosphere, or a vacuum, is used to exclude oxygen and nitrogen, both of which are hardeners and cause loss of ductility.

Powder metallurgy techniques are not used commercially, although some of the pioneering work did rely upon powder metallurgy for conversion of sponge titanium into massive form. Production of usable powders and techniques for compacting and sintering must be improved before powder metallurgy methods can be used commercially.

Mechanical working. Forging temperatures vary from about 1600°F (871°C) for pure titanium to 2100°F (1150°C) for some alloys. Larger capacity hammers and presses are required for titanium than for steel. For instance, the deformation resistance of titanium at 1750°F (955°C) is much greater than the deformation resistance of SAE-AISI 4340 steel at 2250°F (1232°C). A thin, rust-colored scale, possibly an oxide-nitride combination, forms on titanium at the forging temperatures. This scale is believed to increase the wear rate of forging dies. If the forgings are to be machined the scale should be removed by grit blasting, otherwise tool wear is excessive.

Joining. Inert gas-shielded arc welding is successfully applied to titanium. The shielding of the hot metal can be accomplished with either argon or helium. Gas shielding on the underside is preferred to a tight back-up to prevent an embrittling reaction with oxygen or nitrogen. Spot and seam welding are also used with good results, providing the surfaces to be joined are clean. Flash welding is used and offers a possible means of joining titanium to other metals. Inert gas protection improves the results of flash welding.

Machinability of titanium is not good, being about the same as for stainless steel. Low cutting or grinding speeds and feeds and light cuts are recommended along with efficient coolants. Tool wear is probably the result of alloying and welding between the chip and tool with subsequent tool breakdown when the built-up edge (see Chapter 18) sloughs off. The poor thermal conductivity of titanium causes excessive heating at the tool tip and promotes welding. Low rates of metal removal and use of effective coolants aid in dissipation of heat and minimize welding tendencies. Abrasion of tool surfaces is also caused by titanium carbides present in the alloys being cut as well as by oxide-nitride scale on the surfaces of the parts being machined.

10.16. Metallurgical Aspects

Titanium has a hexagonal close-packed structure, known as alpha titanium, at room temperature. When heated to 1650°F (900°C), the alpha phase changes to the beta phase, a body-centered cubic structure. Even though the stable room temperature structure is HCP, ductility is fairly good unless carbon, oxygen, or nitrogen is present as an alloying element. The size of the titanium atom is within 15 per cent of the size of the atoms of many other elements.[5] This factor tends to favor substitutional solid solution. Chromium, manganese, iron, and molybdenum tend to stabilize the ductile beta phase at room temperature. Aluminum, on the other hand, is an alpha phase stabilizer. Alloys are available in which the predominant structure is the alpha phase, the beta phase, or a mixture of the two. Heat treatment offers some possibilities as a means of control of properties and microstructure. Annealing is of course carried out upon cold-worked material for restoration of ductility and softness.

10.17. Uses of Titanium

Titanium is used in aircraft for parts subjected to temperatures between 300–800°F (149–427°C). Below 300°F (149°C) alumi-

---

[5] Among these are: iron, nickel, cobalt, chromium, magnesium, aluminum, copper, zinc, silver, gold, platinum, mercury, tin, tantalum, antimony, columbium, tungsten, molybdenum, and vanadium. Nitrogen and carbon dissolve interstitially as they do in iron.

num is preferred, and above 800°F (427°C) stainless steel or special alloys are superior. Thus, titanium is used for compressor blading, jet engine shrouds, and similar parts. It is also used for special chemical installations where it has proved superior to stainless steel with respect to corrosion resistance and severe service conditions. Anodizing clips and racks used for aluminum processing are made of commercially pure titanium because titanium combines corrosion resistance and strength with suitable electric conductivity. It is also used for prosthetic devices such as bone pins and skull plates because it is chemically inert with respect to body fluids and chemicals.

Titanium in the form of its carbide has been used to control grain size and deoxidize steel for a number of years. It is also used to stabilize stainless steel against carbide precipitation. Titanium is used in pyrotechnics because of its highly combustible nature when in a finely divided state.

Questions

10.1. What metals are classed as light metals?

10.2. Fill out the following table as far as possible.

	Commercially pure, annealed condition:			Highest strength alloy:		
	Yield strength	*Tensile strength*	*Elongation*	*Yield strength*	*Tensile strength*	*Elongation*
Aluminum:						
Magnesium:						
Titanium:						

	Young's modulus	*Wear resistance*	*Fatigue strength*
Aluminum:			
Magnesium:			
Titanium:			

	Creep strength	*Corrosion resistance*	*Special properties*
Aluminum:			
Magnesium:			
Titanium:			

10.3. What casting techniques are commonly applied to aluminum? What problems are encountered in the casting of aluminum? Compare the casting of magnesium with that of aluminum. What special precautions must be taken during heat treatment of magnesium castings?

10.4. Discuss the mechanical working of aluminum and magnesium.

10.5. Discuss the joining of aluminum and magnesium.

10.6. Discuss the machining and finishing of aluminum and magnesium.

10.7. Compare the crystal structures of the light metals. Which of the light metals has the best ductility? Which shows the greatest promise in regard to solid-solution hardening? Why?

10.8. For what reasons are the following metals alloyed with aluminum: (a) copper; (b) silicon; (c) magnesium; (d) manganese; (e) nickel; (f) zinc.

10.9. Give several examples of applications of aluminum and explain why aluminum is used in each case.

10.10. For what reasons are the following metals alloyed with magnesium: (a) aluminum; (b) zinc; (c) manganese; (d) silicon. What elements are considered harmful if present in magnesium alloys?

10.11. Give several examples of applications of magnesium and explain why magnesium is used in each case.

10.12. What are the outstanding characteristics of beryllium? What is the most important use of beryllium?

10.13. Discuss the fabrication of titanium.

10.14. What applications appear promising for titanium? Why?

Bibliography

10.1. *Alcoa Aluminum Handbook.* Pittsburgh: Aluminum Company of America, 1956.

10.2. *Alcoa Structural Handbook.* Pittsburgh: Aluminum Company of America, 1956.

10.3. Numerous publications of Reynolds Metals Company, Louisville, Kentucky, on the subject of Aluminum.

10.4. Numerous publications of Aluminum Company of America, Pittsburgh, on the subject of Aluminum.

10.5. Riley, M. W., "Wrought Aluminum Alloys," *Materials and Methods,* **43-1** (January 1956), pp. 109–124.

10.6. Vanden Berg, R. V., "A Study of the Characteristics of Anodized Aluminum," *Metal Products Manufacturing* (August 1957).

10.7. Vanden Berg, R. V., "Anodized Coatings for Aluminum," *Materials and Methods,* **44-1** (July 1956), pp. 90–94.

10.8. *Designing with Magnesium.* Pittsburgh: American Magnesium Corporation (Subsidiary of Aluminum Company of America), 1945.

10.9. Mote, M. W. and R. J. Jackson, "Magnesium and Its Alloys," *Materials in Design Engineering,* **46-1** (July 1957), pp. 117–134.

10.10. *Properties of Titanium and Titanium Alloys.* Niles, Ohio: Mallory-Sharon Titanium Corporation, 1953.

10.11. *Metals Handbook,* 1948 Ed. Cleveland: American Society for Metals.

10.12. *Metal Progress,* **66-1A** (July 15, 1954). (Supplement to *Metals Handbook,* 1948 Ed.) Cleveland: American Society for Metals.

10.13. Everhart, J. L., "Titanium," *Materials in Design Engineering,* **46-5** (October 1957), pp. 149–168.

10.14. Abkowitz, S., J. J. Burke, and R. H. Hiltz, Jr., *Titanium in Industry.* New York: D. Van Nostrand and Co., Inc., 1955.

10.15. Pagonis, G. A., *The Light Metals Handbook,* Text, Vol. I and Tables, Vol. II. New York: D. Van Nostrand Co., Inc., 1954.

CHAPTER 11

Copper and Zinc

11.1. Principal Uses

Approximately one half the copper and zinc consumed in this country is in the form of the unalloyed metals. Most of the remaining copper is alloyed with zinc to produce brass. Therefore copper and zinc, which are closely related, are both considered in the same chapter. It should be pointed out, however, that the second largest use of zinc is not in brass, but in the production of die castings. In these almost no copper is used.

COPPER

11.2. Service Properties

The most important service properties of pure copper are its *good electric and thermal conductivity and its corrosion resistance.* The electric conductivity of pure copper is exceeded only by that of pure silver, and the difference between the two is small. Copper is the most abundant and cheapest of the good electric conductors. Silver also slightly surpasses copper in heat conductivity, but again the cost differential favors copper for most applications.

Strength, ductility, and modulus of elasticity. Pure annealed copper has a yield strength of 8700 psi and a tensile strength of 32,000 psi.[1] These figures are considerably higher than those for aluminum. By alloying, cold working, and heat treating, yield strengths may approach 100,000 psi and tensile strengths may reach almost 150,000 psi. For beryllium-copper, the figures are even higher than those. Copper alloys, in general, have greater strength

[1] Data on pure copper and its alloys are from the *Metals Handbook*, American Society for Metals, Cleveland, 1948.

319

than aluminum and magnesium. The specific gravity of copper is 8.9, which is slightly more than that of steel. The strength/weight ratio of copper is less than for steel. Pure annealed copper *elongates* about 45 to 50 per cent, but this figure may be improved upon somewhat, by alloying. For instance, in annealed cartridge brass (70 per cent copper, 30 per cent zinc) the elongation is about 65 per cent. The modulus of elasticity of copper and its alloys is in the vicinity of 16.0×10^6 psi. The hardness and wear resistance of many cold-worked copper alloys exceeds that of annealed, medium-carbon steels (R_B 90). In beryllium-copper, the hardness may be as high as R_C 42, depending upon previous history of the piece.

The *fatigue strength* of the copper alloys, expressed as a percentage of the yield strength, varies widely, depending upon the degree of cold work in the pieces tested. This is not because of the effect of cold work on fatigue strength, but rather because of its effect in raising yield strength. Therefore, the fatigue strength of a cold-worked brass may be 30 per cent of the yield strength, while in the same material in the annealed condition, the percentage might be over 100. Fatigue strengths of about 30,000–40,000 psi occur in unpolished beryllium-copper, depending upon the degree of cold work and heat treatment. This and most of the other alloys have better fatigue strength than aluminum and magnesium.

High-temperature performance of the copper alloys is better than for aluminum and magnesium, though not as good as for steel. The copper alloys are not known for particularly good creep strength.

In most metals, ductility at first increases as the temperature is raised above room temperature, and then, as the melting point is approached, ductility decreases. Brasses are peculiar in that ductility decreases up to approximately 850°F (455°C). Beyond this temperature and up to 1300°F (704°C), their ductility increases. Past 1300°F (704°C) and up to the melting point, the ductility again falls off. The range 575°–1100°F (302°–593°C) is a region of hot shortness.

Corrosion resistance of copper and many of its alloys is good when they are exposed to the atmosphere and still, nonoxidizing waters. Resistance to attack by the atmosphere may be traced to the formation of a passive layer of basic copper sulfate. Copper also resists attack by salt water as well as or better than most commercial metals, the rate of attack being about 0.002 inch per year.   Copper is resistant to most acids, bases (except ammonia), and salt solutions providing they are not oxidizing in nature.   Copper resists attack by fresh water, providing it does not contain appreciable amounts of carbon dioxide and oxygen.   If the velocity of fresh or salt water is great enough, copper undergoes erosion-corrosion or impingement attack.   The *brasses*, i.e., copper-zinc alloys, are subject to dezincification when immersed in water, particularly if the water is high in carbon dioxide.   The brasses are not as resistant as copper to the action of acids, either oxidizing or nonoxidizing.   They are also more susceptible to stress corrosion (also called season cracking) and to erosion-corrosion.   Admiralty metal, which contains small amounts of arsenic and tin, is one brass which resists dezincification and erosion-corrosion, and therefore is used for naval condensers.   The *copper-nickel* alloys are superior to the brasses with respect to corrosion resistance, in that they resist stress corrosion better, and show less susceptibility than brass or copper to erosion-corrosion.   Forms of attack similar to dezincification are rarely encountered in the copper-nickel alloys.   The *true bronzes*, i.e., copper-tin alloys, are similar to the brasses, but have better stress corrosion resistance.   They are also better able to resist attack by moving water.   The *silicon bronzes* are superior to the brasses, being more comparable to copper.   They resist stress corrosion much better than brass, but are not as resistant to moving water.   The *aluminum bronzes* compare favorably with copper, but are more resistant to impingement attack.

11.3.   Fabrication of Copper and Its Alloys

Copper and its alloys are readily fabricated by all the methods of fabrication described in Chapters 13 to 18.   These include casting, powder metallurgy, electroforming and electroplating, hot and cold working, joining, and machining and finishing.   With respect to fabrication, copper and its alloys are more adaptable to a greater variety of methods than the light metals.

Casting.   The melting point of pure copper is 1981°F (1082°C), and this is depressed toward 1600°F (871°C) by the addition of most alloying elements.   One important exception to this is nickel, which forms an isomorphous system with copper and raises the temperature at which melting starts (e.g., 2250°F or 1232°C for

70 per cent copper–30 per cent nickel). This is shown in Fig. 4.1. Because of the higher melting temperature, the service life of permanent molds and die-casting molds is lower for copper and its alloys than for aluminum, magnesium, and zinc (which melt at temperatures of about 1200°F or 650°C or lower). The copper alloys shrink about $\frac{3}{16}$ inch per foot, or 1.56 per cent, which is greater than shrinkage for magnesium (1.43 per cent) but less than for steel (2.08 per cent). The fluidity of the copper alloys is very good. When casting copper alloys, the pouring temperature and melting conditions must be closely controlled. The pouring temperature affects the fluidity of the melt, and the soundness and surface finish of the castings. Temperature and time at temperature during melting and before pouring determine the amounts lost of some of the more volatile alloying elements, such as zinc. In die casting, steep thermal gradients exist at and near the die surface during use. These are such that within 0.050 inch of the surface, temperatures both above and below the transformation temperature of steel are experienced. This leads to severe stresses and shortens die life, making necessary the use of special high-alloy steels. Centrifugal casting has been quite successfully applied to copper alloys. Precision casting is also adaptable to copper alloys, and would be more widely used except for other competing methods of fabrication which are less costly. Its use is reserved for intricate shapes.

Powder metallurgy. Brass parts are readily fabricated by powder metallurgy. Although the quantities so produced represent only a small portion of the total brass consumption, they are nevertheless the second most important class of powder metallurgy products.[2] Brass parts made in this fashion include structural parts, such as gears and lock bodies. The powders are made by atomization of brass. *Bronze* parts are most successfully made by mixing copper and tin powders in the desired proportions, followed by the usual compacting and sintering procedures. Some leaded copper bearings are successfully made by powder metallurgy, because it provides a convenient means of uniformly distributing the lead. Bronze bearings are also made by powder metallurgy.

Electroforming and electroplating. Copper is widely electroplated, sometimes to provide a certain finish, and sometimes to provide an intermediate plated layer to which the final plated surface adheres better than to the basis metal. It is also readily elec-

---

[2] Iron parts are produced in greatest quantity.

troformed into shapes which cannot be made or are difficult to make by other methods. Brass is one of the few alloys which can be plated easily. A major application of brass plate is to provide a surface for finishing by polishing or buffing.

Mechanical working. Copper and most of its alloys are readily worked hot or cold. Among the most important of the hot-working operations are extrusion, forging, bending, and rolling of sheets, strips, and shapes. These may be carried out if the material is free from certain embrittling impurities (Pb, Bi) which tend to reduce ductility. Cold working is very common among copper and its alloys. It is used not only for the purpose of shaping the metal, but also to provide strength, at the expense of ductility. Cartridge brass (containing 70 per cent copper and 30 per cent zinc) is used for deep drawing because it has the best combination of ductility and strength of all the brasses. Cold rolling of flat products, rod, and wire, and drawing of wire and tubing are among the more important cold-working processes. However, almost all the cold-working operations are applicable to copper and its alloys.

Joining. Welding, brazing, and soldering are successfully used to join copper and its alloys. The welding of copper and the brasses containing more than 85 per cent copper is complicated by their high thermal conductivity. Not only does this require greater heat input, but, because of a high coefficient of thermal expansion, causes distortion problems. The high electric conductivity of copper and its alloys is an important factor in resistance welding. In copper and brasses which have more than 85 per cent copper, spot, seam, and projection welding are quite difficult. According to Chapter 17, $H \propto I^2Rt$, where $H =$ heat input, $I =$ current, $R =$ resistance, and $t =$ time, for spot welding. Since R is low, heat cannot be developed as readily as in most other metals. It is not practical to attempt to increase H by an increase in t, for longer times also allow greater opportunity for loss by thermal conductivity, which is high in copper. Furthermore, longer times cause greater distortion, lower production, and greater opportunity for the boiling away of zinc or other volatile alloying elements. In copper-base alloys other than these brasses, the electric conductivity is reduced sufficiently by the presence of the alloying elements, so that resistance welding is not so serious a problem. In arc and gas welding, hot shortness of some alloys (silicon bronzes), the formation of oxides which are entrapped in the weld and cause weakening of it (true bronzes, copper-tin), or the formation of oxides which reduce the flow characteristics of the weld metal (nickel-copper alloys) are possible sources of difficulty. The alloys containing lead are almost impossible to weld because they develop porosity when the lead boils out at the high temperatures of welding. Welding also has an adverse effect on the high strength of cold-worked copper and copper alloys in cases where recrystallization takes place. If grain growth also occurs, as is often the case, ductility is impaired along with strength. Carbon-arc, gas, and shielded metal-arc welding are used for joining copper and its alloys. The three processes do not show equal applicability to all copper-base metals, however. In contrast to welding, brazing and soldering are readily adapted to joining copper and its alloys. The joints formed are not as strong as welded joints, but where strength is not a prime requisite they are often satisfactory. Brazing and soldering produce gas- and liquid-tight joints.

Machining and finishing. The machinability ratings for copper and its alloys cover a wide range. The free-machining leaded brasses and bronzes are more machinable than any alloys excepting those of aluminum and magnesium. Copper and the bronzes are about as machinable as the SAE steels. The low-zinc (15 to 20 per cent zinc) brasses are in this same category, but as the zinc content increases, the machinability improves somewhat. Cold work improves the machinability of annealed brass. The nickel-bearing copper alloys, the aluminum-copper alloys, and beryllium-copper are among the poorest, from the standpoint of machinability.

Copper and its alloys are capable of receiving a variety of attractive finishes. The appearance of hardware made from certain compositions is a very important factor in its sales appeal, and for this reason, finishing operations are of importance. Copper and its alloys can be given a high luster when finished by ball burnishing, polishing, or buffing. They may also be finished by pickling to remove oxide scales, followed by another special acid dip to develop luster. This is known as bright dipping. A dull finish called a matte surface, can be obtained by immersion in still another solution after bright dipping. The finish given to copper and its alloys is often preserved by the use of clear lacquers which are applied in a variety of ways. By using appropriate chemical baths it is possible to vary the color of copper and copper-rich alloys (i.e., more than 85 per cent copper). Reddish, brown, black, and blue-black surfaces are possible.

11.4. Metallurgical Factors Affecting Properties and Uses

Copper has a face-centered cubic structure, and like most metals having this structure, has good ductility. Many of the copper alloys, hardened by substitutional solid solution, retain the face-centered cubic structure which is responsible for their good formability. There are somewhere between 50 and 100 copper-base compositions which might be termed common alloys. While some of these do not differ greatly from one another, there is considerable variation over the entire range, involving different elements and different percentages of the same element.

Grades of copper. There are several grades of pure copper having different degrees of purity, each intended for special purposes. The lowest grade is *arsenical copper* which contains up to 0.5 per cent arsenic. Since arsenic in copper diminishes electric conductivity, this grade of alloy is used where other properties are more important. It has good oxidation resistance at elevated temperatures, and has found some application along these lines. The *high-conductivity grades of copper* are by most standards extremely pure materials. As can be seen from Fig. 11.1, the presence of extremely

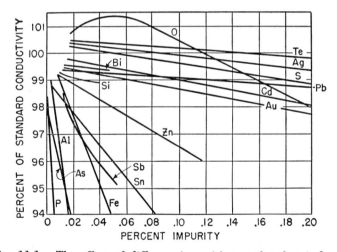

Fig. 11.1. The effect of different impurities on the electrical conductivity of copper. [Original data from Addicks, Lawrence, *Transactions American Institute of Mining and Metallurgical Engineers*, 1905, **36**, pp. 18–27. Figure as drawn subsequently appeared first in Hofman's *Metallurgy of Copper*, 1st edition, p. 7. McGraw-Hill Book Co., N. Y., 1914.]

small amounts of phosphorus, arsenic, iron, and aluminum cause very large changes in electric conductivity. Some years ago, standard copper was given a conductivity rating of 100. Since then, improvements have been made in refining so that today values above 100 are used. It will be noted from the figure that with increasing oxygen, the conductivity rises slightly to a maximum and then falls off. This is due to the oxidation of those impurities which cause a decrease in conductivity. Oxygen in excess of the amount necessary to remove impurities causes a decrease in conductivity. *Tough pitch copper* is an oxygen-bearing, high-conductivity copper which contains about 0.04 per cent oxygen, and is used for electrical purposes. The oxygen in tough pitch copper exists mainly at the grain boundaries in the form of finely divided cuprous oxide particles. These cause a slight impairment of most mechanical properties at room temperature. Because of their restraining effect on grain growth, they may cause a slight improvement in ductility. The effect of oxygen on mechanical properties is significant at elevated temperatures (above 750°F or 399°C) in the presence of hydrogen or reducing gases containing hydrogen. Hydrogen diffuses into tough pitch copper and reacts with the cuprous oxide to form water vapor at the grain boundaries:

$$H_2 + Cu_2O \longrightarrow Cu + H_2O$$

Since the water molecules are large, they cannot diffuse outward as fast as the small hydrogen molecules diffuse inward. Thus pressures are built up, which, when coupled with stresses caused by applied load, may cause rupture. Tough pitch copper may be deoxidized by the use of phosphorus. This grade of copper is known as *phosphorized* or *deoxidized copper*. It has considerably lower electric conductivity (about 75 per cent of standard copper) but is free from the embrittling tendencies of tough pitch copper. *Oxygen-free, high-conductivity* (OFHC) copper is the highest grade of commercial copper available. It is low in oxygen and therefore free from embrittlement, and low in other impurities which cause a decrease in electric conductivity.

Alloys of copper. Most of the hardening of copper by alloy additions is brought about by the mechanism of *solid-solution hardening*. The hardening possibilities based on the use of zinc, tin, aluminum, and silicon as alloy additions are limited by the eventual appearance of a second phase, which is more brittle than the copper-rich solutions. The phase diagrams (see Fig. 11.2) indicate the solubility limits for the above elements. In actual practice the second phase often appears *before* the limit of solubility is reached, as a result of coring and sluggish diffusion in the solid state.

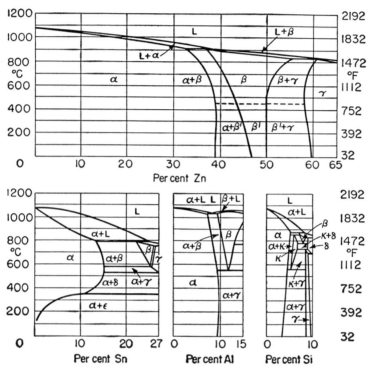

Fig. 11.2. Portions of phase diagrams for some copper alloys. The significant feature of these diagrams is the maximum solubility of alloying element in the α-solution. The appearance of phases other than α is marked by loss of ductility. Note the sharp decrease in solubility of tin with decreasing temperature. This accounts for precipitation-hardening possibilities of copper-tin alloys.

There are few possibilities for heat treating copper alloys. The most heat-treatable alloy is age-hardenable beryllium-copper. Tin also shows a marked decrease in solubility in copper when saturated alloys are cooled, and the bronzes have shown a tendency to precipitate some tin at room temperature following cold working. When quenched, the aluminum bronzes undergo a transformation similar to the austenite-martensite transformation in steel.

The next few paragraphs attempt to summarize (at the risk of oversimplification) the principal effects of the major alloy additions.   These are zinc, tin, aluminum, silicon, nickel, and to a lesser extent lead, phosphorus, and silver.   Other elements are often present in the alloys of copper, either added intentionally or as impurities.   Because of the large number of these alloys, only a few of the more important ones can be mentioned.

Zinc.   Increasing amounts of zinc alloyed with copper result in an increase in strength, and in the range between 10 and 30 per cent zinc, an increase in the ductility of the annealed metal is achieved.   For this reason, a very popular alloy for severe cold-working operations is *cartridge brass,* containing 30 per cent zinc, balance copper.   At 40 per cent zinc, the ductility of the alloys falls off rather sharply, although the strength is higher than in the 30 per cent zinc composition.   This is known as *Muntz metal.*   The effect of increasing the zinc content is to change the color gradually from the deep red of copper to a rich yellow and then to a straw yellow.   Beyond 50 per cent zinc, the color becomes silvery.   Color, as well as mechanical properties, ease of working, and corrosion resistance, enters into the selection of a copper-zinc alloy for a particular purpose.   These alloys are known as the brasses.   They are frequently modified by the addition of lead, which imparts machinability.   The cast brasses may contain tin, in addition to zinc, for the purpose of increasing hardness.   Die-casting alloys are essentially brasses, occasionally modified by the addition of silicon.   Small amounts of tin increase corrosion resistance, as in admiralty metal and naval brass.

Tin.   The effect of tin when alloyed with copper is to increase hardness and strength.   Within the common compositions of the wrought alloys, the ductility in the annealed condition is also improved when tin is added.   The use of more than about 10 per cent of tin causes a drop in ductility, even though strength continues to rise.   This is not much of a disadvantage in casting alloys, and therefore some of these have higher tin contents than the wrought alloys.   The tin alloys are sometimes called the true bronzes.   The true bronzes are somewhat more golden colored than the brasses. The use of tin as an alloying element has been limited by its high cost.   Equivalent less costly effects can sometimes be achieved by using other elements or combinations of them.   Copper-tin alloys have given some indications of forming age-hardenable systems in which precipitation will occur after cold work.   The solubility of tin in copper is probably very low at room temperature.

Aluminum. The behavior of alloys containing increasing amounts of aluminum is similar to that of the tin alloys. The ductility and strength first increase, then ductility decreases while strength increases as the aluminum content is raised. The alloys containing copper and aluminum as the principal components are known as the aluminum bronzes. Some cast aluminum bronzes contain appreciable amounts of iron and nickel which serve as hardeners. Aluminum-bronze castings containing more than 10 per cent aluminum are heat treatable in a manner similar to steel. A martensitic transformation takes place upon quenching these alloys from elevated temperatures.

Silicon produces effects similar to those of zinc, tin, and aluminum when alloyed with copper. However, the range of solubility of silicon in the solid state is much more limited, and embrittling occurs at lower concentrations. The silicon bronzes are quite readily welded, probably because some of the silicon is oxidized during welding, forming a protective silica flux over the molten metal.

Nickel is used in amounts up to 30 per cent in wrought alloys. The nickel-copper alloy system is isomorphous, and the hardness of copper is raised by increasing amounts of nickel up to 50 atomic per cent. Since the atomic weights of copper and nickel are approximately equal, 50 atomic per cent is about the same as 50 per cent by weight. Nickel imparts a white color to copper (five-cent pieces contain only 25 per cent nickel, balance copper).

Lead is usually added to brasses and bronzes to impart free-machining properties. It also acts as a lubricant when present in bearings. *Phosphorus* is useful as a deoxidizer in copper-base brazing alloys. In these, the phosphorus tends to reduce oxides which would otherwise reduce the fluidity of the molten metal. The phosphor bronzes are the most difficult copper-base alloys to hot work. *Beryllium* forms an age-hardenable alloy with copper, as previously discussed. Where strength must be improved with the smallest possible decrease in electric conductivity, *silver* may be used as a hardener. The conductivity of copper is only slightly affected by the presence of silver, as can be seen by reference to Fig. 11.1.

The particular alloys of copper involve so many possibilities that generalizations regarding applications of groups or classes of similar alloys are difficult to make. It should be remembered that the pure forms of copper possess excellent electric and thermal conductivity, combined with good strength and ductility, workability, and corrosion resistance. By alloying, the strength and hardness are almost always increased, frequently accompanied by an improvement in ductility and work hardenability (zinc, tin, aluminum, silicon). However, electric and thermal conductivity always suffer as a result of alloying. Alloy additions may improve the fluidity of molten metal (silicon), making casting and welding easier in this respect. All alloys excepting nickel-copper combinations have lower melting temperatures than pure copper, and if the alloy content is high enough, the composition may be suitable for die casting (silicon, zinc). Still other elements improve strength and corrosion resistance without seriously impairing ductility (nickel in copper-nickel alloys, tin in admiralty metal). Oxidation resistance (arsenic) and other properties at high temperatures may be improved by certain additions. Thus alone and in combination, the alloying elements are used to produce specific compositions which serve special needs, either in respect to good service characteristics or ease of fabrication.

ZINC

11.5. Service Properties

The most outstanding service characteristics of zinc are its *resistance to ordinary atmospheric corrosion* and its ability to *provide galvanic protection* when in contact with other less active metals, notably iron and steel.

The tensile strength of annealed commercial grades of rolled zinc is dependent upon the direction of rolling with respect to the direction of measurement of strength. It is also dependent upon the quantities of impurities present. An approximate average figure would probably be around 23,000 psi.[3] Elongation is also directional and dependent upon composition, varying between 30 and 60 per cent. The strength values are considerably improved by alloying, as indicated by the properties of "Zamak No. 2," a high-strength die-casting alloy. In this alloy, the tensile strength is 52,000 psi with an elongation of 8 per cent. The compressive strengths of these alloys are always appreciably higher than tensile

[3] Data on zinc and its alloys are from the *Metals Handbook*, American Society of Metals, Cleveland, 1948.

strength, and, for "Zamak No. 2," is 93,000 psi. The Brinell hardness number for this alloy is 100, indicating that wear resistance is not very good. The specific gravity of zinc is 7.14, but this is lowered, by the use of aluminum and magnesium in the die-casting alloys, to values near 6.6. Though their strength/weight ratios are not particularly high, mechanical properties for zinc die castings compare favorably with those of aluminum die castings, being perhaps slightly superior to those made of magnesium.

Dies for press-forming of sheet metal parts are made of "Zamak No. 2" or similar alloys. These alloys have good castability, which minimizes the need for subsequent machining operations. The alloys are also suitably strong for moderately severe forming operations on fairly large parts. They are not useful for forming of small parts having abrupt changes in contour.

The *fatigue strength* of the high strength "Zamak No. 2" is in the neighborhood of 8500 psi. The other alloys have even poorer endurance limits down to about 7000 psi.

Zinc alloys *are not suited for elevated temperature service.* They creep at room temperature, as might be suspected from their low melting range, which is from 730° to 930°F. Pure zinc melts at 787°F.

The *corrosion resistance* of commercially pure zinc has already been mentioned. The zinc-base die-casting alloys have about the same resistance to ordinary atmospheric corrosion as zinc or zinc-coated steel.

Die castings show *shrinkage tendencies,* which in some applications is an important consideration. This amounts to between 0.0007 inch and 0.0009 inch per inch, and occurs at room temperature over a period of years. About two-thirds of the total shrinkage occurs, at room temperature, in the first month after casting. This initial shrinkage can be made to take place faster by heating between 3 and 6 hours at 212°F (100°C). Copper is used as an alloying element in die castings to combat these dimension changes.

11.6. Fabricating Characteristics

Zinc lends itself to fabrication as a hot-dipped or electroplated coating on iron and steel. Frequently, it is cast, and finished by electroplating. It is hot and cold worked, and can be joined by welding.

Zinc coatings. The low melting point of zinc makes convenient the application of thin coatings to iron and steel by dipping in the molten metal. Good fluidity of the metal and its wetting characteristics are favorable to the process. Electroplating characteristics are good, and electrogalvanized coatings can be made thicker than dipped coatings where longer life is a requirement. Furthermore, since no heating is required in electroplating, no brittle alloy forms by diffusion at the interface between the zinc and steel. Hence, the zinc-plated materials can be bent without chipping, cracking, or peeling of the coating. Zinc coatings are also applied by directing a stream of fine atomized molten zinc at the surface of objects too large to be coated by other methods. In Sherardizing, objects are packed in powdered zinc and heated.

Casting. Zinc-base alloys are well suited to die casting because of their low melting points, excellent fluidity, and ability to reproduce dimensions accurately. Solidification shrinkage of the die-casting alloys is 1.7 per cent, but because of the chill effect in die castings, values of 0.3 to 0.6 per cent are more common. This means that solidification shrinkage in die castings is uniformly distributed as small internal voids rather than appearing as an overall decrease in size. Some slush casting and permanent mold casting is also carried out using zinc-base alloys.

Finishing. Very little machining is necessary on die castings. Occasional holes must be drilled and tapped, or surfaces planed. The necessary machining operations are carried out without difficulty. The most important finishing operation, as far as zinc alloys are concerned, is electroplating. This is used mainly to improve appearance on decorative die castings. Chromium, nickel, copper, brass, and silver are readily electroplated.

Mechanical working. Zinc is not difficult to work mechanically. It is hot and cold rolled into sheets which are further shaped by spinning, forming, drawing, bending, and similar operations. The annealing temperature for soft zinc alloys is at or near room temperature. The harder grades of zinc may have to be heated to about 212°F (100°C) to prevent excessive work hardening. If heated to too high a temperature, coarsening of the grain results. The finished product then lacks ductility.

Joining. Zinc and its alloys can be joined by gas welding, but this requires considerable skill and patience. Soldering is used to some extent, but produces a low-strength joint.

11.7. Metallurgical Considerations

Alloys for die casting contain *aluminum* (about 4 per cent) as a hardener. The highest strength alloys also contain copper (1 to 3 per cent), which serves as a hardener and retards the phase changes known to cause shrinkage of the castings. If copper is present, the volume changes either do not occur or occur so slowly that the plasticity and low creep strength of the alloy can accommodate them without cracking. *Magnesium* (0.03 to 0.04 per cent) improves resistance to intergranular corrosion, to which the die casting alloys are susceptible. *Cadmium* and *copper* are used as hardeners in rolled alloys.

Heat treatment of zinc alloys is limited to improvement of dimensional stability of the die-casting alloys. This has already been mentioned.

Questions

11.1.   What is the most important property of pure copper?

11.2.   Compare the mechanical properties of copper and its alloys with those of aluminum and steel. How is the ductility of copper affected by alloying? Do copper alloys have good or poor work-hardening characteristics?

11.3.   Why does the fatigue strength of copper alloys, expressed as a percentage of yield strength, vary so widely?

11.4.   Which corrosive media attack copper most severely? To what kinds of corrosive attack are copper alloys susceptible?

11.5.   How do the fabricating possibilities of copper and its alloys compare with those of aluminum and magnesium? Compare the problems connected with the casting of copper with those of casting aluminum. Why is cartridge brass so well adapted to cold work? What alloy is the second most widely used material for powder metallurgy structural parts? What difficulties are encountered in joining of copper and its alloys?

11.6.   Discuss the machinability and finishing of copper and its alloys.

11.7.   What are the uses of: (a) arsenical copper; (b) tough pitch copper; (c) oxygen-free high-conductivity copper?

11.8.   What limits the possibilities of solid solution hardening of copper by alloying with zinc, tin, aluminum, and silicon? How is the ductility of copper affected by small amounts of these alloying elements? Which of the above elements produces the most readily welded alloy of copper? Explain this behavior.

11.9. In what major respect does alloying of copper with nickel differ from alloying with the elements mentioned in Question 11.8?

11.10. For what purposes are the following elements alloyed with copper: (a) lead; (b) phosphorus; (c) beryllium?

11.11. What are the most outstanding service characteristics of zinc?

11.12. How does the strength of zinc-base die castings compare with that of aluminum and magnesium? Why are zinc alloys well suited to die casting?

11.13. Discuss the shrinkage tendencies of zinc-base die castings after they have cooled to room temperature.

11.14. What methods are used for zinc-coating steel? What are the advantages of electroplated coatings over hot-dipped coatings?

11.15. For what reasons are the following alloying elements used in zinc-base die castings: (a) aluminum; (b) copper; (c) magnesium?

Bibliography

11.1. *Metals Handbook,* 1948 Ed. Cleveland: American Society for Metals.

11.2. "Selection of Copper and Copper Alloys," *Metal Progress,* **66-1A** (July 15, 1954), Supplement to *Metals Handbook,* 1948 Ed. Cleveland: American Society for Metals.

11.3. Sachs, G. and K. R. Van Horn, *Practical Metallurgy.* Cleveland: American Society for Metals, 1944.

11.5. Samans, Carl H., *Engineering Metals and Their Alloys.* New York: The Macmillan Co., 1949.

11.6. Uhlig, H. K., *The Corrosion Handbook.* New York: John Wiley & Sons, 1948.

11.7. *Die Casting.* New York: American Zinc Institute, Inc. (Booklet, no date of publication).

CHAPTER 12

Miscellaneous Metals

This chapter is devoted to to a discussion of the properties and uses of the white metals, nickel, cobalt, tungsten, the precious metals, and some of the less common metals.

THE WHITE METALS

12.1. Scope

The term "white metals" is often used to cover alloys in which lead, tin, or antimony predominates. In addition to lead, tin, and antimony, there may also be present bismuth, cadmium, arsenic, silver, copper, zinc, indium, and sodium. There are many possible alloys in this group, each applicable to a special problem. The discussion in this text is confined to the characteristics of the most important of the pure metals, and to the three major classes of white metal alloys, namely: (1) fusible alloys, (2) type metals, and (3) bearing metals.

12.2. The Pure Metals and Miscellaneous Alloys

The principal ingredients of the white metals, namely lead, tin, antimony, and bismuth are characterized by low strength, and therefore their alloys are low-strength metals. The melting points of most of the white metals are also low, as can be seen from the following:

Element	Melting Point
Antimony (Sb)	1168°F (631°C)
Lead (Pb)	621°F (327°C)
Cadmium (Cd)	610°F (322°C)
Bismuth (Bi)	520°F (271°C)
Tin (Sn)	449°F (232°C)
Indium (In)	314°F (157°C)

Of the elements which are used in the white metal alloys, *lead, tin,* and *cadmium* are used in relatively pure form for a number of engineering applications.

Lead is a soft metal (tensile strength between 2000 and 3000 psi), having good corrosion resistance against a number of chemicals, notably sulfuric acid. For this reason, it has been used in plants where sulfuric acid and certain other chemicals are manufactured and handled. It recrystallizes at room temperature, and can be readily formed, cut, and welded (by a process known as "lead burning"). It is fabricated into liners for tanks, reaction chambers, and other chemical apparatus. Lead is readily extruded into pipes and around cable as a sheathing material having good corrosion resistance. Considerable quantities are used for waste and vent pipes and calking material. Lead is also used in large quantities for storage battery plates, hardened by the addition of 9 per cent antimony. Hardness and corrosion resistance are improved by alloying with antimony. Creep strength and hardness are improved by adding a small amount of calcium (0.028 per cent) to the lead used in cable sheathing. Both calcium and antimony produce age-hardening alloys with lead. In the 8 per cent antimony alloy, heat treating at 455°F (235°C), followed by quenching and aging for one day produces a lead-antimony alloy with tensile strength of 12,350 psi. This is almost 8000 psi higher than commercially rolled sheet of the same composition. Lead is used also to make collapsible tubes and protective foil wrappings. This use is probably associated with its ease of fabrication, softness, ductility, and corrosion-resistant properties. Because lead salts are poisonous, lead is not used in connection with the protection or packaging of foods or preparations taken internally.

Terne plate is a competitor of zinc-coated products, and is similar to tin plate. It usually contains, however, less than 25 per cent tin, balance lead. It is corrosion resistant to the atmosphere and petroleum products and is used for roofing and gas tanks, and similar applications.

Tin in the pure form is used in large quantities for producing a coating of tin on steel. Tin coatings are applied by hot dipping or electrotinning, the latter process allowing more efficient use of tin. Tin plate is used for containers, particularly tin cans for food products. In this application, the tin is corrosion resistant and the products of corrosion, if any, are harmless. The coating of tin on steel must be continuous, otherwise a galvanic cell is created in which the attack of the base metal is usually accelerated. Tin is also used for the production of foil wrappings and collapsible tubes, though aluminum, which is cheaper, has largely replaced tin for these purposes.

Cadmium is used in pure form as an electroplated coating for steel. It shows good resistance to atmospheric corrosion and is a competitor of zinc.

12.3. Fusible Alloys

The fusible alloys are useful chiefly because they melt or soften at low temperatures. They most often contain lead, tin, and cadmium for the higher melting ranges (350°–475°F or 176°–246°C), and bismuth, lead, and tin in the lower melting ranges. Very low-melting alloys contain indium and may melt as low as 117°F (47°C). Some of the fusible alloys are eutectic compositions which melt sharply at one temperature, while others freeze over a range of temperatures. Those containing appreciable amounts of bismuth expand upon cooling below the solidification temperature.

The fusible alloys have numerous *applications*, the most common of which is in the release mechanism of automatic sprinkler systems. They are also used as safety plugs in compressed-gas cylinders. Actuating devices for fire-warning systems and automatically closed fire doors often depend upon a fusible operating link. They are also used as a substitute for wax or plastics in precision casting, and for cores or matrices over which other metals may be plated, as described in Chapter 15. Forming dies for sheet aluminum and magnesium are sometimes made of fusible alloys. They are also used as filler material in order to prevent the collapse of thin-walled tubing when it is bent.

12.4. Type Metals

Lead is present in major amount with lesser quantities of antimony and tin in the alloys used for type metals. These alloys are characterized by low melting ranges or, in the case of a eutectic alloy, a low melting point. In addition they have very good fluidity when molten, and because of this are able to yield very sharp reproductions of the molds or dies into which they are cast. Increasing amounts of tin and antimony increase the wear resistance of type metal. By adjusting the composition of type-metal alloys, it is possible to produce a eutectic alloy (84 per cent lead, 4 per cent tin, 12 per cent antimony) which freezes at 462°F (239°C). This composition is useful for linotype machines. The type metals containing sufficient tin and antimony can be precipitation hardened at elevated temperatures. One hour at 185°F (85°C) approximately doubles the hardness of a solution heat-treated alloy.

The *microstructure* of the type metals consists of hard, white primary crystals imbedded in a lamellar eutectic. The hard, white crystals are either antimony-tin, or antimony containing lead and tin in solution. The lamellar eutectic which makes up the matrix is composed of lead, antimony, and tin. It is softer than the primary crystals.

12.5. Bearing Metals

The true babbitts are tin-base alloys containing antimony and copper, and occasionally lead. Because of the high cost of tin, some lead-base babbitts have been substituted for the true babbitts. The microstructures of all the babbitts are similar. They always contain hard particles of an antimony-tin phase imbedded in a softer matrix. The soft matrix is a tin-rich solid solution of antimony in the true babbitts, whereas in the lead-base babbitts it is the ternary eutectic (mentioned above in connection with type metals). Since the hard antimony-tin crystals solidify before the heavier matrix, they tend to float to the top of bearing castings and segregate. (This problem is not encountered in the casting of type metal because freezing is rapid.) In order to prevent gravity segregation, copper is used as an alloying element. The copper alloys with tin to form spiny, starlike, primary crystals which produce an interlocking network entrapping the antimony-tin crystals so that they are evenly distributed throughout the mass. Copper additions also serve to harden the alloys.

The reasons for the wide popularity of the white metals as bearing alloys are found in the combination of various properties which they exhibit. Primarily, they have the good antifriction properties characteristic of lead, antimony, and tin. In addition, their microstructure consists of hard particles (which resist wear) imbedded in a soft matrix (which can deform so as to accommodate varying load conditions). Furthermore, hard particles of foreign matter are forced into the matrix rather than into the shaft, thus minimizing scouring tendencies. When the bearing is used, microscopic depressions form in the matrix because the soft portions are worn away faster than the hard portions. These depressions, acting as reservoirs, assist in maintaining an oil film. The bearings are strong enough to resist moderate loads, and yet are not so weak as to flow plastically out of shape. If flow does occur, the shaft pounds in the bearing and fatigue failure may occur. Sometimes the tendency to flow is reduced by using a thin bearing liner on a thick, strong backing material. Bearings of this type have been developed by the automotive industry.

NICKEL

12.6. Essentially Pure Nickel

In some respects nickel is similar to iron. Tensile strength, yield strength, modulus of elasticity, and elongation are of the same order of magnitude in both metals. Nickel also has magnetic properties, though they are not as strong as in iron. Chemically nickel is similar to iron, though its corrosion resistance is much better, particularly with respect to the atmosphere and water. For this reason pure nickel is used as a protective coating on steel. The coating may be applied by hot rolling a layer of nickel onto a slab of steel, by a process that amounts to pressure welding. This method applies particularly to sheet or strip. Irregular shapes may be coated by electroplating. Electroplated nickel commonly serves as an intermediate layer between steel and chromium plate.

12.7. Effects of Alloying Elements on Nickel

Pure nickel is resistant to oxidation at room temperature and at elevated temperatures up to about 1500°F (817°C). However, if a reducing atmosphere of sulfur is present, attack proceeds rapidly. Nickel is also hot short if it contains appreciable amounts of sulfur, because a network forms having properties similar to the ferrous sulfide network of steel. By addition of *manganese* to nickel, the sulfur present is caused to form harmless manganous sulfide pools, similar to those found in some Bessemer steel. The addition of manganese (4.5 per cent) to nickel also provides resistance to attack by reducing atmospheres which contain sulfur.

The casting characteristics of nickel are improved by the use of *silicon* (1.5 per cent) as an alloying addition. It will be noted, by reference to published data, that many cast nickel alloys contain more silicon than the wrought alloys. Silicon is added to act as a deoxidizer and to improve the fluidity of the molten metal. It also results in solid-solution hardening and shows some promise as an age hardener.

Aluminum shows decreasing solubility in nickel with decreasing temperature. It forms an age-hardenable alloy system with nickel and is also a solid-solution hardener. It is alloyed (4.5 per cent) with nickel to provide an alloy of higher strength and age-hardening characteristics, while retaining the good corrosion resistance of nickel.

12.8. Important Nickel Base Alloys

High strength, corrosion resistant alloys. The *Monel alloys* are essentially copper-nickel alloys to which minor additions of other elements have been made. The nickel content is near 65 per cent, and the copper content is about 30 per cent. It will be recalled that copper has unlimited solid solubility in nickel, and its chief function is that of a solid-solution hardener. The strength of Monel is greater than that of the essentially pure nickel alloys mentioned in previous paragraphs. Toughness is also superior, and the tendency to work harden is very pronounced. However, machinability is poor. The casting grades of Monel (S, and cast Monel) contain higher silicon contents to improve fluidity and castability. S-Monel also contains sufficient silicon (4 per cent) to form an age-hardenable alloy. The wrought Monels are of two grades. K-Monel is high in aluminum (2.75 per cent) and is age hardenable. Free-machining Monel (R-Monel) is high in sulfur and manganese.

There are *other nickel base alloys* whose composition suits them to resist certain types of corrosive attack. Inconel (nickel-chromium-iron) is specially resistant to oxidation and corrosion, particularly at high temperatures. The Hastelloys are resistant to most acids. Stainless steel does not resist strong acids unless there is some tendency toward oxidation and formation of a passive, protective layer on the metal surface. This layer, however, is not necessary for corrosion resistance of the Hastelloys, which resist sulfuric and hydrochloric acids under reducing conditions. One alloy (Illium) is resistant to nitric acid (a very strong oxidizing agent which attacks many nickel-base alloys) and mixed acids.

Creep strength. Monel and the other nickel alloys have good creep strength. Monel is superior to stainless steels for elevated temperature use.

High electric resistance. Another series of alloys of nickel is used for high electric resistance. Some of these are nickel-chromium or nickel-chromium-iron alloys. They are used for resistance units and heating elements. Constantan is a well known nickel-copper alloy (45 per cent nickel) used for electric resistors; it has desirable thermal emf characteristics which suit it for use as a thermocouple alloy.

Desirable magnetic properties. Permalloys are important iron-nickel alloys containing either chromium or molybdenum. They have very high values for magnetic permeability and low values for magnetic saturation. They are therefore used in transformers and similar applications where their magnetic properties are useful. There are other nickel-base and nickel-bearing alloys possessing special magnetic characteristics which suit them to special applications.

12.9. Use of Nickel as an Alloying Element

Nickel is a very important alloy addition for steel. It is added to improve hardenability of SAE steels, and it is a ferrite strengthener in unhardened steels. The unhardened nickel-bearing steels have good toughness, and some are particularly suited to low-temperature work, where other steels lose their ductility and become brittle. Nickel is added to cast iron to promote graphitization and improve strength. For production of the austenitic stainless steels, large quantities of nickel are consumed annually.

Nickel powder is used as a bonding agent in some kinds of cemented carbide tools.

When nickel is added to copper, some of the alloys formed have good corrosion resistance, such as the cupronickels, which resist impingement attack in naval condensers. German silver is a copper-base alloy containing nickel and zinc in appreciable quantities. Nickel is also used in a few aluminum alloys.

COBALT

12.10. Properties and Uses

Cobalt, which is weakly magnetic, has about the same mechanical properties as iron. With respect to corrosion resistance, the behavior of cobalt is more nearly like that of nickel, and superior to iron. Cobalt is used in high-speed steels where it contributes to red hardness by solid-solution hardening of ferrite. It is used in magnet steels and ferrous alloys such as the Alnicos, some of which are alloys containing aluminum, nickel, cobalt, and iron. The Stellites are cobalt-base metals, containing smaller amounts of chromium and tungsten. They are particularly well known for good high temperature properties such as creep strength and oxidation resistance. Because of the difficulty of forging and machining (the cobalt-base alloys are very work hardenable), precision casting of parts is common practice. The first Stellites were cobalt-base alloys developed originally as tool materials, in which capacity they are still used as well as for high-temperature applications. Stellites are available in the form of welding rods and can be applied to softer metals in order to provide a hard, wear-resistant overlay. Cobalt is the principal cementing ingredient in cemented carbide tools produced by powder metallurgy techniques.

TUNGSTEN

12.11. Properties and Uses

Tungsten, which melts at about 6170°F, has a higher melting point than any other metal. Tungsten is also very stiff, having a modulus of elasticity of 50,000,000 psi. In fine wire (18 mils) the tensile strength of tungsten is 264,000 psi. In wire having a diameter of 3.96 mils, its tensile strength is 483,000 psi.[1] Because of its high melting point and high atomic number, tungsten is used as a target material in x-ray tubes. Filament wires for incandescent lamps are also made of tungsten. These must be protected from the air when the lamp is lighted, since heated tungsten forms a volatile oxide, which continually sublimates, exposing fresh metal to

[1] *Metals Handbook*, American Society for Metals, Cleveland, 1948.

oxidation. Tungsten is an important alloy addition to steels; its hard, persistent carbide is effective in resisting wear and softening at high temperatures. It is also used in the cobalt-base alloys to produce good high-temperature properties. Cemented carbide tools consist of hard carbides of tungsten (and often carbides of molybdenum, tantalum, and other metals) cemented together by cobalt or nickel. Since the carbides are almost completely insoluble in cobalt and nickel, the bonding material retains the melting point of whichever pure metal is used. The resistance to softening of these tools is dependent upon the resistance to softening of the almost pure cobalt or nickel bond at the temperatures involved. Wear and abrasion resistance are provided by the carbide particles.

An interesting point concerning tungsten is the fact that it was one of the first metals to which powder metallurgy was industrially applied as a means of fabrication. Because of its high melting point, casting and melting are impracticable. Tungsten is therefore produced by hydrogen reduction of its oxide to produce a powder which is compacted and sintered into bars. These are then mechanically worked by special techniques to produce wire.

THE PRECIOUS METALS

12.12. Scope

The most important of the precious metals are gold, silver, and platinum. The "precious metals" also include rhodium, palladium, ruthenium, osmium, and iridium. These metals are similar in their failure to form stable oxides under atmospheric conditions. All precious metals have good corrosion resistance, although silver tarnishes readily by formation of a black sulfide.

12.13. Silver

From an industrial standpoint silver is probably the most important of the precious metals. It exhibits the highest electric and thermal conductivity of any known metal. It is used for electric contactors in the form of pure silver or as a powder metal product alloyed with tungsten, molybdenum, or other materials which improve its life for heavy-duty service. Largely because of its appearance, ease of forming, corrosion resistance, and reasonably good wear resistance and strength, it is used for jewelry and silverware.

Silver is hardened by the addition of copper as an alloying agent. The copper acts as a solid-solution hardener and the resulting alloy is age-hardenable. Sterling silver contains about 7.5 per cent copper, while coin silver contains about 10 per cent copper. Silver is also used in bearings and as an electroplated coating.

12.14. Gold

From an engineering viewpoint, gold is not very important. It is free from oxides (its oxide has a negative heat of formation) and is very soft and ductile. It can be beaten out into the thin sheets known as gold leaf. Gold is used to some extent in jewelry, as a decorative material for glazed chinaware, for coins, and for dental fillings. It has exceptionally good corrosion resistance, and may be hardened by alloying with copper, silver, platinum, or many other metals.

12.15. Platinum

This is a soft, ductile material possessing excellent corrosion resistance to most attacking media. A most important use in industry is as a high-temperature thermocouple material against platinum-rhodium alloys. It may be used for temperature measurements up to 3000°F (1650°C). It is also used in chemical equipment, such as crucibles, containers, and electrodes, but because of its high cost, these applications occur mainly in laboratories. It is very susceptible to attack by phosphorus, arsenic, lead, antimony, bismuth, tin, and their oxides. It is also used in spongy form as a catalyst in many organic chemical reactions. When contaminated by foreign substances (such as those just listed) platinum loses its catalytic properties and is said to be "poisoned." To a somewhat lesser extent than gold, it is used for decorative purposes.

LESS COMMON METALS

12.16.

Columbium is used principally as an alloy addition to stainless steels. It appears promising as a cladding for uranium in reactors because of its compatability, strength, and low neutron absorption.

Germanium plays a significant role in electronic applications. It is used in rectifiers and in transistors, which replace vacuum tubes in many applications. Transistors offer the advantages of compactness, light weight, and durability as compared to vacuum tubes.

Hafnium occurs as a sometimes troublesome impurity in zirconium. Hafnium is used principally in rectifiers and for electronic applications.

Rhenium has good electron emission characteristics and better resistance to water-cycle attack than tungsten. (*Water-cycle attack* is the name given to formation of a volatile oxide on tube filaments by reaction with residual water vapor in the tube. The oxide condenses on the cold wall of the tube where it is reduced by the hydrogen formed in the original reaction. The regenerated water vapor reacts with additional metal and the process repeats itself.) An additional noteworthy characteristic of rhenium is the good electric conductivity of its oxide. This and good electron emission characteristics account for improved performance of electric contacts made from rhenium.

Tantalum has corrosion resistant properties similar to those of zirconium (see below), except that it is not resistant to alkalies. However, its inertness to chlorine, bromine, and iodine is superior to that of zirconium. Tantalum is most extensively used in the chemical process industries for corrosion resistance. It is also used in rectifiers and for vacuum tube components. Its hard carbide is found in cemented carbide tools.

Thorium is used in electronic tubes and as a source of nuclear fuel obtained from breeder reactors. It has poor corrosion resistance, being highly reactive and readily attacked by water and oxygen of the air. It is alloyed with other metals to improve their electron emission characteristics.

Zirconium is probably best known for excellent corrosion resistance. It is inert to attack by alkalies and most acids with the exception of hydrofluoric and hot concentrated sulphuric and phosphoric acids. Zirconium is therefore extremely useful as a material in chemical processing equipment. Zirconium alloys, which are low in hafnium, are used in water-cooled reactors for the production of atomic energy. Zirconium has a low neutron absorption when freed from hafnium. In the pure state it has low strength and highly variable corrosion resistance. Alloys of zirconium have been developed which are stronger and behave more consistently when exposed to water and high temperature steam than pure zirconium. In addition, these alloys are ductile and retain the low neutron absorption coefficient of pure zirconium.

Questions

12.1. What three metals are included in the usual meaning of the term *white metals?* What other metals may also be present in white metal alloys? What are the three major functional classes of white metal alloys?

12.2. What are some of the principal uses of lead? What properties of lead make possible these applications?

12.3. What is the most important application of tin? What properties have led to this use? For what purpose is cadmium used?

12.4. What uses are made of the fusible alloys? Over what approximate range of temperatures do they melt?

12.5. What properties are of importance in alloys used for type metals? What is the characteristic microstructure of the type metals?

12.6. What properties render the white metals useful as bearing materials?

12.7. What metal is most nearly like nickel as regards physical and mechanical properties? In what respect is nickel far superior to this metal which it otherwise resembles?

12.8. For what purposes are the following alloying elements added to nickel: (a) manganese; (b) silicon; (c) aluminum; (d) copper; (e) sulphur?

12.9. What four properties are outstanding in the major functional classes of nickel alloys?

12.10. In what applications is nickel used as an alloying element?

12.11. List some of the important uses of cobalt. What other common metals closely resemble cobalt?

12.12. List some of the outstanding properties and uses of: (a) tungsten; (b) silver; (c) gold; (d) platinum.

12.13. List the outstanding properties and applications of: (a) columbium; (b) germanium; (c) hafnium; (d) rhenium; (e) tantalum; (f) thorium; (g) zirconium.

12.14. With the aid of chemical equations, explain the *water cycle.*

Bibliography

12.1. *Lead in Modern Industry.* New York: Lead Industries Association, 1952.

12.2.   *Nickel* (binder of current publications).   New York: The International Nickel Company.

12.3.   Miller, G. L., "Cobalt and Cobalt Alloys," *Materials and Methods*, **44-4** (October 1956), p. 141.

12.4.   Li, K. C., and C. Y. Wang, *Tungsten.*   New York: Reinhold Publishing Corp., 1955.

12.5.   Vines, R. F., *The Platinum Metals and Their Alloys.*   New York: The International Nickel Company, 1941.

12.6.   Miller, G. L., "Columbium and Its Uses," *Materials and Methods*, **45-5** (May 1957), pp. 131–135.

12.7.   Sims, Chester T., "Rhenium Metal," *Materials and Methods*, **41-3** (March 1955), pp. 109–111.

12.8.   Gayle, T. M., "Where to Use Tantalum," *Materials and Methods*, **39-1** (January 1954), pp. 94–95.

12.9.   Everhart, John L., "Commercial Zirconium," *Materials and Methods*, **41-4** (April 1955), pp. 112–115.

12.10. Sims, Chester T., "Present and Future Uses of Scarce Metals," *Materials and Methods*, **43-1** (January 1956), pp. 80–84.

12.11. Sherwood, E. M., "Less Common Metals," *Ind. and Engin. Chem.*, **47-9** (September 1955), pp. 2044–2050, 2054–2064.

12.12. Shockley, William, "Transistor Physics," *American Scientist*, **42-1** (January 1954), pp. 41–72.

CHAPTER 13

Primary Methods of Fabrication: Casting

13.1. Introduction

Most common engineering metals and alloys, tungsten being one important exception, can be melted and cast into useful shapes. Some castings are used as they come from the mold, some undergo minor finishing operations, and still others require major shaping operations. This latter type of casting is more properly called an ingot. In any event, the casting represents a finished part or the first step in making a finished part. Hence, in this text, casting is considered a primary means of fabrication.

Several casting techniques at the disposal of engineers are discussed in this chapter. The particular technique adopted for manufacture of a part depends upon a number of considerations. The metal or alloy of which the part is to be made influences the selection of a process. Some metals are amenable to one type of process but not to another, depending upon their physical properties in the molten state, during solidification, and during cooling. Other considerations are the quantities to be made, tolerances, and the relative cost of subsequent shaping operations as contrasted with the cost of more elaborate casting techniques. This discussion of casting is aimed at pointing out the comparative advantages and limitations, methods of control, and general characteristics of the various casting methods. Preceding the details of specific casting processes are some general comments.

PHYSICAL BEHAVIOR OF METALS DURING SOLIDIFICATION

13.2. Shrinkage

Shrinkage is the result of the contraction of metals upon freezing. Bismuth and some of its alloys expand when they solidify, but the other common metals contract upon freezing, and continue to contract as they cool further in the solid state.

Shrinkage cavities tend to occur in the portions of the metal freezing last, and are the result of the progressive freezing of metals. The first solid to form undergoes shrinkage, but voids do not remain in it because molten metal flows in and compensates for the contraction. When the last metal freezes there is no reservoir from which feeding can occur, and a shrinkage cavity results. Cavities of this type are quite troublesome in ingots, where they take the form of long fingerlike holes called shrinkage pipes. One of these is illustrated in Fig. 13.8. Shrinkage pipes are a form of macroshrinkage. Shrinkage may also occur on a microscopic scale between the dendrite arms. Voids of this type are known as *microshrinkage* cavities, and these likewise are due to progressive freezing. As shown in Fig. 13.1, if a quantity of molten metal is entrapped between the dendrites so that feeding cannot occur, a microshrinkage cavity forms when this entrapped liquid solidifies.

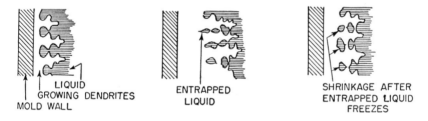

LIQUID
GROWING DENDRITES
MOLD WALL

ENTRAPPED
LIQUID

SHRINKAGE AFTER
ENTRAPPED LIQUID
FREEZES

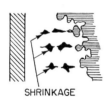

SHRINKAGE

Fig. 13.1. Formation of microshrinkage cavities. Dendrites form and grow in the melt, eventually trapping some liquid which later freezes and contracts. Since additional liquid cannot flow into the regions of entrapment to compensate for solidification shrinkage, a cavity is formed as freezing proceeds.

Shrinkage cracks are due to stresses produced by nonuniform thermal contraction which results in separation of the grains at the time of solidification. Nonuniform thermal contraction is caused by thick sections cooling more slowly than thin sections, by faces cooling more slowly than edges, or by edges cooling more slowly than corners. The stresses are concentrated in the piece by changes in section thickness, and shrinkage cracks occur at these points in castings unless precautionary measures are taken. Higher pouring temperatures which result in slower, more uniform cooling in the freezing range, and the use of liberal fillets, if design permits, reduce the tendency to form shrinkage cracks.   Mold materials with a lower heat conductivity (e.g., sand, as compared to metal molds) and cores which yield upon solidification of the casting also aid in the prevention of shrinkage cracks.

Cracks may also occur in an apparently sound and completely solidified casting at temperatures much lower than those at which shrinkage cracks occur.   Cracks of this type are due to residual stresses resulting from uneven cooling and are known as *cooling cracks*.   They may occur after the part has been placed in use and a service stress of sufficient magnitude has been superimposed on the piece.   There is no indication that residual stresses are present, and the part fails by cracking without warning when it is put into service.

There is also an *over-all shrinkage* of the casting as it solidifies and pulls away from the mold walls.   In steel castings the over-all shrinkage is about $\frac{1}{4}$-inch per foot, while in other structural metals shrinkage is less than this.   Adjustments for over-all shrinkage are made by use of oversize molds.

13.3. Gas Evolution

An evolution of gas accompanies cooling of molten metal.   Since the solubility of gases in metals is sharply reduced at the freezing temperature (Fig. 13.2), the most vigorous evolution of gas occurs as castings or ingots solidify.   When layers of liquid change to solid, gas is evolved at the interface between the two.   Unless the evolved gas escapes, as it often does during the early stages of freezing, it becomes entrapped, and shrinkage cavities are replaced by gas cavities.   Gas cavities tend to be rounded, while the shrinkage cavities exhibit sharp crevices and abrupt changes in shape, as shown in Fig. 13.3.   If the gas which is being evolved can oxidize the metal, the surfaces of the gas cavities become covered with an oxide film, and have a dull appearance.   Small gas cavities are called *pinholes*, and produce what is commonly known as *gas porosity*.   Large gas cavities are called *blowholes*.

Gases may be considered helpful in certain instances.   For example, in the production of rimmed steel ingots the evolution of gas compensates for shrinkage of the freezing metal and reduces the size of the pipe.   This results in a greater yield of sound metal from each ingot.

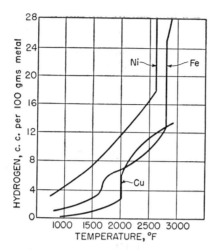

Fig. 13.2. The solubility of hydrogen in various metals at different temperatures. [After G. Sachs and K. R. Van Horn, *Practical Metallurgy*, p. 191. American Society for Metals, Cleveland, Ohio, 1947.]

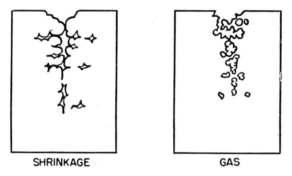

Fig. 13.3. Gas porosity and shrinkage cavities compared. Gas cavities tend to be rounded; shrinkage cavities tend to have sharp re-entrant angles.

Different gases are found in different metals under varying conditions of processing. Hydrogen is absorbed by several metals, this absorption being particularly objectionable in iron and steel. Although the weight of hydrogen is small, the volume of hydrogen (measured at atmospheric pressure and a processing temperature of 2000°C) may be four times the volume of the metal in which it is dissolved. Hydrogen usually is produced by the reaction between hot metal and water vapor, but it may also result from decomposition of hydrocarbons, such as oils and greases. Carbon monoxide, nitrogen, oxygen, and sulfur dioxide have been found in structural metals when the metals are exposed to sources of these gases during processing. The chemistry of the gases is quite complicated as a result of the reactions which they undergo at the high temperatures and pressures involved.

13.4. Segregation

This is the name applied to an uneven distribution of the alloying elements in the casting or ingot. Segregation can occur on a microscopic or macroscopic scale. *Microscopic* segregation is known as *coring;* it has already been discussed in connection with equilibrium diagrams. (See Chapter 4.) Coring consists essentially of concentration of the highest melting alloy compositions in the centers of the dendrites, while the lower melting compositions are concentrated near the boundaries between dendrites. One form of *macroscopic* segregation known as *normal segregation* is similar to coring. In normal segregation, there is a high concentration of the lower melting compositions in the central portion of the ingot or casting, which is the last portion to freeze. Thus in some steel ingots there is a higher carbon content in the center of the ingot than near the surface. Phosphorus in steel is similarly concentrated. *Inverse segregation* is often found in nonferrous metals. It is probably just as common a form of segregation as is normal segregation. It was investigated after normal segregation had become an accepted fact, and since the lower melting compositions were found to occur in the outer layers rather than in the center of the ingot, *inverse segregation* was adopted as a name. Alloys with a wide freezing range seem to be particularly susceptible to this type of segregation. Current theory suggests that the dendrites grow until they meet at the center of the melt, trapping the low-melting composition between them. As freezing progresses, the solid shell shrinks and pulls away from the mold walls. Then the low-melting liquid in the center of the casting leaks or is forced (by the pressure of evolved gases) through the solid shell, where it freezes next to the mold wall. At temperatures within the freezing range of alloys of this type, diffusion through the solid shell is rapid enough to make this possible.

Gravity segregation is produced by differences in the specific gravity of the solid and liquid phases, or between two immiscible liquid phases.   Copper and lead exist as two layers in the molten state, and unless agitated thoroughly during freezing, the copper-rich layer freezes first and remains on top of a copper-lead casting. In tin-antimony alloys, which are used for bearings, the first crystals to form are antimony-rich crystals, which float to the top of the castings.   It is desirable in bearing castings that these particles be evenly distributed throughout the mass.   This can be accomplished only if special precautions are taken, as described earlier.

13.5. Detection of Defects in Castings

Shrinkage, gas evolution, and segregation are undesirable in most instances.   Therefore methods have been devised to detect their presence.   *Shrinkage* can often be discovered by visual examination of the exterior of the ingot or casting.   Sometimes macroscopic or microscopic examinations of sections of the casting are needed to detect internal shrinkage cavities or perhaps shrinkage cracks. Shrinkage of some types can be found by x-ray examination, but thin cracks are elusive and may escape discovery unless several radiographs are made from different directions.   Internal defects of this type are detected by supersonic inspection.   *Gas porosity and blowholes* are quite easily detected by radiographs, or, if the piece can be sacrificed, by sectioning and macroscopic study.   *Seggregation* may be detected by metallographic methods, by chemical analysis of samples taken from different parts of the casting, and in some instances by the use of special x-ray techniques.   The latter depend upon the principle that different metals possess different powers of absorption of x-rays (see section 1.2), and hence different concentrations of alloying elements produce variations in the darkening of the film.

13.6. Physical Properties of Metals Affecting Casting

Two physical properties of metals deserve special attention with respect to casting processes.   These are melting point and fluidity.

The *melting points* of metals vary widely.   One low-melting alloy of lead-bismuth-indium melts at 117°F (47°C) while molybdenum melts at 4760°F (2625°C).   Obviously, mold materials which are suitable for the low-melting metals may not be satisfactory for the high-melting metals.   The freezing points and the freezing ranges of particular metals and alloys at atmospheric pressure can not be changed and the casting processes must be adapted to them.

Fluidity is the ability of a metal to flow freely and evenly into a mold so as to fill it completely and faithfully reproduce mold details. The fluidity of metals depends largely upon: (1) the surface tension of the metal, (2) the presence or absence of surface oxide films on the metal, and (3) the kinematic viscosity of the metal. *Surface tension* has been observed to vary with the melting points of metals, being greater, in general, for the metals with high melting points, and less for those with low melting points. The greater the surface tension, the lower the fluidity of a metal. *Oxide films* form skins around the molten metal which must be broken if the metal is to penetrate tiny crevices and depressions in the mold cavity. Oxide films cause loss of fluidity, as though the surface tension of the metal had been increased. Oxide films, while particularly troublesome in aluminum, are also found in brass (where a zinc oxide film forms), bronze, and other nonferrous alloys. *Kinematic viscosity* refers to the modifying effect which the specific gravity of the metal has on viscosity. If the viscosity of metals is compared with the viscosity of water, the metals are found to have a viscosity two to four times as great. However, when the viscosity is divided by the specific gravity to obtain the kinematic viscosity, the value for metals is lower than for water. This indicates good flow characteristics. At temperatures near the freezing point or within the freezing range where crystals may be suspended within the melt, the effective viscosity falls off rapidly and flow becomes sluggish. If adequate pouring temperatures are used so that the metal temperature remains well above the freezing range until the mold is filled, the kinematic viscosity of most metals is adequate. It is the effect of surface tension rather than viscosity which usually controls the ability of a metal to reproduce mold details.

13.7. Casting Processes

In this text some space will be devoted to each of the following casting processes: sand casting, permanent and semipermanent mold casting, die casting, precision casting (which is also called investment mold casting or lost wax casting), slush casting, centrifugal casting, and ingot casting. Each of these casting methods has certain advantages and limitations which suit it to particular metals or the accomplishment of specific tasks. If the same part should be made of the same alloy by different casting techniques, the parts so made would have different properties. It has been attempted, as far as is practical, to treat each process from the standpoint of its general nature, its particular advantages and limitations, and the properties of the finished product.

SAND CASTING

13.8. General Nature of Sand Casting

Sand casting acquires its name from the fact that the principal molding material is sand. A pattern is made of wood or metal in the shape of the finished casting. Size allowances are included to compensate for shrinkage. The pattern is then placed in a container known as a flask and sand is forced around it. The sand is rammed, squeezed, jolted, or thrown (known as sand-slinging) into place. The pattern is then withdrawn from the sand and a mold cavity remains. If void spaces are to be cast into the part, sand cores having the shape of the void are placed in the mold cavity. The essential features of a sand mold are shown in Fig. 13.4. The sand is usually held together by a moist clay bonding agent, although cereals such as corn flour are sometimes used. For better reproduction of mold details, a special grade of fine sand known as *facing sand* may be placed over the pattern before the balance of the flask is filled with backing sand. Very fine facing material such as graphite may be dusted over the surface of the mold cavity before the parts of the mold are assembled. Such a procedure improves the surface finish of the casting.

Molds which are used in the moist condition are known as green sand molds. These are the lowest cost molds and have a low crushing strength which permits the mold to yield after solidification; thus stresses, shrinkage cracks, and cooling cracks in the casting are minimized. If the mold is dried by baking, it becomes stronger and has greater resistance to erosion by molten metal. Green sand molds, having a higher moisture content than dry sand molds, tend to cause greater porosity in the casting. Drying, however, is slow and increases molding costs.

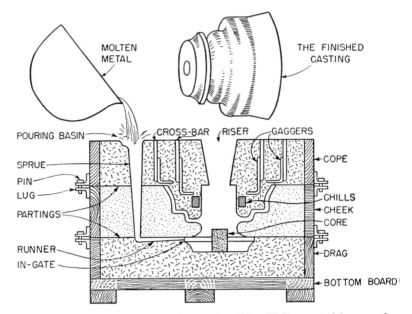

Fig. 13.4. Essential parts of a sand mold. Molten metal is poured into the basin and flows down the sprue (vertical passage), through the runner (horizontal passage), finally entering the mold cavity through the in-gate. The sand core produces a void in the finished casting. The chills are metal blocks inserted in the mold to produce rapid cooling and a chilled structure. The cross-bars and gaggers provide support for portions of the mold suspended from the cope. The riser acts as a gas vent and as a reservoir of molten metal to compensate for shrinkage. Pins and lugs align cope, cheek, and drag. [After W. H. Clapp and D. S. Clark, *Engineering Materials and Processes*, p. 229. International Textbook Company, Scranton, Pennsylvania, 1946.]

A modification of sand casting known as shell molding [1] was developed in Germany during World War II. The method has received much attention in the United States in recent years, and has improved the competitive position of sand casting as a means of mass production. In this process, a metal pattern is heated to about 350°F (176°C) and clamped over a box containing a mixture of fine sand and thermosetting resin. The box is inverted for 10 to 12 seconds and the resin, softened by the heat, forms a thin shell which adheres to the pattern. The box is returned to its original position

[1] Other names are C-process (named after Croning, the inventor) and plastic-bonded shell molding.

and excess sand and resin fall to the bottom.   The pattern and its
excess sand and resin fall to the bottom.   The pattern and its
shell are then baked for a few minutes at about 600°F (315°C), following which the shell is stripped from the pattern.

A finished mold consists of two matching shells, held firmly together and surrounded by metal shot (or some other backing material) which is kept in place by a flask.   The plastic-bonded shell
can be used only once.   However, surface finishes are produced
which are almost as good as those obtained by die casting.   Dimensional accuracy is good and machining requirements are reduced.
The use of metal shot as a backing material provides a dense, strong,
chilled structure in the finished casting.   The molds can be made
quickly and economically on a highly mechanized basis, if a sufficient number of parts are required to justify equipment costs.   The
process does not seem particularly suited to small quantity production.

13.9. Sand Casting Defects and Their Control

Risers are used, as noted in Fig. 13.4, to compensate for shrinkage of the metal during freezing.   The mold is designed so that the
riser is the last portion of the casting to solidify.   Therefore the
pipe forms in the riser rather than in an essential portion of the cast
shape.   The risers are knocked off or cut from the casting after
removal from the mold, and are then remelted.   This procedure
involves labor and melting costs, and efforts have been made in
recent years to reduce the size of risers by the use of exothermic
compounds.   Similar to thermit, these compounds give off heat and
keep the riser molten for a longer time so that it can feed more
efficiently.   Exothermic compounds permit use of smaller risers.
Sand castings may contain inclusions of molding sand resulting
from erosion of mold walls by the molten metal.   This can be
minimized by the use of mold washes such as shellac, by very careful control of the pouring rate, and by adjusting the size of the
ingate through which metal enters the mold cavity.   Stresses due
to uneven rates of cooling at sections of varying thickness can be
reduced by pouring at higher temperatures, the use of more liberal
fillets, by avoidance of abrupt changes of section, and by the use
of chill blocks.   Chill blocks are metal inserts placed in the mold

in order to remove heat more rapidly from a particular region, such as a thick section. Chill blocks may also be used to produce localized chilled structures such as fine-grained areas in an otherwise coarse-grained casting, or a region of hard white cast iron in a casting which consists essentially of gray cast iron. Cold shuts are defects commonly found in sand castings and occur when two molten surfaces meet and entrap an oxide film between them. A misrun is a casting defect which occurs when metal does not fill the mold. Often a misrun is due to too low a pouring temperature or a mislocated sprue and gate. Segregation occurs in sand castings and seems best controlled by varying the cooling rates and pouring temperatures.

13.10. Advantages and Limitations of Sand Casting

Sand casting requires a new mold for every casting. Since the mold represents much skill and effort, its cost is an important consideration. By the use of multiple patterns the production of a dozen or more small cast parts from one mold has become possible. This has effected economies, but the method is limited to fairly small valves, pipe fittings, and similar objects. Sand molds and cores permit undercut and complicated designs which could not be achieved with a permanent mold process because it would be impossible to remove the casting from the mold. Both ferrous and nonferrous metals are successfully cast in sand molds. Steel, brass, bronze, aluminum, and magnesium are frequently sand cast. The largest castings made are always sand castings, and pieces up to several tons are not uncommon. Sand casting, compared on the basis of a given investment in mechanical equipment and a given expenditure of man hours, is one of the slowest casting methods. It is particularly suited for small quantities of parts, as the cost per part is largely the cost of making the mold, the cost of the metal, and the melting cost. The cost of the pattern becomes negligible when spread over a few hundred parts, unless it is an intricate pattern. Sand casting probably produces the poorest surface finish of all the casting methods, even when high quality facing sand is used. Sand-cast parts may exhibit the coarse grain size of slowly cooled metal, because of the relatively low thermal conductivity of the sand.

PERMANENT AND SEMIPERMANENT MOLD CASTING

13.11. General Nature of Permanent and Semipermanent Mold Casting

Metal molds and metal cores are used for permanent mold castings. Metal molds with sand cores are used for semipermanent mold castings. The cores, which are usually dry sand cores, can be used only once, but the metal molds and cores are used over and over again for many castings. The molds are often hinged and are closed by means of a screw mechanism, or in some other fashion to provide a rapid means for removal of the casting. A mold coating or wash is used to prevent sticking; it consists of a refractory, a lubricant such as graphite or rouge, and a binder. For casting of the higher melting metals such as iron, a fairly heavy refractory coating is used to reduce erosion and checking of the mold. Multiple cavity molds are used to speed production, just as in the case of sand casting. Different mold materials are necessary for casting different metals and alloys. For the low-melting alloys, bronze, carbon steel, or cast iron molds are used; for the copper-base alloys and for magnesium and aluminum alloys, the molds are made of cast iron or alloy steel; for casting iron, steel molds are used with the refractory coating already mentioned. For casting all metals excepting iron, the mold wall is given a high finish, which improves the surface of the cast part.

13.12. Defects and Their Control in Permanent and Semipermanent Mold Casting

The selection of the proper alloy composition has an important bearing on the successful production of castings by this process. Since metal molds and sometimes metal cores are used, considerably more resistance to shrinkage of the casting is offered than by use of sand molds and cores. Thus it is essential to select alloys which undergo a minimum of shrinkage and have good hot-strength properties. This helps to avoid shrinkage and cooling cracks. The use of sand cores which crush and yield during solidification widens the field of alloys from which selections can be made. The same result is achieved by use of metal cores designed so that portions can be removed after solidification has started, allowing the remaining portion of the core to contract. Control of quality is also dependent upon the temperature of pouring. Pouring temperatures which are too high have the effect of preheating the mold, and the advantages offered by rapid freezing are lost. If the temperature is too low, the metal may freeze before the mold is completely filled. The temperature of the mold, like the temperature of pouring, is also of importance, and this is controlled largely by timing the sequence of operations.

13.13. Advantages and Limitations of Permanent and Semipermanent Mold Casting

With permanent mold casting there are *limitations* to the use of undercut cores because it is impossible, except in a few special instances, to remove such a core from the casting. The dry sand cores of semipermanent castings overcome this difficulty, but these may increase costs because such a core is used only once. The maximum and average sizes of the parts which are made by these methods are smaller than in the case of sand casting. This is partly because large numbers of very large parts are rarely needed, and production of a small number of parts will not cover the increased cost of manufacturing large molds. Technical difficulties have restricted castings of this type to less than about 20 pounds of aluminum in most cases, although a few aluminum castings weighing 500 pounds have been made. Aluminum and magnesium alloys are most widely cast in permanent and semipermanent molds. Some castings of bronze, lower-melting metals and alloys, and some cast iron parts are made in this way. The difficulty in casting high-melting metals (i.e., those melting above 2000°F or 1100°C) arises from the thermal shocks produced when hot metal hits the relatively cool die surface, and causes erosion and checking and shortening of the die life so as to make the process uneconomical.

There are numerous *advantages* to the permanent and semipermanent mold processes. They are economical, high speed methods, if the number of parts is sufficient to warrant the cost of die manufacture. At least 500 castings should be made from a single mold, and usually the number is much higher than this, depending upon the metal being cast, the finish required, and the shape of the part.

Because of rapid freezing there is little opportunity for shrinkage pipe formation. Therefore it is not necessary to provide the molds with risers of the volume required for sand castings. This results in an appreciable increase in yield and effects an important economy. The surface finish and reproduction of detail are far superior to those produced by sand casting. A big advantage is found in the superior mechanical properties of these products over sand-cast parts. The rapid, controlled freezing rate produces a uniform, fine-grained casting, with higher yield and tensile strengths, and often a slightly higher ductility than obtained by sand casting. Less gas porosity is found in permanent and semipermanent mold castings than in either sand or die castings. Any gas which is dissolved remains in supersaturated solution or comes out in a finely dispersed condition because of rapid freezing. In sand castings, large gas pockets are quite common, the mold itself acting as a source of gas. In die castings, although the dissolved gas is retained in solution by the chilling action of the mold, porosity is produced by air entrapped in the casting because it cannot escape from the mold. This entrapped air makes subsequent heat treating of die castings impractical, because the air expands on heating and causes the casting to blister or bulge. On the other hand, permanent and semipermanent mold castings *are* suited for heat-treating operations. For this reason, many precipitation-hardenable castings are made in permanent and semipermanent molds.

DIE CASTING

13.14. General Nature of Die Casting

If the molten metal is forced into a highly finished permanent mold under pressure, the casting is known as a die casting. Die-casting molds are made in two pieces, one piece (the cover die) being rigidly attached to the frame of the die-casting machine and the other (the ejector die) being movable to facilitate removal of the casting. The mold is designed so that the casting will adhere to the ejector die and be carried back with it until knocked clear by the ejector pins. (See Fig. 13.5.) The dies are made of plain carbon steel for tin and lead die casting, and from alloy steels for aluminum, zinc, magnesium, and copper alloy castings. Often the die is water cooled to prevent excessive heating, provide good chill

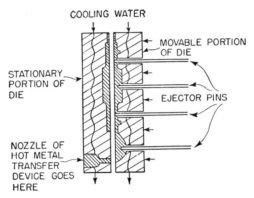

Fig. 13.5. Essential features of die-casting die. In the position shown the casting has been ejected and the movable portion of the die is closing to receive more hot metal.

effects, and permit more rapid operation. Escape of air from the die cavity as the metal is forced into it is accomplished by vents. These are channels about 0.005 to 0.010 inch deep and about one-half inch wide, ground into the parting surface of the die. There are various methods for providing a supply of hot metal and injecting it into the die cavity, as shown in Fig. 13.6.

13.15. Defects and Their Control in Die Casting

Probably most efforts to control the process are aimed at preventing excessive porosity in critical sections of the casting. When new

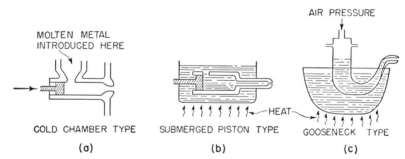

Fig. 13.6. Different kinds of die-casting machines. (a) Cold chamber die-casting machines are characterized by the fact that the source of hot metal is not an integral part of the machine. In the submerged-piston type (b), and in the gooseneck type (c), the heating device and molten metal reservoir are parts of the machine assembly. The gooseneck is filled by submerging it in the molten metal.

die designs are put into use, checks for porosity are made by x-ray methods and mechanical tests. If excessive porosity is present, changes in die design may correct the situation. The temperature of the die is controlled by water cooling. If the die temperature is allowed to get too high, the surface of the casting tends to be oxidized; if the die temperature is too low, porosity occurs and run marks appear in the surface. The temperature of the molten metal has an important bearing on the temperatures reached in the mold cavity for any particular rate of casting. Die-casting machines are designed to reduce the quantity of oxide entrapped in the metal being injected into the die. Evacuation of the die cavity prior to injection of the metal is a recent development. This improves the soundness of the die castings. It is also likely that evacuation will make possible the use of alloy compositions which have hitherto been considered unsuitable because of lack of fluidity.

13.16. Advantages and Limitations of Die Casting

Die casting has been particularly successful in the handling of zinc-base alloys. Aluminum, tin, lead, and magnesium alloys also are cast in large quantities by die casting. Development of die-casting methods for the copper alloys is proceeding, the limiting factor being the relatively short die life of presently available die alloys. Copper alloys have been die cast on an industrial scale since about 1930, but not as widely as the lower melting alloys. The thermal shock produced by hot metal striking the cold die surface is so severe that it has been found impractical to die cast steel or iron parts. In fact, die casting has achieved its greatest application in the casting of those alloys which melt below 1300°F (704°C). Die casting is restricted also to applications where large numbers of identical parts are to be made, so that die cost can be spread over a large production. In copper alloy casting, where die life is the shortest, a run of 10,000 to 50,000 cycles is customary. The dies require great design and manufacturing skill, and are made at considerable cost from high-quality materials. The average size of die castings is probably slightly less than permanent mold castings of similar alloys. This is partly due to the difficulty of constructing a frame rigid enough to hold the dies in place. Pressures used commonly run from 5000 to 10,000 psi, and on rare occasions as high as 20,000 psi. Therefore the forces acting to part the two halves of the mold become excessively great for castings having large surface areas. The problem of completely filling the mold becomes increasingly difficult, as the area of the casting increases. Die castings are not generally amenable to heat treating, because air entrapped in the casting blisters and bulges when the part is heated. Since a die casting usually has a thin, hard, leakproof skin (if properly made) and a soft porous core, it is not suited to heavy machine cuts unless leakproof qualities may be sacrificed. A heavy machine cut disproportionately reduces the strength of die-cast parts.

There are numerous *advantages* peculiar to the die-casting process, of which excellent surface finish (obviating the need for machining) and reproduction of extremely fine detail are quite important. Machining is reduced to a minimum, and hence fabricating economies are effected for certain parts. Sections as thin as 0.03 inch for tin and lead alloys, 0.05 inch for zinc alloys, and 0.08 inch for aluminum alloys can be die cast.[2] The process operates at high speed, up to 150 cycles per hour being possible with aluminum die-casting machines. For large numbers of parts, die casting is an economical means of production. Inserts such as studs or bushings, and cavities (providing the core can be made an integral portion of the mold) can be cast into the part. No risers are provided, and the size of the gates is extremely small, so that yields are obtained which are much higher than in the case of sand castings, and appreciably higher than for permanent mold castings.

PRECISION CASTING

13.17. General Nature of Precision Casting

Lost wax or investment mold casting are terms which are also used to describe what is commonly called precison casting. This is really a modern industrial application of a method used for thousands of years in the casting of bronze statuary, and for many years as a means of producing jewelry and dental castings. Variations suit the process to particular industrial needs. The modern industrial method relies on the use of a perishable pattern to make the mold in which the metal is to be cast. Thermoplastic and thermo-

---

[2] Sachs, G., and K. R. Van Horn, *Practical Metallurgy*, American Society for Metals, Cleveland, 1943, p. 276.

setting resins, low-melting alloys (even mercury), and waxes are used to make the patterns. The pattern itself can be considered to be a die casting or injection-molded part which reproduces every detail of the finished part. The thermoplastic materials seem to be superior from the standpoint of creep strength, resistance to damage by rough handling in the plant, and production of the cleanest molds at the lowest cost. The pattern is removed from the injection molding machine and a thin coating of claylike slip (perhaps a fine phosphate-bonded refractory flour, which corresponds to facing sand) is then applied by dipping. Coarse-grained silica sand is next sifted over the slip and some of the particles are retained to act as an anchor for the backing of the mold. The pattern is then placed in a container which is filled with backing material. Silica flour bonded by plaster of Paris or by ethyl silicate has been successfully used for this purpose. The backing material sets, and the contents of the container are fired at high temperatures. In firing, the plaster of Paris loses all its water of hydration, undergoing a recrystallization which produces a strong mold. The plastic pattern is volatilized and burned away (hence "lost wax," in the case of wax patterns) leaving behind a clean mold cavity of the same shape as the original mold in which the perishable pattern was made. Casting into this mold may be accomplished by centrifuging during which several molds are filled simultaneously as they spin around a central gate to which they are connected. Another variation of the casting technique involves clamping the mold on top of a tilting furnace of about 10 to 15 pounds capacity. The furnace is inverted and mild pressure by an inert gas is applied, forcing the metal into the mold. Application of pressure is not, however, essential to the method. The part is removed from the mold by smashing or chipping the mold away. Thus the process is unique in that for each casting both a new mold *and* a new pattern are needed. The sequence of operations is shown in Fig. 13.7.

13.18. Control of Precision Casting

A good portion of the control efforts for industrial precision casting methods are directed at the selection of the best and cheapest material for manufacture of the perishable pattern. For best reproduction of parts, this material should have good creep resistance at room temperature, along with fairly high strength, so as to with-

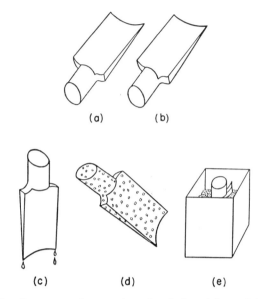

Fig. 13.7. Sequence of operations for industrial precision casting.
(a) The part to be made. (b) A plastic replica of the part is
made in an injection molding machine. (c) The replica is dipped
in fine slip and the excess is allowed to drain. (d) Slip-coated replica is sprinkled with coarse silica sand to act as anchor for backing
material. (e) Replica is placed in flask and backing is poured
around it. The backing material may consist of silica flour bonded
with plaster of Paris. The flask and its contents are fired, thus
burning out the plastic and hardening the molding material. The
void space left after the plastic has been burned away has the
same shape as the part being made. After the pouring operation
and solidification, the mold is broken away from the finished part.
There are many variations of the process.

stand handling before and during the processing of the mold.
Plastics are preferred over waxes for high-precision work, because
the waxes tend to bend slightly and warp, and the raw wax does
not always lend itself to storage. Thermoplastics have the disadvantage of being considerably more expensive than waxes. The
use of low-melting metals for perishable patterns involves the
difficulty of stripping them completely so as to leave a clean mold
surface. This can be accomplished, but involves handling costs
higher than those for waxes or plastics, the last traces of which
are removed by burning at the time the mold is fired. The material
used for the pattern should have thermal expansion characteristics
which are similar to those of the mold material, otherwise excessive

stresses may occur during firing. Graded particle sizes are essential for molding materials. Control of this is important for it has a significant effect on the drying rate, the amount of investment material required to fill the mold, and the strength of the mold. Occluded air in the mixed slip must be carefully removed in a vacuum tank or difficulties will be experienced during firing, and the finished mold will lack strength. The rejection rate for patterns runs in the neighborhood of 2 to 3 per cent, while for finished castings it is about 15 to 20 per cent. For certain critical castings the rejection rate may be as high as 50 per cent. Dimensional control is maintained closely, though it usually involves complications. There are four sources of dimensional change which must be considered. For example, in the casting of copper these are as follows: [3]

Shrinkage of the wax pattern	−1.0%	Total	−2.8%
Shrinkage of the metal casting	−1.8%		
Expansion of the mold during setting	0.3%	Total	1.3%
Expansion of the mold during heating	1.0%		
Net shrinkage			−1.5%

Thus the pattern die is made 1.5 per cent larger than the size desired in the finished casting.

13.19. Advantages and Limitations of Precision Casting

It is obvious from consideration of the control, handling operations, and skill which go into a precision casting that this is not a process used for everyday casting problems. The high cost largely results from the cost of the materials and labor which are involved in making the mold. The actual cost of the metal in the casting is often only a small part of the total cost of the finished casting, excepting of course, the precious metals used by the jewelry trade. Precision casting is not a method which competes with ordinary casting, or with forging and machining of parts which can be made readily by these means. Dimensional tolerances are sometimes

[3] *Metals Handbook*, American Society for Metals, Cleveland, 1948, p. 853.

achieved by trial and error after production has commenced. The size of the castings is usually fairly small, running between 1 and 5 pounds, although some copper castings as large as 100 pounds have been made.

The precision casting process does have some special *advantages* which make it practical from an industrial standpoint. It is specially adapted to achievement of close dimensional control in parts which are made of metals not suitable for forging or machining, or which melt at too high a temperature to be die cast. Among these are the high temperature cobalt-base alloys used for turbine blading. Some alloys have superior high-temperature properties in the form of castings and hence forging is avoided. Machining of the cobalt-base alloys is difficult because they work harden too readily. Precision casting is therefore well suited to the manufacture of these and other high-temperature parts. It is also useful in the production of castings which have intricate shapes, such as thin airfoil sections or parts having internal threads or cores. The surface finish of precision castings is much better than that of sand castings, but not quite as good as for die castings. Dimensional tolerances from 0.015 to 0.002 inch are considered good. Control of grain size is achieved by control of solidification rate, and since large grain sizes are desirable for creep resistance this is an important advantage. (It is not desirable to have a grain size so large that it extends across the entire thickness of a piece, because directional properties of the grains may show up to disadvantage.)

SLUSH CASTING

13.20. General Nature of Slush Casting

A special type of permanent mold casting, known as slush casting, is used to produce hollow, shell-like parts having an external shape which reproduces the shape of the mold cavity. For this method a low-melting alloy which freezes over a narrow range of temperatures is poured, at a temperature just above the freezing range, into a metal mold. After an interval of a few seconds, the mold is inverted and the still molten metal is allowed to drain out. This leaves behind the shell of metal which has solidified in the time between pouring and inversion of the mold.

13.21. Control of Slush Casting

For slush casting most of the control efforts are directed at regulation of the pouring temperature and the time between pouring and inversion. These variables largely determine the thickness of the wall of the casting. The wall thickness determines the strength of the casting and also affects appearance and economy in the use of metal. The composition of the alloys must be adjusted from time to time, because there is a tendency to concentrate the higher-melting component in the shell, while the drainings tend to become richer in the lower-melting component.

13.22. Advantages and Limitations of Slush Casting

The process is used mostly for the casting of decorative non-structural parts, probably because the alloys for which it has been developed are relatively weak materials such as zinc-base, lead-base, and tin-base alloys.   Furthermore, by using the other casting methods for these same metals it is possible to obtain stronger, more uniform parts than can be achieved by slush casting.   The process is suited to the economical casting of "tin" soldiers, toys, candlesticks, and similar objects, where strength is not of major importance. Slush castings are well adapted to finishing by plating or painting.

CENTRIFUGAL CASTING

13.23. General Nature of Centrifugal Casting

Another special form of permanent mold casting is known as centrifugal casting.   There are two kinds of casting which are given this name.   In the first type (which really should be called centrifuge casting) molds such as precision or permanent molds are mounted on a rotating frame with a central sprue and radiating gates.   When the molds and framework are spun, centrifugal action forces the metal into the molds and maintains a steady pressure until freezing is complete.   The resulting casting has lower porosity than if it had been gravity cast.   (The effect of centrifugal force is not considered especially important for some precision castings.) *What is usually meant* by centrifugal casting is the production of hollow parts having rotational symmetry such that the mold can be rotated about the axis of symmetry. Such objects as plain tubing, tubing with external fins for heat exchangers, bearings, gun tubes, gears, and similar shapes have been successfully cast by this process. The mold is usually mounted with its rotational axis in a horizontal position, although by tilting slightly a parabolic internal surface can be produced. Metal is thrown outward against the mold walls by rotation of the mold during solidification. Freezing commences at the mold surface and progresses toward the center of rotation. Depending upon the amount of metal poured, the finished casting may be thin or thick walled. An excess of metal is usually used, and impurities and porosity accumulate in the innermost and last portions to freeze. This material is then machined out, so that only sound metal remains in the finished casting.

13.24. Control of Centrifugal Casting

The chief variables involved in the control of centrifugal casting are those which prevent gravity segregation and which promote the formation of a sound casting. The speed of rotation is an important consideration; the higher the speed, the greater is the centrifugal force. As the centrifugal force increases, gravity separation of impurities and gas is favored and the soundness of the castings is improved. At the same time in some alloys gravity segregation of constituents is promoted, and this is undesirable in certain instances. Similar tendencies are enhanced by increasing the temperature and rate of pouring, and by preheating the mold. All these allow more time for the escape of gas and separation of oxide and other insoluble impurities before solidification is complete. Rapid cooling of the outside of the mold by means of a water spray is used to increase the speed of solidification and prevent segregation in tin-base babbitt castings.

13.25. Advantages and Limitations of Centrifugal Casting

Most centrifugal casting is limited to shapes in which the casting itself, or at least the internal surface, is symmetrical about an axis of rotation. It is therefore a special type of casting process suited to a rather restricted class of products. It has been applied successfully to the casting of steel, copper alloys, aluminum alloys, and tin-bearing alloys.

There are some noteworthy advantages such as the improved mechanical properties of the product, which result from the increased soundness of the metal. An example is found in the properties of brass, in which the tensile strength, yield strength, and ductility are higher in centrifugal than in gravity castings.[4]

Table 13.1

Mechanical Properties of Gear Rings [4]

Alloy	Methods of Casting	T.S. (psi)	Y.S. (psi)	% Elong. in 2 in.	% Reduc. Area
Navy G	Static (sand mold)	46,675	23,900	24.8	27.8
	Centrifugal	51,500	27,100	55.0	53.5
High lead	Static (sand mold)	35,680	19,460	24.4	22.7
	Centrifugal	51,250	24,800	42.0	41.0
Manganese bronze	Static (sand mold)	71,700	26,400	30.3	30.1
	Centrifugal	71,700	33,200	37.2	38.0

In addition to having superior mechanical properties, the centrifugally cast metal lacks directional properties such as are found in sand castings and in some wrought products. Another significant advantage of this process is the higher yield it produces. For steel castings, the yield may approach 100 per cent, and for copper alloys it is usually 90 per cent or higher. High yields result from the fact that no riser or gate is necessary, although the central portion of the casting performs the function of a riser. This portion is often somewhat porous since it provides the reservoir of metal which compensates for the shrinkage occurring in the first regions to solidify. The inner surface layers are often removed by machining, but they involve only a small fraction of the total weight of the casting. Still another advantage is found in the adaptability of the process to the casting of alloys which show hot shortness tendencies. Since there is usually no central core to interfere with shrinkage, a primary source of shrinkage cracks is eliminated.

INGOT CASTING

13.26. Introduction

An ingot is a casting which is to be further shaped by rolling or forging, and perhaps by machining operations. An ingot repre-

---

[4] *Metals Handbook*, American Society for Metals, Cleveland, 1948, p. 853.

sents the first step in producing a metal shape by one of the second-ary methods of fabrication. There are many different types of ingot molds and casting methods intended to accommodate the properties of the different metals. Variations in mold design affect quality and type of product. Most conventional ingot molds are made of copper or cast iron.

13.27. Vertical Molds

The cross sections of the vertical molds show wide variations. Vertical molds have square, rectangular, or round cross sections. The square and rectangular molds usually have rounded corners. The sides may be smooth or vertically corrugated. Corrugations in the mold produce more rapid cooling by increasing the ratio of surface to mass, thus reducing the tendency to form large columnar crystals. Rounding the corners of the molds reduces the tendency toward formation of planes of weakness where the ends of columnar crystals meet. Square vertical molds are designed as big-end-up or big-end-down molds as shown in Fig. 13.8. The big-end-down molds are easier to strip from the ingot and have a lower initial cost. However, they seem to promote pipe formation, and this

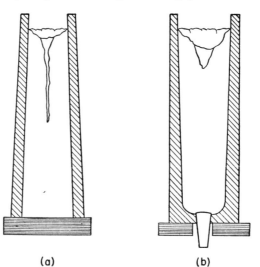

(a)   (b)

Fig. 13.8. **Big-end-up and big-end-down ingots.** (a) Big-end-down ingots yield less sound metal because of the long pipe which forms in them. They are easier to strip than big-end-up ingots. (b) Big-end-up ingots have smaller cropping losses, but require more complicated stripping methods. The plug in the bottom of the mold is intended for use in stripping.

results in lower yields. The big-end-up molds are more difficult to strip, and have a removable plug in the bottom of the mold to facilitate this operation. They also have a higher initial cost, but produce a higher yield, since pipe formation is greatly reduced. Steel ingots are usually cast in vertical molds of either the big-end-up or big-end-down variety.

13.28. Horizontal Molds

For the metals having low melting points such as zinc, lead, and copper, horizontal tray-type molds may be used. These produce slabs suitable for rolling operations. This type of ingot tends to have a fairly heavy oxide coating on its top surface, along with a concentration of other impurities. This requires removal of the top portion of the ingot, which is an expensive operation. Flat, tray-like molds produce ingots in which there is an absence of pipe formation and very little gas porosity, because freezing is progressive from the bottom of the mold. As the columnar crystals grow upward, gas is evolved at the liquid-solid interface and rises to the surface of the molten metal where it escapes into the air; thus blowholes and gas porosity are mostly eliminated. Shrinkage, instead of being concentrated in a single pipe, is distributed across most of the surface area.

13.29. Continuous Casting

There are also continuous casting methods. In these processes higher yields are a big advantage, and also, handling costs are reduced. The basic principle of continuous casting machines is illustrated in Fig. 13.9. Variations in the process provide for elimination of turbulence in the molten stream and protection against oxidation. In some installations the ingot itself is cooled by water sprays as it emerges from the mold. Frequently, the mold is caused to move downward for a short distance at the speed of the casting, followed by a rapid upward movement to the starting position. Large internal stresses, which can cause warping or rupture of the casting, and inverse segregation are metallurgical difficulties commonly encountered. When copper and steel are cast, erosion of the nozzle by reaction with molten metal is an additional problem. Aluminum, magnesium, copper, and steel are all continuously cast with varying degrees of success. Much aluminum

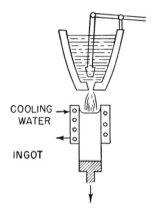

COOLING →
WATER

INGOT

Fig. 13.9.   Schematic sketch of a device for continuous casting of ingots.

is cast by the continuous method for subsequent forging, rolling, or extrusion.   Likewise, brass slabs are very successfully cast for rolling mill operations.

13.30.   Avoidance of Oxide Entrapment

Aluminum is typical of metals which oxidize readily to form dross, which becomes entrapped in the metal if there is sufficient turbulence during pouring.   For metals of this type, side pouring may be used, as illustrated in Fig. 13.10.   The molten metal flows under the tough oxide skin, which remains unbroken during the operation.   Another scheme involves siphoning the metal from the ladle.   The intake of the siphon is below the surface of the metal in the ladle and only clean metal can enter it.   The outlet of the siphon is kept below the surface of molten metal in the mold, the flow being so regulated that the oxide film is not disturbed.   Magnesium is a particularly active metal which is melted and cast under an atmosphere of sulfur dioxide, to prevent oxidation.   Some highly reactive metals are melted and cast under a high vacuum to obtain maximum freedom from gas absorption and contamination by oxide formation.

13.31.   Defects and Their Control in Ingots

The defects found in ingots are quite similar to those found in other castings.   *Shrinkage* manifests itself as a pipe, microshrinkage, or over-all shrinkage. Pipes are the most undesirable form of shrinkage in ingots, because their surfaces are usually oxidized, and the oxide film prevents them from welding together during forging or rolling. The portion of the ingot containing the pipe must be cropped off and remelted. Pipes may be reduced in size by using big-end-up ingots. When shrinkage is prevented by gas evolution, pipes may be replaced by *blowholes and gas porosity*.

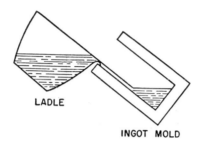

Fig. 13.10. Side-pouring an aluminum ingot. By carefully controlling the pouring rate, the tough oxide skin is not broken, and the hot metal remains free of oxide contamination.

This results in a higher ingot yield because the cropping losses are reduced. Blowholes and gas pores usually weld together when the ingot is subsequently mechanically worked. *Slag and oxide inclusions* are additional defects found in ingots. The prevention of dross entrapment in aluminum has been mentioned already. Avoidance of turbulence, skimming, or allowing the metal to settle before pouring tends to eliminate slag and oxides. Vacuum melting and casting apparatus has been used to prevent oxide formation, but not on a large industrial scale. The *avoidance of large grain sizes* improves the working qualities of the ingot. Smaller grain sizes are achieved by increasing the freezing rate. The latter is accomplished by use of water-cooled molds and copper base plates or stools (which have good thermal conductivity) under the molds, by keeping the pouring temperature as low as practical, or by a change in mold design, e.g., making plane sides corrugated. Finer grain sizes also may be achieved by the addition of nucleating agents as already mentioned. *Segregation* is found in ingots, and generally is considered undesirable from the standpoint of nonuniform mechanical properties which lead to later difficulties. Control of freezing rates seems to be the best way to reduce segregation. *Cold shuts* result from hot metal splashing on the mold wall above the level of molten metal during pouring. These droplets solidify and their surfaces rapidly oxidize. When the level of the metal finally rises above them and solidifies, the droplets are separated from the ingot by oxide layers. These and similar faults caused by the failure of two oxidized surfaces to weld together during forging and rolling may be the source of poor surface appearance or stress raisers, which initiate fatigue failure in service.

PROPERTIES AND HEAT TREATMENT
OF CASTINGS

13.32. Mechanical Properties of Castings

Cast shapes generally exhibit a lower fatigue strength than do corresponding wrought parts. This is an important fact to bear in mind. However, notches, surface scratches, or surface corrosion produce a greater reduction in the fatigue strength of wrought parts than in cast parts. The low fatigue strength of most cast parts apparently is not as greatly affected by the introduction of a few additional stress raisers on the surface. The source of the low fatigue strength of castings is found in entrapped oxides and slag, microshrinkage, porosity, shrinkage cracks, cold shuts, segregation, and stress raisers caused by residual stresses and design. *Yield strength, tensile strength, and ductility* are usually lower for castings than for comparable wrought parts. However, by more rapid freezing rates, by control and selection of casting techniques, by the introduction of nucleating agents, and in fact by almost any means which produces smaller, more equiaxed grains, it is possible to improve the mechanical properties of castings. This is shown by comparison of the properties of sand-cast, permanent mold-cast, and die-cast parts of the same composition. (See section 5.2.) The elongation of many castings is so low as to render them useless where shock loads are encountered. *Residual stresses*, which are found in castings as a result of uneven cooling in varying section thicknesses, may cause failure under static or dynamic loads.

13.33. Heat Treatment of Castings

The properties of castings may be improved by heat treating. Heat treatments are carried out for a variety of purposes. Annealing of castings sometimes is used to relieve residual stresses; such a treatment is known as a *stress-relieving anneal.* Residual stresses which are not removed may lead to fatigue failure or stress corrosion. Although most residual surface stresses in castings are compressive in nature and hence do not promote stress corrosion, there may be local areas of residual tensile stresses in the surface which do promote stress corrosion. *Spheroidizing anneals* may be used to change the shape of the microconstituents from sharp angular particles, plates, or laminations, to spheroids, as illustrated in Fig. 13.11. This usually produces a casting which is more machinable and ductile. Spheroidizing is applied also to wrought steel parts, and has been discussed in more detail under the heat treatment of steel. The casting may be subjected to a *homogenizing anneal* which is intended to eliminate coring and macrosegregation. Homogenizing anneals often result in an improvement in strength and ductility. *Solution heat treatment* is a form of homogenizing anneal, followed with a quench and subsequent reheating to cause controlled precipitation of the constituents.

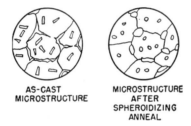

AS-CAST
MICROSTRUCTURE

MICROSTRUCTURE
AFTER
SPHEROIDIZING
ANNEAL

Fig. 13.11. Effects of a spheroidizing anneal.

Precautions regarding the heat treatment of castings. The heat treatment of castings may lead to the formation of blisters if appreciable gas porosity is present. Because of this tendency, die castings are rarely heat-treated. There is also a tendency for columnar grains to change into equiaxed grains and for some grain growth to occur. When grain growth occurs the effects of chilling are partly removed. Softening may also be promoted, which may more than offset the increase in strength resulting from homogenizing.

Questions

13.1.   What important physical changes, which affect the properties of castings, occur during the solidification and cooling of cast metal?

13.2.   Describe the ways in which shrinkage may manifest itself.

13.3.   In what forms are gas cavities found?   At what stage during the cooling of molten metal does the most vigorous evolution of gas occur?   Are gas cavities more or less harmful than voids which result from shrinkage?   Explain your answer.   Under what conditions might gas cavities be considered useful?

13.4.   Describe the kinds of segregation.

13.5.   What physical properties of metals influence the suitability of a casting process for a particular application?

13.6.   Name seven casting techniques.

13.7.   Describe how sand castings are made.   Discuss defects and their control in sand casting.   What are the advantages and limitations of sand casting?

13.8.   What is meant by *permanent and semipermanent mold casting?* Discuss defects and their control in these types of castings. What are the advantages and limitations of permanent and semi-permanent mold casting?

13.9.   How are die castings made?   Discuss defects and their control in die casting.   What are the advantages and limitations of die casting?

13.10.   Describe the precision casting process.   Discuss the control of the precision casting process.   What are the advantages and limitations of precision casting?

13.11.   Discuss: (a) the nature of; (b) the control of; (c) the advantages and limitations of slush casting.

13.12.   Discuss: (a) the nature of; (b) the control of; (c) the advantages and limitations of centrifugal casting.

13.13.   Discuss the variations found in ingot mold material and design. Describe continuous casting.   How is quality controlled in ingot casting?

13.14.   Compare the properties of cast parts with those of wrought parts. Explain as far as possible why these differences exist.

13.15.   What heat treatments are applicable to castings?   What precautions should be observed when castings are heat treated?

Bibliography

13.1.   *Cast Metals Handbook.*   Chicago: American Foundrymen's Association, 1944.

13.2.   Heine, R. W., and P. C. Rosenthal, *Principles of Metal Casting.* New York: McGraw-Hill Book Co., Inc., 1955.

13.3.   Ekey, D. C., and W. P. Winter, *Introduction to Foundry Technology.*   New York: McGraw-Hill Book Co., Inc., 1958.

13.4. Doehler, H. H., *Die Casting*. New York: McGraw-Hill Book Co., Inc., 1951.

13.5. Smart, J. S., "Continuous Casting," *Metal Progress,* **68-4** (October 1955), pp. 117–125.

13.6. Marek, C. T., *Fundamentals in the Production and Design of Castings*. New York: John Wiley & Sons, Inc., 1950.

13.7. Wood, R. L., and D. Von Ludwig, *Investment Castings for Engineers*. New York: Reinhold Publishing Corp., 1952.

CHAPTER **14**

Primary Methods of Fabrication: Powder Metallurgy

14.1. Introduction

This chapter deals with the production of metal powders and the means of forming these powders, sometimes combined with non-metallic materials, into useful shapes. Powdered metals are used also to produce protective metal coatings, as in Sherardizing, where a coating of fine zinc particles is bonded to another metal. They also find wide application in paint pigments, for example, aluminum and bronze powders.

Metal powders have been produced and used for various purposes for centuries, but probably the first application of the process as we know it today occurred in the early nineteenth century. At this time, spongy platinum was compressed in a mold at room temperature and then hammered into dense, strong billets. The billets were further worked into various shapes by mechanical means.

The manufacture of tungsten wire for use in electric light bulbs depends upon the manufacture of tungsten bars from compressed and sintered tungsten powder. These bars are then wrought into smaller diameters and finally drawn into wire, cemented carbide dies being used for this purpose. These dies, developed in the early twenties, heralded the expanding application of powder metallurgy.

PRINCIPLES OF POWDER METALLURGY

14.2. Fundamental Procedure

The manufacture of powder metal parts involves two fundamental steps:

(1) The metal particles are compressed into the desired shape.

The particles thus form a compacted mass strong enough to withstand ordinary handling.

(2) The compacted mass is heated, during which time its strength is increased. The step is called sintering;[1] it usually results in dimensional changes such that there is an increase in density. In other versions of the process, compression may be carried out hot or cold, and additional compression cycles may follow the sintering cycle. Both pressure and heat are, however, almost always required at some stage of production.

If two clean metal surfaces are forced together under sufficient pressure at room temperature a weld will form between them. During compression of powders, the fine metal particles are distorted and forced into intimate contact. Forces of attraction between the surface atoms of adjacent particles and diffusion across

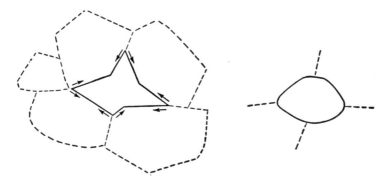

Fig. 14.1. **Effects of sintering.** A schematic sketch showing a void space (solid lines) between several particles (whose former boundaries are shown by dashed lines). The forces of surface tension are shown by arrows. When the yield strength of the metal is sufficiently lowered by the use of high temperatures, the surface tension causes flow and the angular voids become rounded.

the interface are believed to be the source of the strength of the "green" or compacted mass. Gases contained in the spaces between the particles are partly expelled and partly trapped during compression.

[1] Sintering in this text is defined as "the process of heating the article to a temperature below the melting point of the highest melting constituent for such a length of time and in such an atmosphere as will impart to that article the properties which will permit it to serve a useful purpose." R. P. Koehring, in *Powder Metallurgy*, ed. John Wulff. (Cleveland: American Society for Metals, 1942, p. 278.)

During sintering, the strength of the union between adjoining particles is increased. This may be attributed to the forces of surface tension and the effects of temperature on diffusion and softening of metals. As shown in Fig. 14.1, forces of surface tension exist where particles meet, such that the sharper the angle between any two particles, the greater the resultant force. These forces are able to cause flow only when the elastic strength of the metal is sufficiently lowered by the use of suitable high temperatures. Under these conditions the voids change from angular to spheroidal shapes, as shown in Fig. 14.2. As the voids become spherical, the ratio of free surface to mass, the forces of surface tension, and the internal energy of the mass all approach a minimum. There may be an initial decrease in density (probably caused by expansion of

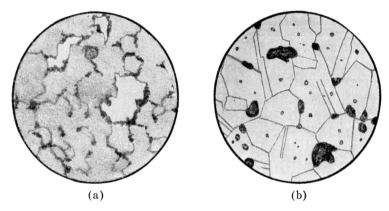

(a)   (b)

Fig. 14.2.   The effects of sintering on powder metal compacts.   (a) A 90 per cent copper, 10 per cent nickel compact is shown in the as-pressed condition. The copper grains are gray and the nickel grains are white. Void spaces show up as black areas. (b) The same compact as in (a), excepting that sintering has been carried out at a high temperature for a long period of time. The material has been homogenized, recrystallization has occurred, and the void spaces have become rounded. Etchant: $H_2O_2 + NH_4OH$. Magnification: 500×.

trapped gases) followed by an increase upon prolonged heating. In other cases, the opposite of this behavior may occur. A second pressing operation following the sintering cycle increases the strength and density of the part. Re-pressing is used when high strength, dimensional acuracy, and maximum density are required. Re-pressing is also called sizing or coining.

PRODUCTION OF POWDERS

14.3. Methods

The production of powders is accomplished by physical, chemical, or electrolytic means. These are explained in detail in the following paragraphs.

Physical methods for producing powders. (1) Metal powders have been made by various *machining, grinding,* or *filing operations.* Powders made in this way are fairly coarse and are rarely used in the production of powder metallurgy parts. They may, however, be the starting point for other means of producing powders. (2) *Milling* has been used to produce particles for metal compacts. The operation is usually carried out in ball, roll, or stamping mills. The product of such devices is flakelike. In general, flaky powders find wider use as paint pigments than as raw materials for compacted and sintered parts. In the Eddy mill, disintegration results from the interaction of the metal particles being milled, and is achieved by the use of impellers or fans in a tightly enclosed mill. Particles from the Eddy mill are more or less spherical and are more widely used for compacts than the flaky powders. (3) *Shotting* is used as an initial step in the production of powders. The metal, at a temperature slightly above its melting point, is poured in a fine stream into air or a neutral gas atmsophere and allowed to fall into water. If solidification is completed in the air, the particles are rounded. On the other hand, if solidification occurs in the water, the shot is feathered. (4) *Condensation of metal vapors* is used principally in the manufacture of fine zinc powders. These are by-products of the distillation process used for manufacturing zinc. The powder tends to be spherical in shape and is generally finer than 100 mesh. It is widely used for compacting. (5) *Atomizing* produces irregularly shaped particles with rounded surfaces, and in some respects is similar to shotting. The metal is forced through an orifice into a stream of high-velocity air, steam, or an inert gas. The metal is broken into fine particles which are so small that heat is rapidly extracted from them and they quickly solidify. If air or steam is used as the atomizing stream an unobjectionable thin oxide film forms which amounts to about 0.3 per cent by weight of the total mass. If an inert gas is used, the finely divided powders with their bright surfaces tend to ignite spontaneously upon exposure to the air, unless steps are taken to prevent overheating. Dust explosions present a hazard when air streams are used. The process is applicable to the manufacture of powders suitable for compacting if the metal being atomized has a melting point below that of copper. It offers the possibility of wide variations in particle size through variations in (1) the size of the orifice through which the metal is forced, (2) the temperature and rate of flow of the metal, (3) the temperature, velocity, and type of atomizing atmosphere. The variations of particle size which are possible by this method make it a very important physical method of producing powders for compacts.

Chemical methods for producing powders. (1) Precipitation of metal particles from a solution of one of its salts produces powders suitable for some applications. Another metal higher in the electromotive series is immersed in the solution of the metal to be precipitated:

$$AgNO_3 + Fe \longrightarrow Ag + FeNO_3$$

The precipitation technique is used successfully for silver, tin, platinum, and copper-coated iron particles. The latter are used in the production of copper-iron alloys in which a particularly uniform distribution of copper and iron is required. (2) Chemical disintegration has been used to produce stainless steel powders. If stainless steel is heated for a sufficient time in the neighborhood of $1160°F$ ($625°C$), it undergoes damage which renders it susceptible to intergranular corrosion. (See section 9.11.) When the damaged steel is immersed in a solution of copper sulfate and sulfuric acid, intergranular attack occurs. The steel disintegrates into individual grains which are useful for compacted parts. The particle shape and size are controlled by the grain size and shape prior to decomposition. (3) The carbonyl method is used to produce nickel and iron powders. The first step in this process is the formation of iron carbonyl:

$$Fe + 5CO \longrightarrow Fe(CO)_5 \qquad \text{(iron carbonyl)}$$

The reaction can be controlled by manipulation of temperature and pressure so that:

$$Fe(CO)_5 \longrightarrow Fe + 5CO$$

The iron formed from this decomposition is a finely divided, almost perfectly spheroidal powder. Nickel powders produced by the carbonyl reaction are very expensive, and not widely used. Iron powders, though expensive, are well suited to the manufacture of magnet cores. (4) Oxide reduction is probably the most important chemical method for the manufacture of metal powders whose melting points are equal to or above that of copper. In fact, oxide reduction occupies the same position of importance with respect to these metals that atomizing occupies with respect to metals which melt below copper. The metal oxide is first ground to a finely divided state, and is then reduced by mixing with a solid (e.g., carbon) or gaseous (e.g., hydrocarbon) reducing agent:

$$Fe_3O_4 + 2C \longrightarrow 2CO_2 + 3Fe$$

The particles formed by this method tend to have an irregular shape, and can be made in a wide variety of particle sizes. Irregularity of shape produces high green-strength, and low final porosity in parts. The cost of the process is relatively low.

Electrolytic method for preparing powders. Electrolysis of solutions of metal salts is used to produce powders having a dendritic shape. Instead of a hard, adherent layer, as is produced by electroplating, a brittle, soft layer, having large dendritic grains, is deposited. If necessary this layer is subsequently ground to produce fine particles. Electrolysis is applied to the manufacture of copper and iron powders.

The above summary of methods of producing powdered metals is not all-inclusive, although it does list the more widely used techniques. For use in making powder metal parts, atomizing (for the lower-melting metals) and oxide reduction (for the higher-melting metals) are probably the most important methods.

CONTROL OF THE POWDER METALLURGY PROCESS

14.4. Control Factors

In this section of the text, the factors which exert the most important influences on the nature of the finished product are briefly pointed out. Among these are (1) the physical character of the powders, (2) the chemical character of the powders, (3) the pressure and time cycle during compacting, (4) the temperature and time of sintering, (5) the effects of hot pressing, (6) the atmosphere during sintering or hot pressing, and (7) the use of lubricants.

14.5. The Physical Character of the Powders

The *size of the particles* is an important consideration in determining the final properties of the compacted part. Other variables being kept constant, the smaller the size of the particles which fill a container, the smaller is the ratio of voids to total volume. Since the presence of voids is harmful in some applications and helpful in others, control of particle size is closely checked and adjusted.

More important than merely having a uniform, fine particle size, is a good *variation in particle sizes*. This is an application of the principle of graded particle sizes, which may be stated as follows. *In masses made of compacted particles, the greatest strength and density can be achieved at lowest cost by using graded particle sizes.* This principle finds application in the design of concrete mixes, manufacture of clayware from finely ground clays, and in the mixing of paint pigments, as well as in powder metallurgy. It is an extremely valuable principle to bear in mind. The effect of particle size and size distribution is shown in Fig. 14.3.

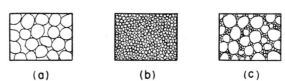

(a)   (b)   (c)

Fig. 14.3. Effect of particle size on voids. (a) Large particles of uniform size produce compacts with a high proportion of void spaces. (b) Very fine particles produce a compact with few voids. (c) A mixed particle size containing suitable proportions of different particle sizes will produce a compact which is fairly free of voids at the lowest cost. It is easier to attain high density by using graded particle sizes than by use of a very fine particle size, because of the difficulty of obtaining and handling particles which are sufficiently small.

The *shape of the particles* has an effect on the nature of the product. Flaky powders are generally considered to be undesirable for fabrication of parts. Spheroidal particles produce a rather uniform distribution of porosity and produce compacts of lower green-strength than irregularly shaped particles. There is considerable difference of opinion as to the effect on final porosity and strength of compacts produced by spheroidal particles as compared with those produced by irregularly shaped particles.

14.6. Chemical Characteristics of Powders

Of course, wide variations in the properties of powder metal parts result from the use of different powdered metals. Purity and nominal composition also have pronounced effects on final properties. Oxygen is one of the major offenders in work with powdered metals. If appreciable oxide forms on the surfaces of the powders, cold welding is seriously impaired. Likewise, if oxide formation continues during the sintering process, the strength and other properties may be appreciably diminished. In some powders sulfur is an impurity of importance. The purity of powders with respect to oxygen and sulfur content may be determined by loss in weight when hydrogen is passed through them.

14.7. The Pressure and Time Cycle During Compression

When the clean, smooth surfaces of two pieces of the same metal are brought into intimate contact, interatomic forces of attraction in the surface layers cause the pieces to weld together. The strength of this weld increases with increasing intimacy of contact, as the spacing between the atoms in the two surfaces approaches the atomic spacing of the crystal involved. Self-diffusion occurs across the interface and further strengthens the bond. This is sometimes called cold welding. In this fashion, metal powders compressed at room temperature change into compacted masses. Since intimacy of contact and diffusion determine the strength of cold welds, both pressure and time are factors to be considered.

Pressure serves to increase areas of contact by eliminating voids and expelling air or entrapped gases. The particles are deformed, and initial *points* of intimate contact are enlarged and become *areas* of contact. Thus interatomic cohesive forces increase in magnitude. The importance of pressure and its effect on deformation has been pointed out by experimental work. For instance, pressures of 5 tons per square inch are sufficient to produce good cohesion in compacts of soft metals like copper and tin. The same pressure is barely sufficient in the compression of hard, deformation-resistant tungsten particles.

High compacting pressures at room temperature may produce compacts with higher final porosity of the part after sintering, than low compacting pressures. This unexpected effect may be traced to the fact that high pressures produce such a tight interlocking of particles that gases cannot escape from the piece. Upon sintering, the gases expand, and sizable pores or even ruptures may result. This is sometimes called blistering. The speed of applying pressure has an effect on entrapment of gases, but it is not safe to make generalizations.[2,3]

Recrystallization occurs at the interfaces between particles, and is a source of strength in compacted parts. Recrystallization at any interface is dependent upon deformation of the surface layers of the particles. Therefore, the greater the pressure used in compacting, the greater the deformation, and the greater the extent of recrystallization during the sintering operations which follow.

The *time during compression* is of considerably less importance than the pressure used. It will be recalled that diffusion occurs at the interface between two adjoining particles. The longer the time of compression, the greater the opportunity for diffusion, while pressure maintains close contact between particles. It appears that equivalent results can be obtained by fairly long times at low pressures or somewhat shorter times at higher pressures.

14.8. The Temperature and Time of Sintering

The relationship between temperature and time during sintering is similar to the relationship between temperature and time for annealing. After the part has been compacted it is heated to improve its properties. The major effect of increased temperature is to increase the mobility of the atoms in the metal particles. At room temperature the forces of surface tension are ineffective in reducing the voids which are present in the compacted mass, because the yield strength of the metal is great enough to resist these forces. Only when the temperature is raised does the yield strength fall off sufficiently so that surface tension can cause inelastic flow. Time enters into the picture because increasing the time at a particular temperature tends to increase the total amount of flow.

In addition, diffusion and recrystallization occur at the interfaces

---

[2] Hardy, C., *Metal Progress*, **29**, April 1936, pp. 63–67.
[3] Balke, C., *Trans. AIMME*, 1938.

between particles.   Both of these processes depend upon the time
and temperature during the sintering operation.

It might be expected that heating would always cause contraction
of the green compact when the forces of surface tension become
operative.   In many metal compacts, however, the expansion of
entrapped air may cause an increase in the proportion of void
spaces and an increase in dimensions.   In other cases, a reduction
in density results when adsorbed or dissolved gases are evolved at
critical temperatures.   This is shown by Fig. 14.4, which sum-
marizes some work with cold-pressed copper compacts.   In other
powder metal parts, contraction proceeds unhindered because the

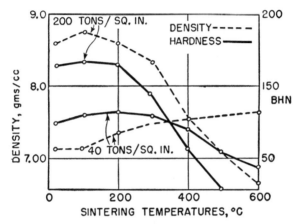

Fig. 14.4.   **Density and hardness of copper compacts after sintering
at various temperatures.**   Density may at first increase and then
decrease as a result of evolution of gases at high temperatures.
Ultimately hardness always falls off because of recrystallization and
softening of the particles which were cold worked during the initial
pressing.   [After W. D. Jones, *Powder Metallurgy*, p. 88.   Edward
Arnold and Company, London, 1945.]

metal particles tend to assimilate gases by adsorption or solution.
Usually prolonged heating or the use of excessive temperatures
results in an eventual increase in density.   This occurs after elimination of gases, and is shown in Fig. 14.5 for iron compacts.

Increasing temperature or time of heating causes an initial increase in tensile strength, followed by a decrease if heating is prolonged or the sintering temperature is raised sufficiently.   This is
probably due to excessive grain growth and softening following recrystallization of the cold-worked particles, and is illustrated by
Figs. 14.4 and 14.6.

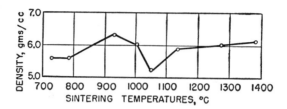

Fig. 14.5. Density of iron compacts after sintering at various temperatures. The density falls off at about 1050°C, at which temperatures evolution of gases causes expansion. At temperatures above that at which gases are evolved, the density increases again. [After W. D. Jones, *Powder Metallurgy*, p. 85.]

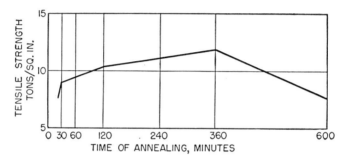

Fig. 14.6. Tensile strength of copper compacts after compressing at 24 tons per square inch and sintering at 715°C. Recrystallization and annealing are the cause of final softening. [After W. D. Jones, *Powder Metallurgy*, p. 86.]

14.9. The Effects of Hot Pressing

Cemented carbides are successfully produced on an industrial scale by hot pressing. Hot pressing of metals shows promise of producing superior compacts, but the process is an expensive one. Disadvantages of hot pressing as compared with cold pressing are (1) the time required for the heating and pressing cycle, (2) the increased cost of dies, because die life is shortened by high temperatures, (3) the necessity for providing atmosphere control in cases where the powder is suspectible to oxidation, (4) the cumbersome and expensive heating equipment which is often required. In some instances the length of the pressing cycle is reduced by preheating the powder before use. However, hot pressing does have certain advantages. Among these are (1) improved tensile strength and hardness, and in some cases, elongation, (2) higher densities, (3) better dimensional accuracy, and (4) avoidance of oxide difficulties in cases where a controlled atmosphere is used.

14.10. Atmosphere Control

If control of the atmosphere during compacting involves purging or flushing the die and powder, fairly complex equipment is required. On the other hand, if a reducing atmosphere is sufficient, this may sometimes be obtained simply by using lubricants or die dressings which decompose to produce the desired control.

Atmosphere control during sintering is achieved by one of two methods in most cases. Dry ammonia may be dissociated over a catalyst at elevated temperatures. This produces a gas containing 75 per cent nitrogen and 25 per cent hydrogen, which is used to blanket the work in the furnace. Also widely used are converters in which gaseous hydrocarbons are burned with controlled amounts of oxygen to produce the required atmosphere for the sintering furnace. See sections 8.3 and 8.4.

14.11. Lubricants

When metal powders are compressed in a die, the pressure is not transmitted equally in all directions as it would be if a *fluid* were being compressed. In cylindrical compacts made by forcing a punch downward into a die cavity, the pressure decreases toward the bottom of the compact as a result of friction. Thus the greatest density is achieved at the top of the mass, and the least density at the bottom. This gradient can be reduced somewhat by the use of lubricants. When cold-pressed objects which contain lubricants are heated, the lubricants volatilize, leaving voids. The voids can be reduced by a subsequent coining operation, but this involves added cost. The use of lubricants requires a decision as to whether greater uniformity of density will offset the disadvantages of porosity or the added cost of a coining operation. Among the lubricants which have been used are graphite powder, stearic acid dissolved in an organic solvent, lubricating oil, glycerin, and volatile organic solvents such as alcohol. Usually less than 1 per cent of lubricant is used, and more often only traces are present. Larger amounts of volatile substances are often added to metal powders in order to produce porosity. In this case, lubrication is an incidental effect. The organic lubricants also serve to reduce oxidation of surfaces during the sintering operation. Lubricants reduce wear on dies and allow the use of lower compacting and push-out pressures.

EQUIPMENT

The essential items of equipment required for the production of powdered metal parts are mixers, presses, dies, and furnaces.

14.12. Mixers

Mixers are used to blend powders for the production of alloy parts, or for mixing metal particles with lubricants and porosity-producing ingredients. Mixers used in bakeries are adequate, as are ball mills, tumbling mills, and similar devices.

14.13. Presses

Presses are either mechanically or hydraulically operated at speeds up to about 30 strokes per minute. Pressures required are most often in the range between 15 and 50 tons per square inch, but may go as low as 5 tons or as high as 100 tons per square inch. The volumetric ratio of uncompressed to compressed powder may be as high as 6 to 1, but more often it is nearer 3 to 1.

14.14. Dies

Dies are made of hardened tool steels or cemented carbides. Nitralloy, alloy cast iron, or sintered carbide liners are also used, the latter being particularly desirable because of the high finish which is possible. A high surface finish on the die and punch is essential for good finish on the completed part. In addition, a mirror finish minimizes the tendency for the compacts to stick and crack during the ejection cycle. Since the punches are not subjected to appreciable abrasive action of metal particles, punch hardness can be sacrificed for improved toughness, and oil-hardening steels are often used. The pressures involved in hot pressing are lower than for cold pressing. However, die life at elevated temperatures is much shorter than for cold pressing. High-speed tool and stainless steels are used for some hot-press work. Graphite is used for the high-temperature compression of cemented carbides at low pressures. A cross section of a simple die for production of compacts is shown in Fig. 14.7. In the example illustrated, even though pressure is applied only from the top, a fairly uniform density results because of the thinness of the compact being formed.

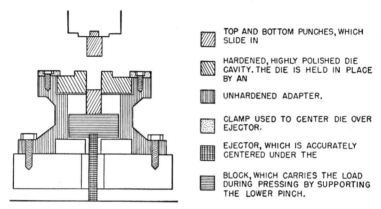

TOP AND BOTTOM PUNCHES, WHICH SLIDE IN

HARDENED, HIGHLY POLISHED DIE CAVITY. THE DIE IS HELD IN PLACE BY AN

UNHARDENED ADAPTER.

CLAMP USED TO CENTER DIE OVER EJECTOR.

EJECTOR, WHICH IS ACCURATELY CENTERED UNDER THE

BLOCK, WHICH CARRIES THE LOAD DURING PRESSING BY SUPPORTING THE LOWER PINCH.

Fig. 14.7. A simple die for production of compacts. After filling the die cavity with powder, the upper punch is moved down a pre-determined distance by a mechanical press or until a certain pressure has been attained by a hydraulic press. The pressure is then released, the upper punch is withdrawn, and the compact is pushed out of the die by means of the lower punch. In production work the powder is introduced into the die from a funnel. The mound of powder is then smoothed level with the top of the die before compressing. Sometimes previously weighed charges of powder are placed in the die. [Adapted from *Powder Metallurgy*, edited by John Wulff, p. 252. American Society for Metals.]

For thicker sections, pressure is applied from both top and bottom to overcome the poor flow characteristics of powders. The tolerances between punches and dies, the high surface finish, and the cost of die materials all contribute to the cost of the finished die assembly, which is an important item in the cost of pressed-metal parts.

14.15. Furnaces

Furnaces of both the batch and continuous types are used for powder metallurgy. The batch furnaces may be small muffle furnaces or furnaces heated by direct radiation. Some are equipped with fans to circulate the atmosphere and maintain uniform temperatures throughout the furnace. Continuous furnaces are often used for high-speed production of small parts. The work may be carried on wire mesh belts or mechanically driven hearth rollers through a preheating zone, sintering zone, and finally through a cooling zone. For these types of furnaces, the work is usually neatly arranged in trays to assure uniform exposure to the hot atmosphere. Still another type of furnace is the so-called pusher type of continuous furnace, in which the compacts on trays are pushed through the hot zone by a mechanical drive. The sintered parts drop one at a time from the exit end of the furnace in some installations so that they can be hot coined. See section 8.5.

APPLICATIONS OF POWDER METALLURGY

A large number of applications of powder metallurgy can be listed. Rather than attempt a complete listing, a few examples are mentioned for each of the fields in which powder metallurgy has gained importance. Among these fields are fabrication of (1) high-melting metals, (2) cemented carbides, (3) porous objects, (4) physical mixtures of two or more metals or metals and nonmetals, and (5) structural parts.

14.16. High-Melting Metals

Powder metallurgy as a modern method of fabricating metals really started about 1909 with the production of tungsten billets from tungsten powder. Tungsten melts at too high a temperature (6170°F or 3410°C) for fabrication by melting and casting. Tungsten powder is therefore compacted into briquets which are sintered, then swaged (see section 16.15) at high temperature, and finally drawn down into the fine wire which is used for electric light bulbs. Molybdenum (mp 4760°F or 2625°C) and tantalum (mp 5425°F or 3000°C) are also fabricated from their powders.

14.17. Cemented Carbides

Important products of powder metallurgy are the cemented carbide tools. They are sometimes considered physical mixtures, but they are so important in themselves that they are considered separately in this text. The basic ingredient in most cemented carbides is tungsten carbide, WC, which is an extremely hard material. Smaller amounts of tantalum carbide or titanium carbide may be present in this material. The carbide powders are mixed with cobalt powder or, in some cases, with nickel powder. The mixture is pressed, presintered, given any machining or grinding operations which are required, and then given a final sintering for maximum hardness. The final microstructure consists of hard carbide particles imbedded in a cement. The cement is essentially cobalt or nickel, since very little, if any, alloying occurs between the carbide particles and the lower-melting cement. Cemented carbides are used for cutting, burnishing, and spinning tools, where a cemented carbide tip is brazed onto a shank. In cutting operations, the cemented carbides can operate at higher speeds than the tool steels because of better high-temperature properties. In addition the tool tip requires less attention because wear occurs at a much lower rate than for tool steels. Cemented carbides are used for dies in wire drawing, extruding, powder metallurgy, and in other processes where hardness and strength are required. They are also used as abrasion-resistant materials in applications such as for pump valves and in the wearing surfaces of gages.

14.18. Porous Objects

It is possible to control the porosity of powder metallurgy parts by varying the amount and kind of volatile, nonmetallic material mixed with the powder before briquetting. Substances of this nature are usually selected to provide lubrication during compacting as well as porosity in the finished product. Interconnecting pores result when the volatile substances are driven from the cold-pressed masses by heating. Graphite and organic substances which are easily burned off are used to create the voids. Two rather important classes of porous materials are *bearings and filters*. Porous bearings, after sintering, may be evacuated and then impregnated with oil. In use, friction drags a thin film of oil out of the bearing. When the shaft stops, capillary attraction sucks most of the oil film back into the voids of the bearing. These bearings are often called "oilless" because the original supply of oil provides sufficient lubrication for the life of the machine. Porous metal filters are another example of useful porous products. Since they are made of metal they are stronger and have better resistance to thermal shock than ceramic filters. Porous metal filters are used in Diesel fuel injection systems to filter out tiny particles which might clog the small orifice through which the oil is injected into the cylinder. When made of corrosion-resistant metals and alloys, these filters compete with ceramic filters for use with corrosive liquids.

14.19. Physical Mixtures

The practical manufacture of parts consisting of physical mixtures of two or more metals, or of metals and nonmetals has been accomplished by powder metallurgy. One of the important applications of this is found in the manufacture of *electrical parts*. Brushes for use in electric motors and generators are made by compacting carbon and copper, which are then heated in a neutral or reducing atmosphere. The copper results in improved conductivity, while graphite acts as a lubricant and thereby reduces wear. Electric contacts are made of silver-tungsten mixtures. The silver provides good conductivity, and the tungsten resists damage from arcing during making and breaking of the circuit. The contacts retain the good conductivity of pure silver, because no solid-solution alloying is involved. Self-lubricating bearings made of graphite and bronze are another example of a physical mixture. In these bearings, the graphite serves as a lubricant while the bronze carries the load. Parts also can be made of metals which are immiscible in the liquid state. Lead-copper bearings, made with great difficulty by more conventional methods, can readily be made by powder metallurgy. The difficulty in casting these bearings arises from the fact that copper and lead are not miscible in the molten state. The lead, being heavier than copper, sinks to the bottom of the casting before freezing can occur. The successful performance of this type of bearing depends upon a good distribution of hard and soft particles. This type of structure is most easily obtained by powder metallurgy methods in which the liquid phase does not form and gravity segregation is thereby avoided. Friction parts are made of metal powders compacted with ceramic or other nonmetallic particles. The nonmetallic particles provide friction, while the metal particles provide high strength, toughness, and a degree of heat conductivity which was not possible in older types of friction materials. Thus metallic-base brake bands and clutches withstand much more abuse than do conventional materials. Metal-ceramic combinations are being investigated for use in jet engines and similar applications.

Superior high temperature aluminum "alloys" have been made by powder metallurgy techniques. Aluminum powder (99+% Al) is mixed with 8 to 16 per cent aluminum oxide; the mix is then compacted and sintered. The slug so obtained is then shaped by forging, impact extruding, or extruding in a conventional manner. Such materials have better strength and high temperature stability than conventional wrought alloys. Ductility is not as good, however. The fine oxide particles restrain grain growth and act in a fashion similar to precipitated particles in a precipitation-hardened alloy.

14.20. Structural Parts

Small structural parts are being more and more widely made by powder metallurgy. This process is useful where large volume, high-speed production is a requirement, or where reduction of scrap losses and partial or complete elimination of machining operations is possible. Powder metal structural parts are porous, and their tensile strengths and elongations are lower than for conventional parts. However, by re-pressing and resintering it is possible to produce parts whose properties very closely approach those of wrought or cast parts. Coining and reheating treatments produce densities approaching 95 per cent of normal. However, these additional operations raise costs, and are rarely used for making structural parts. It is easier to compensate for the lower strengths of powder parts by slightly increasing their size.

Voids in powder metallurgy parts lead to brittleness in objects made of notch sensitive materials. Stress concentrations at the voids are believed to account for this. Materials which are not normally notch sensitive do not exhibit notch sensitivity when fabricated by powder metallurgy. The tendency to be notch sensitive can be reduced by impregnating or infiltrating the part with plastics or with a metal or alloy which melts at a temperature lower than the melting temperature of the compact. Voids in structural parts are the source of lower fatigue strength than that of similar parts made by more conventional methods.

Figure 14.8 illustrates a few structural parts which have been successfully produced from powdered metals. Iron powders, iron and graphite, iron and copper, and bronze powders have found the widest application in the manufacture of structural parts.

Fig. 14.8. Typical structural parts made by powder metallurgy. [Courtesy of the Presmet Corporation, Worcester, Massachusetts.]

ADVANTAGES AND LIMITATIONS OF POWDER METALLURGY

14.21. Limitations

(1) Production of some kinds of undercut sections, such as threads or grooves is not practical because of ejection difficulty and non-uniform pressure distribution. (2) The size of the parts which can be produced is limited by several considerations. In parts having excessive thickness the density of the center sections is too low. In addition, thick parts require a very deep die because of the high compression ratios used. The area of the surface of the part at right angles to the direction of pressing is limited by the pressure required and the force which the press can

exert. Presses are available which can exert a force of 3000 tons. These are slow-acting presses, but are capable of producing bronze parts having a projected area of 200 sq in. and steel parts having a projected area of 100 sq in. (3) Parts having large variations in thickness in the direction of pressing cannot be readily made. It is possible to a certain extent to overcome the difficulties associated with this, but die requirements become increasingly complex. (4) Except in the production of parts which cannot be made by any other means, the manufacture of small numbers of parts is impractical. The cost of dies, experimental work, and setting up is such that for the simplest parts an order for 10,000 is generally accepted as the minimum. Orders in the hundreds of thousands or millions are preferable. (5) Porosity usually remains in structural parts, and this leads to lower strength and endurance limits, and a decrease in ductility. In the case of notch sensitive materials it also leads to brittleness. (6) Corrosion resistance may be impaired because of voids expose a large area to attack. (7) The cost of metal powders sometimes places the process at a disadvantage when compared to machining, forging, casting, and other conventional methods.

14.22. Advantages

(1) One of the outstanding advantages of the process is the fact that it makes possible fabrication of high-melting metals, whose fabrication is all but impossible by other methods. (2) The fabrication of metal parts having controlled, uniformly distributed porosity is possible. A similar achievement is not so easily attained by other methods. (3) Alloys can be made of immiscible or only slightly soluble metals, in which the alloying components are evenly and finely dispersed throughout one another. Such distribution is not possible by casting and subsequent forming operations. In this same class mixtures of metals and nonmetals might be considered. (4) The finished powder-metallurgy part can be made to a tolerance of 0.01 inch, and in some cases to 0.0005 inch. Thus the need for machining operations is often eliminated, thereby effecting savings in labor and scrap. This is particularly important as applied to structural parts. (5) Production is faster than by conventional methods in certain instances. This advantage is realized where die

design and manufacture, experimentation, and setup time can be spread over a sufficiently large production.

Questions

14.1. What two fundamental steps are involved in the production of powder metallurgy parts? Describe the changes which take place during compacting and sintering.

14.2. List the methods used for producing metal powders. Which methods are probably the most important means of producing metal powders?

14.3. List the factors which exert a significant influence on the properties of the finished powder metallurgy part.

14.4. Discuss the physical character of the powders.

14.5. Discuss the chemical character of the powders.

14.6. What are the effects of the application of pressure to metal powders? Why does high compacting pressure frequently result in greater porosity in the finished part than low pressure?

14.7. What changes are brought about by the application of heat during sintering? Explain how heating may cause either an increase or decrease in density of the finished part. What is the effect on strength of increasing the temperature or time of heating? Why?

14.8. What are the advantages and limitations of hot pressing?

14.9. Why is atmosphere control sometimes required? How is atmosphere control achieved during compressing and during sintering?

14.10. Explain why lubricants are used. What additional functions are sometimes performed by lubricants?

14.11. Describe the essential features of the equipment used in the production of powdered metal parts.

14.12. Discuss the application of powder metallurgy to the following fields: (a) high-melting metals; (b) cemented carbides; (c) porous objects; (d) physical mixtures; (e) structural parts.

14.13. What are the advantages and limitations of powder metallurgy?

Bibliography

14.1. Goetzel, Claus, *Treatise on Powder Metallurgy*, Vol. I. New York: Interscience Publishers, 1949.

14.2. Goetzel, Claus, *Treatise on Powder Metallurgy*, Vol. II. New York: Interscience Publishers, 1952.

14.3.   *Powder Metallurgy*, ed. John Wulff.   Cleveland: American So-
        ciety for Metals, 1942.
14.4.   Jones, W. D., *Principles of Powder Metallurgy*.   London: Edward
        Arnold and Co., 1937.
14.5.   Lyle, J. P., "Aluminum Powder Metallurgy Products," *Materials
        and Methods*, **43-4** (April 1956), pp. 106–111.

CHAPTER 15

Electroplating and Electroforming

15.1. Definitions

Electroplating and electroforming involve similar principles, equipment, and techniques, and are closely related to one another. However, they are not used for the same purposes. Electroforming may be thought of as a primary means of fabrication, i.e., as a basic means of creating shapes. Electroplating, on the other hand, involves finishing, and therefore may be thought of as a secondary means of fabrication, i.e., a means of altering an existing metal shape. In this chapter, the principles of electrodeposition are discussed, followed by a report of how these principles are applied to electroforming and electroplating.

PRINCIPLES OF ELECTRODEPOSITION

15.2. Basic Mechanism of Electrodeposition

In connection with corrosion (see sections 3.24–3.29), the basic mechanism of electrodeposition has been pointed out. In the galvanic cell described, copper dissolved from an anode, thereby forming copper ions. These, having positive charges, were attracted to the negatively charged cathode, where the charges they carried were neutralized and copper plated out. As mentioned under the topic of corrosion, the anode is always dissolved or tends to dissolve, and plating occurs at the cathode. The difference between corrosion and plating is basically one of sense or direction. Corrosion involves solution of a metal by formation of metallic ions:

$$Me \longrightarrow Me^+ + e$$

where Me represents a metallic atom, Me^+ represents a metallic ion, and e represents an electron. During plating, the reverse is true:

$$Me^+ + e \longrightarrow Me$$

In most baths for electrodeposition, solution (or corrosion) occurs at the anode, while deposition occurs at the cathode. The same is true of simple electrochemical cells, as can be seen by referring to Fig. 3.34.

15.3. Basic Electrical Considerations: Faraday's and Ohm's Laws

Since quantities of electric charge can be expressed in terms of numbers of electrons, it can be seen from the second equation above that the quantity of metal deposited is proportional to the electric charge consumed. That is to say, one electron is required for the plating of each monovalent atom; two electrons are required for each bivalent atom, and so on. This is actually Faraday's law, which in more formal terms states:

(1) The quantity of a substance liberated at an electrode is proportional to the quantity of electric charge which flows through any given electrolyte.

(2) The quantities of different substances which are liberated at an electrode by the same quantity of electricity passing through solutions of different electrolytes are proportional to the equivalent weights of the substances liberated.

Ohm's law is another basic precept used in electrodeposition. Mathematically this can be stated:

$$E = IR$$

where E stands for voltage, I represents current, and R signifies resistance. Low voltages are ordinarily used with solutions having good conductivity (i.e., a low value of R) so that large amounts of current flow. The greater the flow of current the greater the rate of deposition. The term "current density" usually means cathode current density, and is expressed as I/A, where I is current in amperes and A is cathode area. Anode current density is not usually intended by use of the term current density. The units of A are usually square feet, but square centimeter and square decimeter are also used.

15.4. Structure

The nature of the structure of deposited metal and the rate of deposition are important considerations. Microstructure has been correlated with physical and chemical properties of the deposit. Structure and rate of deposition are closely related to one another because they are influenced by the same variables. The effect on properties of (1) the structure and (2) the variables in electrodeposition are taken up next.

15.5. The Nature of the Deposited Layer

Some electrodeposited metal structures consist of columnar grains. The major axes of these grains run at right angles to the plated surface (or parallel to the direction of current flow). Such a structure is shown in Fig. 15.1. Crystal formation is by a process of nucleation and growth similar to that described in sections 2.3–

Fig. 15.1. Columnar structure of plated metal. This is not a particularly desirable structure for corrosion resistance or maximum strength. It can be avoided by proper control of plating variables. Etchant: $NH_4OH + H_2O_2$. Magnification: 50×. [Courtesy of the School of Engineering, Metals Laboratory, University of Massachusetts.]

2.6. Columnar growth tendencies, coupled with high current density at projections on the deposited layer, lead to increased roughening of the surface as plating proceeds. The more pronounced the projection, the greater the disparity in current distribution between the peaks and valleys of the surface. Thus, once roughening of the surface starts, it is perpetuated and amplified. See Fig. 15.2. Such growth characteristics may produce a porous structure which has cracks running from the exposed surface down to the basis metal.

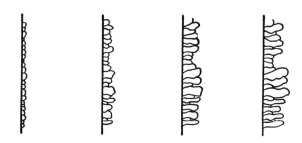

Fig. 15.2. **Progressive roughening of surface during plating.** Once roughening starts it is perpetuated and grows worse as a result of the high current density from projecting grains.

Columnar and other common types of structure have been studied using the electron microscope. The character of the deposit depends upon the crystal structure (i.e. face-centered cubic as opposed to hexagonal close-packed) and the presence and quantity of growth-impeding films in the cathode area. The structural characteristics of the deposit may vary with thickness up to about 0.16 mil, but beyond this thickness structural characteristics become fixed. Even though the character of the deposit does not vary, the *size* of the structural features may vary beyond a 0.16 mil thickness.

Electron micrographs reveal that the grains sometimes contain platelets or subgrains. The orientation and size of the platelets is important because of their effect on brightness of the deposit. It was formerly thought that uniformly fine grained surfaces were necessary for brightness. It has now been established that a structure of coarse grains can be bright if the grains contain platelets all of which are approximately in the same plane.

Throwing power, which is related to uniform current density, is an important property of plating solutions. Throwing power may be qualitatively described as the ability of a solution to plate down into crevices, where the current density normally tends to be relatively low. Steps to improve throwing power result in improvement in the uniformity of thickness of the deposited metal. More can usually be accomplished to improve macrothrowing power by changing the geometry of the anode-cathode relationship than by changing the bath. In general, uniformity of deposit thickness tends to be improved by increasing the anode-cathode distance. Various anode arrangements, shadowing, and robbing are used. See section 15.11.

Considering only the effect of grain size in the deposited metal, it usually is found that the larger the grain size, the greater the softness and ductility. In general, decreasing grain sizes means smoother, brighter surfaces, which are less porous and more corrosion resistant. An exception to this generalization was mentioned above. For electroformed or plated parts which are to be subjected to plastic forming operations, deposits having a coarse grain size are often desired, whereas for wear, impact resistance, and toughness, a fine grain size is frequently preferable. Exceptions to this may be found in the case of thin deposits.

15.6. Control of Quality

The means of controlling the quality of the electrodeposited layer are (1) regulation of current density, (2) use of agitation, (3) control of temperature of plating bath, (4) preparation of basis metal, (5) maintenance of clean plating baths and tanks, and (6) use of addition agents.

Current density has been found to have a marked effect on the grain size of deposited metal. In the plating of copper, increasing current density tends to decrease the grain size. If the current density is high enough, a spongy, treelike deposit results. The latter structure is sometimes called a *burned* deposit. Although burned structures appear to be coarse grained to the naked eye, micrographs show them to be very fine grained. Experiments with nickel and cobalt plating baths show that increasing current densities do not always result in finer grain sizes. Thus the only safe generalization that can be made is that current density and grain size are related, but not in any universal manner for all plating baths.

The use of agitation, with other variables constant, results in better deposits. By increasing the rate of agitation, it is possible to use current densities which otherwise would result in burned deposits. Thus agitation makes practical the use of high current densities with high rates of deposition.

Lower temperatures of plating have been observed to result in finer grain sizes in copper plating. Fairly small temperature changes are sufficient to cause marked changes in properties. Blum and Hogaboom [1] report that for copper plated at 77°F (25°C) an ultimate strength of 40,000 psi was obtained, whereas at 104°F (40°C), the ultimate strength dropped to 20,000 psi. However, the effects on grain size and strength are not the only changes resulting from variations in temperature. It is important to remember that higher temperatures always increase the conductivity of electrolytes and also the solubility of plating salts. The pH of the plating solutions also is affected by temperature changes.

The preparation of the surface on which deposition is to occur has a marked effect on the character of the deposit. If deposition is to take place on a metal base, the higher the polish of the basis metal, the smoother is the finish of the deposit. This is particularly important in plating. The cleanliness of the basis metal has a direct bearing on the adhesion of the deposit. For plating, cleanliness of the basis metal surface is imperative, whereas in electroforming, compounds are used which prevent good adhesion and promote ready stripping of the electroform from its core.

Maintenance of clean plating solutions and tanks results in a smoother surface, free from included particles of dirt. Plating and electroforming tanks are often considerably deeper than required by the shape of the part. This provides space beneath the suspended work in which dirt particles and sediment can collect. In agitated baths, care is usually exercised not to disturb the layer of sediment on the tank bottom. Where the agitation is such that this is not possible, the solution may be continuously filtered. In any event, tanks must be cleaned periodically and old plating solutions replaced.

The addition of chemicals to the bath has a pronounced effect on the nature of the deposit. Addition agents may serve any of several purposes, among which are the following. Colloidal substances are added to decrease the grain size for a given set of plating conditions. Some of the fine colloid particles adhere to the surface and nucleate the formation of new grains, thus decreasing the value of G/N. Wetting agents prevent pitting and improve smoothness and appearance. The wetting agents, by reducing the surface tension of the plating solutions, apparently maintain a cleaner surface with

[1] Blum, W., and G. B. Hogaboom, *Principles of Electroplating and Electroforming*, McGraw-Hill Book Co., Inc., New York, 1949, p. 69.

better contact at the metal-solution interface, and reduce the tendency for hydrogen or air bubbles to stick to the surface of the work. Addition agents which control the conductivity, metal ion concentration, and pH are also used. An improvement of conductivity results in power economies because the voltage required to produce a given current density is reduced. Furthermore, good conductivity also improves the smoothness of the deposits. By reducing the metal ion concentration, the fineness of crystal size is decreased, presumably because G/N is decreased. The pH is controlled closely because it is a factor in the brightness and fineness of grain in some solutions. When plating from acid solutions, too low a pH produces a spongy or cracked deposit.

ELECTROPLATING

15.7. Reasons for Electroplating

Electroplating usually involves the application of a fairly thin (often 0.00003 inch to 0.001 inch) coating of metal on metallic or nonmetallic objects. Probably the intention of plating most materials is to improve their finished appearance. For this reason electroplating is often classed as a finishing operation. The finish may be required to provide a special texture, such as bright or matte, or a particular color. The coating itself should be capable of resisting corrosion, and should retain a good appearance. Another important reason for plating is to protect the basis metal against corrosion. While this also affects appearance, the prevention of corrosion and corrosion fatigue are of primary importance. Plating is also used to improve the physical properties of parts, such as wear resistance, surface hardness, and fatigue strength. Finally, plating is used to build up undersize or worn parts, where the cost of the part justifies a simple repair operation. This is done on shafts, cams, and other moving parts requiring close dimensional tolerance.

15.8. Plating Operations

The first operation involves cleaning the surface to be plated. This is accomplished by the use of organic solvents and emulsifiers which remove oils and greases. Alkali solutions also may be used as solvents for oily substances. If oxides are present, they can be removed by acid dips or pickling. Frequently steel which is to be plated is made anodic, and a thin layer of metal is electrolytically removed. The steel is made anodic in order to obtain a scrubbing action by evolution of oxygen, thus avoiding the possibility of hydrogen embrittlement. These operations are often followed by acid and water rinses before plating actually starts.

Large objects are plated by hanging them in the plating tanks. Agitation is achieved by pumps or other mechanical means, or by bubbling air through the bath. Occasionally the racks supporting the objects in the bath are moved back and forth. For plating large numbers of objects of similar size and shape, completely automatic equipment may be used. Conveyors carry the work through the various cleaning solutions, plating baths, and finally through the proper rinses. The motion and speed of the conveyor control the time devoted to each operation. Installations of this type involve a large initial expense, but are economical for plating large quantities of similar parts.

Parts too small to be handled individually are usually barrel plated. In an installation of this type, the parts are placed in a nonconducting sievelike barrel, which can be rotated mechanically. Inside the barrel are a number of exposed metal ribs. Current is conducted through insulated conductors to the projecting ribs, and from these to the work with which they are in contact. Rotation of the barrel provides agitation as well as a burnishing action which improves the quality of the plate, particularly its porosity. A plated layer builds up on the ribs, and these are occasionally removed and used for anodes. Sometimes the deposit on the rib is stripped and the stripped metal is used as anode material.

After plating, the objects are either rinsed, or rinsed and buffed, depending upon whether a bright surface is desired. As pointed out earlier in this chapter, cracks and porosity may extend through a plated surface down to the basis metal. This is undesirable where good corrosion resistance is the object of the plating. The pores can be sealed by subjecting the plated surface to mild plastic deformation. This is often achieved by polishing or buffing operations which smooth over the projections, as shown in Fig. 15.3. In addition to sealing the pores, operations of this type brighten subsequent layers of plated material. The brightness and luster of the final plated layer directly reflects the care in preparation of the basis metal. Scratches and surface imperfections in the basis metal or initial layers of plated metal tend to show up in the finished article, although this tendency is minimized by the use of leveling solutions.

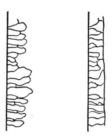

Fig. 15.3. Smoothing plated layers. A sketch showing the effects of smoothing a rough plated surface by rubbing, brushing, or gentle peening.

In most plating baths, chromium being one notable exception, the anodes are of the same material as the metal being plated. They dissolve at the same rate at which metal is deposited, and are often in the form of plates or bars. Sometimes the small scraps of anodes which are left over are hung in bags from which they slowly dissolve. Chromium plating is usually carried out on a highly polished base of nickel plate under which there is a layer of copper plate.

A unique type of electroplating is given the name *brush plating.* The anode for this process is an electrically conducting holder to which is attached a cotton pad or cotton-wrapped carbon roller supplied with electrolyte by dipping in a solution or by a drip feed. The work is made cathodic. Very high current densities are used and cooling of the brush or stylus holder is necessary. Abrasion between the stylus and work gives exceptionally good adherence and generally a deposit which is free from pores and cracks. The process is useful particularly for build-up and repair of worn parts, copper, nickel, and chromium commonly being used as plating material. It is also possible to plate onto aluminum directly without special surface preparation, by this method.

Electroless nickel is a special nickel coating which, as the name implies, does not depend upon electrolytic action. However, the coating produced does compete with electrolytic deposits, and so the process is discussed here. Deposition occurs as a result of sodium hypophosphite reduction of a nickel-bearing solution. It takes place spontaneously when the bath comes in contact with the object, either internally or on the outer surfaces. Nickel deposits on steel, copper, and aluminum are made from 0.0005 to

0.003 in. thick. The coating contains 5 to 7 per cent phosphorus, is free from hydrogen embrittlement, and is extremely wear and corrosion resistant. The as-plated hardness of R_c 45 can be raised to R_c 55 by heat treating. The coating does not build up on projections, as is the case of electrolytic deposits. This process is useful as a means of coating inaccessible internal surfaces.

15.9. Uses of Plated Coatings

The following table indicates, in a general way, the principal uses of a few of the common metals which have been found suitable for plating.

Table 15.1

Useful for Corrosion Resistance	Useful for Appearance	Useful for Build-Up and Improvement of Physical Properties
Zn, Cd, Sn, Cr, Brass, Ni, Cu	Cr, Ni, Ag, Au, Pt, Brass, Cu	Cr, Ni, Fe

In addition to brass, terne plate (75% Pb–25% Sn) is a commonly plated alloy. Other alloys are plated when special properties are required.

ELECTROFORMING

15.10. Reasons for Electroforming

Electroforming, in contrast to electroplating, involves deposition of fairly thick (0.01 to 0.625 inch) layers of metal over a mandrel or mold. The mandrel or mold is later removed, leaving behind a metal shape. Electroforming is particularly useful where greater dimensional precision is required than is obtainable by conventional methods. This is quite an advantage in the production of complicated internal shapes, which must be produced with a tolerance of ± 0.001 inch or less. As a matter of fact, tolerances within ± 0.0002 inch are a practical accomplishment in certain types of work. Electroforming makes possible the production of some parts at a much lower cost than more conventional methods. In fact, some of the items manufactured by electroforming could not possibly be made by other means. Furthermore, some metals particularly suited to a special task can be shaped for that task only by electroforming methods. Electroforming is not a method which is likely to eliminate conventional means of fabrication on a wide scale. It is not used to produce parts having projections or bosses which are higher than they are wide. It is, however, a useful process which is suited to production problems falling in the above-mentioned categories.

15.11. Electroforming Operations

The thickness of electroformed parts is considerably greater than the thickness of electroplated layers. *The techniques of electroforming are therefore aimed at greater rates of deposition.* Copper is often plated at about 0.003 inch per hour, but in electroforming, the rate may be as high as 0.1 inch per hour. These high rates of deposition are attained by use of high current densities coupled with vigorous agitation of the solution or the object being formed. Current densities as high as 2000 amperes per square foot have been used when agitation is achieved with high-speed jets. Current densities of 200 to 400 amperes per square foot commonly are used for electroforming. Because of the need for agitation, the baths must be kept clean by frequent filtering, and care must be exercised so that sludge on the bottom of the tanks is not stirred up.

The first step in electroforming is production of a form on which the object is to be made. These forms go under many different names, among which are *mandrel, matrix,* and *core.* The matrix may be expendable, used for the production of only one item. On the other hand, if it is used repeatedly it is termed "permanent." The method of making the matrix depends largely upon the material from which it is to be made. Permanent matrices usually are made of metals such as alloy steels, aluminum, magnesium, chromium-plated steels, and lead. Metal mandrels have the advantage of being conductors, and therefore their surfaces require no treatment to render them conductive. Ceramics, glass, quartz, and hard plastics are also considered permanent materials, but their use requires application of a thin coating of a conducting material before they can be used. Rubber cores are a rather special type of permanent matrix. The dimensional accuracy of electroforms from permanent mandrels tends to run higher than when temporary mandrels are used. Sometimes the surfaces of permanent cores are electroplated with tin or cadmium to facilitate subsequent stripping.

Permanent mandrels are made by die, permanent mold, and slush casting. They are also made by machining or hubbing. Hubbing, sometimes called die sinking, is the same process used in the manufacture of molds for plastics. It involves impressing a hard master die into a soft block of steel. If large amounts of plastic deformation are required, the operation may be executed as a series of alternate deforming and annealing cycles. The temporary mandrels are either fusible materials such as plastics, wax, lead and low-melting alloys, or metals such as zinc and aluminum, which are readily dissolved by certain chemicals. The temporary metal matrices are made by die casting or other conventional methods. The plastics and similar materials are often formed by transfer or compression molding.

Rendering the surface of insulating materials conductive is often accomplished by coating with a water suspension containing about 10 per cent colloidal graphite. Dry colloidal graphite mixed with copper or other metal powders is also used as a coating material. Coatings are applied by spraying, brushing, or dipping. Silver coatings are also used. These are chemically applied by methods similar to those used for silvering mirrors. Sometimes coatings are applied to metal mandrels to facilitate stripping, as already pointed out. Fusible metal films of low-melting metals or alloys and oxide or metallic compound films are used for this purpose. The latter prevent good adhesion.

The placement of the cores and anodes in the plating bath must be given careful consideration if uniform deposition is required. Conforming target anodes may be mounted in the bath to cause deposition in recessed areas. Since the shape of soluble anodes changes, the conforming target anodes are usually of the insoluble type. Projections are shielded from current by the use of insulating materials such as glass, ceramics, and polystyrene. Shields or dams are designed on the basis of experimentation with each particular job or application. Current robbers or "thieves" consist of wire racks surrounding projecting areas. These steal current from points which otherwise would have a high current density. Where deposition on a core is to be prevented, areas of the core are coated with nonconducting lacquers.

Work which consists of thick deposits will often remain in the bath for a number of days. Under these conditions pieces should be removed frequently for inspection. If unwanted surface projections are observed they should be smoothed off. Insoluble anodes eliminate the tendency to form nodules from anode particles, and for this reason, they are preferred for certain types of work.

After the part is formed, it is removed from the bath and *stripped* from the mandrel. Stripping is achieved mechanically by impact, tension, prying, or tumbling. Rubber cores may be removed by deflating or by stretching them out of shape. In some cases, use is made of differences in the rate of thermal expansion of the matrix and the electroform. In this instance, heating is sufficient to free the part from its core. Sometimes simple cutting operations must be carried out in order to free the edges of the mandrel.

Occasionally thin electroformed parts are made, of which electrotype is an example. The thin shell, after stripping from the mold, is strengthened by a cast backing of a suitable low-melting alloy. This saves time and reduces the cost of making the shape.

15.12. Properties

The properties of electroformed parts vary widely, depending upon the technical details of their formation. This is shown in Table 15.2, the data [1] for which were obtained from electroformed tubes, rod, and sheet.

Table 15.2 [1]

Metal	Hardness (Brinell or Vickers)	Tensile Strength psi	Elongation in 2 inches
Nickel			
Hard, stress free, as formed	130–500	< 132,000	< 20%
Very hard, as formed	400–575	< 160,000	< 9%
Very hard, stress annealed	300–400	< 90,000	< 30%
Fully annealed, recrystallized	no data	45,000– 50,000	< 50%
Copper			
Stress free, as formed	30–120	30,000– 68,000	5–20%
Cold worked, ductile	65	< 102,000	40%
Iron			
Stressed, as formed	225–350	50,000–110,000	5–20%
Cold worked, ductile	140–165	40,000– 55,000	27–40%
Cobalt			
As formed	150–375	no data	no data
Silver			
As formed	50–300	no data	no data

[1] Safranek, W. H., F. B. Dahle, and C. L. Faust, *Plating*, **35**, January 1948, p. 44.

Residual stresses in electroformed parts are sometimes lower than for similar parts made by casting, cold working, forging, or machining. This is partly responsible for their good dimensional accuracy. Bright nickel deposits, iron, and cobalt have been known to contain appreciable residual stresses. Iron parts have been carburized and heat treated to a R_c 62 reading.

15.13. Applications of Electroforming

Electroforming is not a new process. It has been used for years in making electrotype, and for the manufacture of phonograph master record discs, copper foil and tubing, and leather-embossing dies. Its use has been expanded to the manufacture of high-frequency wave guides for radar and television. These are hollow tubes of various cross sections. They require good internal surface finish, and may involve complicated twists and bends, such as two adjacent 90° bends lying in two planes at right angles to one another. Sometimes the cross section of the wave guide gradually changes in shape and size along its length. Electroforming is used for manufacture of searchlight reflectors, molds for forming plastics, copper floats, Pitot tubes, fine screening, seamless tanks, sheet, and strip. Some nickel alloy molds for die casting and rubber tire molds are produced by electroforming.

Questions

15.1. What chemical equation illustrates the mechanism of electrodeposition? Does this equation indicate Faraday's or Ohm's law? State Faraday's and Ohm's laws.

15.2. What is the nature of the electrodeposited surface? Describe its formation and growth. What is *throwing power*? What is the effect of grain size on the properties of the deposit?

15.3. List and elaborate briefly on the methods used to control the quality of electrodeposits.

15.4. What are the principal ways in which electroplating differs from electroforming? For what purposes is electroplating used?

15.5. List and describe the steps in electroplating.

15.6. Discuss the nature and advantages of electroforming as a manufacturing method.

15.7. Describe the steps involved in electroforming.

15.8. List some applications of electroforming. For what reasons has electroforming been applied to each of the applications listed?

Bibliography

15.1. *Electroplating Engineering Handbook*, ed. A. K. Graham. New York: Reinhold Publishing Corp., 1955.

15.2. Field, S., and A. D. Weill, *Electroplating*, 6th ed. New York: Pitman Publishing Corp., 1951.

15.3. Blum, W., and G. B. Hogaboom, *Principles of Electroplating and Electroforming*, 3rd ed. New York: McGraw-Hill Book Co., 1949.

15.4. Rubinstein, Marvin, "Brush Plating Now Practical," *Materials and Methods*, **40-6** (December 1954), pp. 98–101.

15.5. "Finishes for Metals Products," Staff Report, *Materials and Methods*, **42-3** (September 1955), pp. 125–127.

15.6. Rice, H. D., "A New Look at Electroformed Parts," *Materials and Methods*, **42-3** (September 1955), pp. 99–101.

15.7. Cook, M. C., "Acid Etching and Electroforming Precision Parts," *Product Engineering*, **27** (July 1956), pp. 194–199.

15.8. Weil, R., and H. J. Read, "The Structure of Electrodeposited Metals," *Metal Finishing*, **53-11** (November 1955), pp. 60–65, **53-12** (December 1955), pp. 60–64, and **54-1** (January 1956), pp. 56–59.

15.9. Mohler, J. B., "Practical Throwing Power," *Metal Finishing*, **54-1** (January 1956), pp. 53–55.

CHAPTER 16

Secondary Methods of Fabrication: Mechanical Working

PRINCIPLES OF MECHANICAL WORKING

16.1. Introduction

Mechanical working produces permanent deformation of metals by stressing them beyond their yield strengths. By mechanical working, ingots are partially or completely shaped into useful objects. In addition to changes in the shape of the cast metal, changes also occur in the physical properties of the metal. Mechanical work can be carried out near room temperature or at elevated temperatures, and the effect on properties varies with the temperature used. Since the yield strengths of metals fall off with increasing temperature, a given amount of hot deformation is possible at lower stresses than an equivalent cold deformation. Large pieces which are to undergo appreciable changes in shape cannot be worked cold because the forces required are too great for existing equipment. It is therefore necessary to heat the metal before deforming it. Thus the first shaping operations on large ingots are invariably carried out at elevated temperatures.

16.2. Principal Stresses and Deformation Resistance

By approaching the topic of mechanical working from the standpoint of the principal stresses, the discussion can be somewhat simplified. In this discussion the symbol σ is used to represent tensile or compressive stresses, i.e., stresses normal to a plane. The symbol τ is used to represent shear stresses, i.e., stresses lying in the plane. For a body in equilibrium, six stress components must be stated in order to specify the stress at a point. Consider a body subjected to several forces as shown in Fig. 16.1(a). The stress at a point can be expressed by working with an infinitesimally small cube inscribed at the point.   Since the body is in equilibrium, the sum of the forces along the three axes of the infinitesimally small cube must equal zero, and the sum of the moments about the axes must equal zero.   Therefore

(1) $\sigma_x = \sigma_{x'}$,   (2) $\sigma_y = \sigma_{y'}$,   (3) $\sigma_z = \sigma_{z'}$,

(4) $\tau_{zx} = \tau_{xz}$,   (5) $\tau_{yx} = \tau_{xy}$,   (6) $\tau_{zy} = \tau_{yz}$

It is possible, by selecting the orientation of the axes of the inscribed cube, to cause all shear stresses on the surface of the cube to equal zero.   When this is done, the surfaces of the cube become

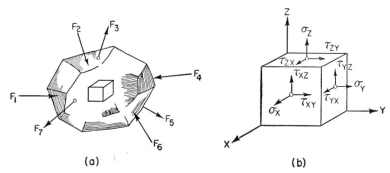

(a)   (b)

Fig. 16.1.   Stresses on a small cube in a body subjected to several forces.   (a) An infinitesimally small cube inscribed at a point in a body subjected to forces $F_1, F_2, \ldots F_7$.   (b) The nomenclature for stresses acting on the cube shown in (a).   The Y-plane is the plane perpendicular to the Y-direction, the X-plane is the plane perpendicular to the X-direction, etc. τ_{yx} is the shear stress in the Y-plane acting in the X-direction, etc. σ_y is the normal stress acting on the front (positive) face of the cube in the Y-direction, $\sigma_{y'}$ is the normal stress acting on the rear (negative) face of the cube in the $-Y$ direction, etc.

the so-called principal planes, and the stresses acting normal to these planes are known as the principal stresses.   By convention,

σ_1 = maximum stress in tensile sense (or minimum stress in compressive sense)

σ_3 = maximum stress in compressive sense (or minimum stress in tensile sense)

σ_2 = stress intermediate between σ_1 and σ_3.

This might be represented:

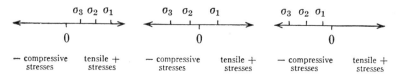

Thus σ_3 might be a tensile stress, but it is always the lesser tensile stress.   Conversely, σ_1 might be a compressive stress, but it is always a minimum compressive stress.

For a bar under axial loading, the plane of maximum shear stress is at 45° to the direction of loading.   Likewise, for a bar subjected to triaxial stresses, the plane of maximum shear stress exists at 45° between the directions of σ_1 and σ_3.   The shear stress in this case is given by the formula: [1]

$$\tau_{max} = \tfrac{1}{2}\,(\sigma_1 - \sigma_3)$$

For axial loading, the yield strength or yield point (if one exists) is the stress at which the deformation resistance of a metal is overcome.   Deformation resistance is often indicated by the letter k, and is sometimes called the flow stress.   In uniaxial tension, as in tensile testing, when $\sigma_1 = k$, flow occurs and the metal undergoes permanent deformation.   A similar statement can be made for conditions of loading other than uniaxial.   For this, the formula above may be rewritten:

$$2\tau_{max} = (\sigma_1 - \sigma_3)$$

Now in simple tension, $\sigma_3 = 0$, and hence $2\tau_{max} = \sigma_1$.[2]   Obviously flow continues as long as $2\tau_{max} \geqq k$.   Or we may say that as long as $(\sigma_1 - \sigma_3) \geqq k$, flow will occur.   This relation is not a precise one, because the effect of σ_2 on yielding is neglected.   However, the resulting error cannot exceed 15 per cent, and hence the relationship is very useful.   Furthermore, the error decreases with increasing temperature.[3]   In effect, this relationship states that when the difference of the major and minor principal stresses is equal to or exceeds k, flow occurs.   The significance and application of this concept to several different stress systems is shown in Fig. 16.2.

16.3. Factors Affecting the Value of k

The value of k for a particular metal is affected principally by the *temperature*, the *degree of strain hardening*, and the *rate of straining*.   During straining at any particular temperature, the

---

[1] *Z. Ver. deut. Ing.*, **72** (1928), pp. 734–736.

[2] This is a statement of the well-known fact that for uniaxial stresses, the maximum shear stress is equal to one-half the normal stress.   It acts along a plane inclined at 45° to the normal stress.

[3] *Z. Ver. deut. Ing.*, **72** (1928), pp. 734–736.

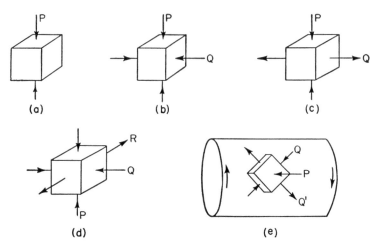

Fig. 16.2. Flow in metals under different stress systems. (a) Uniaxial compression, where $\sigma_1 = 0$. $\sigma_3 = -P$; $k = 0 + P$, hence flow occurs when $P \geq k$. (b) Biaxial compression, with $P > Q$. $\sigma_1 = 0$, $\sigma_3 = -P$; $k = \overline{0} + P$, hence flow occurs when $P \geq k$, and the second compressive stress, Q, is ineffective in promoting flow. (c) Biaxial loading, with $\sigma_1 = Q$, $\sigma_3 = -P$; $k = Q + P$, hence flow occurs when $P \geq k - Q$. Thus, the tensile force Q assists P in causing flow at a lower value than if Q were absent. (Stresses similar to these are found in rolling and drawing operations in which back and forward tensions are applied.) (d) Triaxial loading, with $P > Q$, $\sigma_1 = R$, $\sigma_3 = -P$; $k = R + P$, hence flow occurs when $P \geq k - R$. This case is similar to (c). (e) Triaxial loading resulting from torsion and compression, where $Q = -Q'$, $P > Q$, $\sigma_1 = Q'$, $\sigma_3 = -P$; hence $k = Q' + P$, and flow occurs when $P \geq k - Q'$.

degree of strain hardening depends upon the opposing relative rates of straining and annealing. This important relationship was pointed out in section 6.6.

For increasing temperatures, the value of k decreases. Thus at higher temperatures, lower stresses are required to overcome deformation resistance. This is one reason for hot-working large, massive pieces, where a given force is capable of producing only small stresses because of size considerations.

As a metal is cold worked, the deformation resistance increases. This is known as strain hardening, and is due in part to a reduction in grain size and distortion of the lattice. The effect of strain hardening was discussed in sections 3.9 and 5.3.

The *value of k* has been observed to *increase with increasing rates of straining.* This is probably because decreasing the time for a given degree of straining also decreases the time for softening which results from annealing. Therefore the value of k is increased.

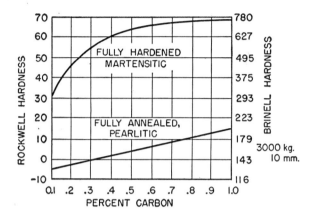

Fig. 16.3.   Variation in hardness of steels.   The versatility of steel is realized when hardening possibilities are considered. Proper heat-treatment of a piece of steel makes it possible to produce a soft metal, amenable to shaping. After shaping, the steel can be hardened to resist wear and provide good service. [After C. G. Johnson, *Metallurgy*, p. 241. American Technical Society, Chicago, 1948.]

Heat treatment is another factor which may influence the value of k. One type of heat treatment which does this is annealing, discussed in Chapter 6. Precipitation hardening, explained in Chapter 5, also affects the value of k. The heat treatment of steel has a more pronounced effect on the value of k than either annealing or precipitation hardening. This topic is covered in Chapters 7 and 8. It is desirable that a metal be capable of having both high and low values of k. Steel, as is shown in Fig. 16.3, does this. When fully soft, the steel can be shaped readily, and then after shaping the steel can be hardened as desired. This behavior makes steel a versatile material and accounts for the great importance attached to heat treating it.

16.4.   Hot Working

By definition, hot working involves permanent deformation of a metal at temperatures and rates of straining such that strain hardening does not occur. The temperature involved in hot working, therefore, depends upon (1) the metal involved, and (2) the rate of straining during deformation. In general, the temperature required for hot working is high for metals having high melting points, and low for metals having low melting points. The temperature actually used in hot working is usually appreciably greater than the lowest temperature which will prevent strain hardening for a given rate of deformation. For instance, steel can be prevented from strain hardening by working at about 1000°F. In practice, it is worked at temperatures closer to 2000°F. The minimum acceptable temperature depends in many instances upon the degree of softening desired. However, the upper temperature cannot be so high that melting commences. The temperature selected is always below that at which the lowest melting constituent liquifies.

The *physical properties* of the finished piece may be significantly affected by the use of a particular hot-working temperature. This must be taken into account when a working temperature is being selected. Hot working actually involves simultaneous grain distortion and fragmentation, along with recrystallization and annealing. The same variables which determine final grain size in a cold-worked and annealed piece (see Chapter 6), influence final grain size in a hot-worked piece. If, for a given amount of deformation, the hot-finishing temperature is raised, the final grain size will tend to be larger. The use of lower hot-finishing temperatures, for the same amount of deformation, tends to produce smaller final grain sizes. The grain size thus reflects the particular finishing temperature used. Therefore, the finishing temperature will affect the final strength, hardness, and ductility of the hot-worked metal. Uniformity of grain size within the piece depends upon the uniformity of deformation and temperature throughout the piece. In any event, since recrystallization occurs, cast grain structures are replaced by refined grain structures, relatively free from the residual stresses usually found in cold-worked pieces.

Hot working results in greatly improved *homogeneity* of the metal. This is a partial result of the severity of mechanical deformation which often characterizes hot work. There is a mechanical breakdown of massive microconstituents and a physical redistribution of the fragments. In addition, diffusion is accelerated at the hot-working temperature, and this assists in improving homogeneity. The surfaces of discontinuities in the metal are welded together, providing those surfaces are clean and free from oxide. Dendritic shrinkage, blowholes, cold shuts, and other defects found in cast structures tend to be eliminated. Since these are sources of weakness, brittleness, and fatigue failure, hot-worked pieces are superior to castings in most respects. Cold working also causes the surfaces of discontinuities to weld together, but not as thoroughly as does hot working.

During hot working, an objectionable *scale* or oxide may form on some metals. If this is not removed, it is pressed into the metal surface, resulting in discoloration and surface defects. Prior to hot working an ingot, the scale may be removed mechanically or by scarfing with an oxyacetylene torch. While hot working is in progress, the scale is often popped off by a spray of cold water. Salt thrown on the hot surface also causes the scale to break loose.

The effects of hot working can be summarized as follows:

1. Hot working makes possible equivalent deformation at lower stresses than cold working.
2. Recrystallization and deformation occur together so that (a) for a given amount of deformation, the higher the hot-working temperature, the softer and more ductile the finished piece, (b) the cast grain structure is refined and replaced, and (c) residual stresses are absent from the finished piece.
3. Most of the physical properties are improved (as compared to castings) by improvement of the homogeneity and soundness of the metals.
4. An oxidized surface is formed on the finished piece. This is objectionable in many instances.

16.5. Cold Working

When a metal is permanently deformed at a temperature and rate of straining such that the hardness of the metal increases, the metal is said to be cold worked. Since the yield strength of metals is greater at the low temperatures of cold work than at the high temperatures of hot work, the stresses induced by cold work are greater than for hot work. Thus the size of the part to be cold worked, and the degree of its deformation, are limited by the force which the equipment is capable of exerting.

The *physical properties* of metals are markedly affected by cold work and its effects on grain structure. During cold work the metal increases in strength and loses ductility. The increase in strength and loss in ductility are directly related to the amount of cold work. Cold work causes grain distortion and introduces imperfections in the crystal structure. Unless the degree of cold working is equal in all directions (an unlikely occurrence) the grain shape is changed. In addition, twins (known in this case as mechanical twins), may form within the grains. Cold work may also result in preferred orientation (i.e., alignment of the major crystal axes) of the grains. When this occurs the anisotropic properties of crystals show up in the finished piece. Cold-rolled sheets in which preferred orientation exists show directionality of properties. Of those properties which are thus effected, mechanical directionality (i.e., strength and ductility vary in different directions) and magnetic anisotropy (in magnetic materials) are most often considered. Mechanical directionality causes difficulties in the cold drawing of sheet metal, and is for the most part undesirable. Magnetic anisotropy is desirable in the production of laminated magnetic parts. Anisotropy has been observed to occur in hot-worked metals, but it is rather rare as compared to its occurrence in cold-worked metals. (Directionality of a different origin occurs in hot-worked metals, particularly forgings, due to mechanical fibering of inclusions of oxide, slag, etc.)

Cold work often results in *residual stresses* in the metal after deformation. Nonuniform cold work, in which some portions of the piece are deformed plastically, while other portions are deformed elastically, is the source of residual stresses. For instance, consider a plate into which a Brinell ball is impressed. (See Fig. 16.4.) The metal in the immediate vicinity of the impression is plastically deformed as the load is applied. The amount of plastic deformation decreases with increasing distance from the impression, and eventually an area is reached in which elastic deformation replaces plastic deformation. Still farther away, there is an absence of detectable deformation. When the load is removed, the elastically deformed metal tries to return to its origin shape. However, resistance is offered by the plastically deformed regions in which are induced residual stresses resulting from the attempt of the elastically deformed metal to resume its original shape. The residual stresses in this case are compressive at the surface of the impression and tensile at a distance below the impression. This is shown in Fig. 16.4(a) for a ball impression, and in Fig. 16.4(b) for other cold-worked pieces. The residual stresses produced by cold working may be useful, as those in autofrettaged gun barrels and in metal subjected to shot peening and cold rolling for improvement of fatigue strength and resistance to stress corrosion. On the other hand, residual stresses are harmful if a slight additional service load exceeds the yield or tensile strength. Residual stresses are removed by proper annealing, as explained earlier.

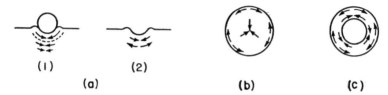

(1) (2)

(a) (b) (c)

Fig. 16.4. Residual stresses. (a) Stresses induced by impressing a Brinell ball into a piece of metal. (1) shows stresses while the load is being applied and (2) shows residual stresses after removal of load. The size of the arrows indicates diminishing stresses with increasing distance from the ball in (1). Below the dotted line the elastic limit is not exceeded. (b) Residual tensile stresses on the surface and residual compressive stresses in the center of cold-drawn wire. (c) A section of a gun barrel following autofrettage, in which internal hydraulic pressure has stressed the inner layers of metal beyond the elastic limit. The outer layers were stressed below the elastic limit and upon removal of pressure, residual stresses remain as indicated by the arrows.

Cold working, when used skillfully in conjunction with annealing, produces products whose physical properties can be closely controlled. If a particular hardness and strength is desired in a piece of metal, it may be possible to achieve this hardness by two different cycles of cold work and annealing. For instance, the piece may be fully annealed just before a final cold-working operation. The final cold work produces the proper size and shape and at the same time also provides sufficient deformation to produce the desired final hardness. The same result can be achieved by cold working the piece to its final dimensions, followed by a partial anneal which reduces hardness and strength to a desired value, but not to the point of dead softness. Anisotropy also can be controlled by varying the conditions involved in alternate cycles of cold work and annealing.

Cold work affects homogeneity and soundness in much the same way that these properties are improved by hot working. However, most cold-worked objects are initially shaped by hot working. As a result they are fairly homogeneous and sound when finally subjected to cold shaping and finishing. Diffusion occurs and homogeneity is considerably improved during the annealing which often accompanies cold work. Diffusion occurs fastest along imperfections in the crystal structure, and cold work increases the number of crystal imperfections. Therefore a homogenizing anneal is more effective in a cold-worked piece than in one which has not been cold worked.

The effects of cold working can be summarized as follows:

1. The stresses involved in equivalent deformations are greater for cold than for hot work.
2. Cold work causes distortion of the grains and introduces imperfections in the crystal structure, resulting in: (a) increase in strength and hardness, and (b) loss of ductility. In some cases, directionality of properties also results.
3. Residual stresses remain in the cold-worked piece; these may be harmful or helpful, depending upon the use for which the piece is intended.
4. When combined with annealing, cold work provides a means of controlling final physical properties, and may significantly improve homogenizing tendencies.

16.6. Classification of Mechanical Working Methods

The remaining portion of this chapter deals with various means of hot and cold working. There is no hard and fast rule for determining which processes are suited to hot work and which ones to cold work. Furthermore, certain types of deformation may be carried out hot under one name, and the corresponding cold process may be given another name. In other cases, both the hot and cold process may have the same name. Nevertheless, an attempt has been made to take up mechanical working methods according to the following classification:

1. Processes which may be carried out hot or cold.
2. Processes which usually are carried out cold.
3. Processes which usually are carried out at elevated temperatures.

HOT- OR COLD-WORKING METHODS

16.7. Rolling

For the initial shaping of ingots by rolling, high temperatures are used. Rails and structural shapes are of such size that they are finished by hot rolling. Sheet, strip, and some kinds of pipe may be finished hot or cold, depending upon the properties desired in the final product.

Hot rolling of **ingots** is carried out in breakdown or blooming mills, which reduce the cross sections of the ingots and improve their properties. Depending upon the particular process, a bloom may be further reduced to a billet or slab. A billet is a bloom whose length has been increased and whose cross section has been decreased. A slab is a bloom which has been flattened and elongated. Blooms may be hot rolled directly to structural shapes and rails. Billets are formed into pipe and wire by hot rolling and by other methods. Slabs are used for the rolling of plates, strips, and sheets.

In the hot rolling of **blooms and shapes** the powered rolls are grooved to produce the cross section desired. Each pair of grooves in the rolls is known as a pass. The ingot being shaped is rolled through a succession of passes, each of which differs slightly from the preceding one. This is shown in Fig. 16.5 for the rolling of blooms from ingots. This particular mill is a three-high mill in which each groove on the center roll serves for two passes, except for the final pass.

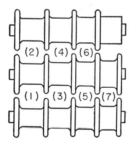

Fig. 16.5. Rolling mill for blooms. The arrangement of rolls in a blooming mill, showing the successive passes. This is a three-high mill in which the center roll is a common roll for three pairs of successive passes.

In the rolling of **plate and sheet,** continuous mills may be used. A continuous mill is one in which power-driven rolls are arranged in a continuous line. Each succeeding mill travels at a higher speed to compensate for the reduction in thickness and corresponding increase in length of the piece.

Mill design. It has been found that the use of large rolls in rolling mills increases power requirements. If the temperature of rolling is low enough, oil may be used to reduce frictional power losses. Small-diameter working rolls also reduce power losses and improve efficiency, but they are not capable of so great a reduction in thickness per pass. This disadvantage may be overcome by using forward and back tension on the sheet. In some installations, the work is pulled through the working rolls, which are not power-driven, but serve only as a source of pressure. If the sheet being rolled is fairly wide, the working rolls tend to bend and must be reinforced with backing rolls. In mills of this construction, the working rolls may be of highly polished, high-speed tool steel, while the backing rolls are a lower alloy heat-treatable steel. The small size of the working rolls effects economies in finishing, heat treatment, and replacement. Figure 16.6 illustrates a four-high mill and a twelve-high cluster mill, in which small-diameter working rolls are given support by backing rolls. Some mills are equipped with edge rollers, whose axis of rotation is at right angles to the plate or sheet being rolled. Mills of this type roll products of controlled width, and are known as *universal mills*.

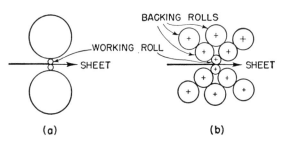

(a)   (b)

Fig. 16.6. **Rolling mill for sheet and strip.** (a) A four-high mill, showing the small working rolls and large backing rolls. In mills of this extreme design, the working rolls are often not power-driven. Instead the sheet is pulled between them with forward and back tension. (b) A twelve-high cluster mill in which there are five backing rolls for each working roll.

Rods and wire are manufactured by rolling, in a manner illustrated by Fig. 16.7(*a*). It has been found more practical to reduce the section of the rod in only one direction at a time. Therefore the piece may be rotated between passes as shown in the illustration. In another method of accomplishing the same result, the axes of a sequence of rolling mills are tilted as shown in Fig. 16.7(*b*).

Roller leveling is always a cold-working operation which is in-

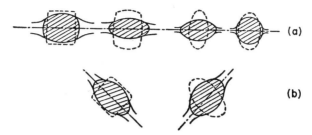

Fig. 16.7. Rolling mill for rods. (a) An open-pass rod mill in which the stock is tilted 90° between successive passes. It is reduced in one direction only during each pass. (b) The same results can be attained by tilting the axes of successive rolls through an angle of 90° as shown. [After G. Sachs and K. R. Van Horn, *Practical Metallurgy*, p. 331. American Society for Metals, 1944.]

tended to flatten sheet or strip. The sheet, containing waves and bends, is passed between staggered power-driven rollers. The rollers are located so that the sheet is bent back and forth with a constantly increasing radius as it moves toward the exit end of the leveler. This is shown in Fig. 16.8(a).

Roll forming is a process used for bending large sheets used in the manufacture of tanks or pipes of large diameter. The principle is illustrated in Fig. 16.8(b).

Roll threading and knurling are cold-working operations similar to some of the processes just discussed. In a widely used form of roll threading, the shaft to be threaded is placed between two parallel die plates. The faces of these plates consist of straight parallel grooves having the same pitch and contour as the threads to be rolled. One of the two plates is movable and the other fixed. The shaft to be threaded is placed between the two plates and the movable plate is rolled across the fixed one, carrying the shaft along and impressing the thread design on it. Rolled threads have fatigue strength superior to machined threads, but are not as precise. To overcome this latter difficulty, the threads may be machined part way to size followed by a sizing roll. This combines the superior dimensional accuracy of machined threads with the good fatigue resistance of rolled threads. For knurling operations, the thread grooves on the die plates are replaced by knurl designs. Threads may also be rolled on lathes and automatic screw machines. The roll threading and knurling operations are cold-working processes.

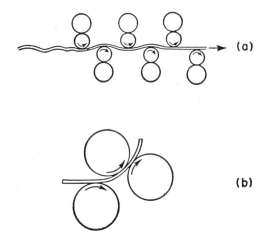

Fig. 16.8. Rolling operations. (a) Roller leveling in which a sheet is straightened by rolling through successive rolls so located that the radius of curvature of the sheet diminishes as it approaches the exit end of the mill. (b) Roll forming in which heavy gauge stock is curved or bent to shape. This device is useful in bending sheet for tanks or round containers. The curvature is controlled by varying the distance between the centers of the rolls.

Hot-rolling operations are used also to produce **pipe and tubing.** The first step involves the cross rolling of a billet by a mill of the type shown in Fig. 16.9(a). This type of mill is known as a Mannesmann mill, and produces a thick-walled seamless pipe. In effect, the Mannesmann mill and others developed from it may be thought of as a three-high mill, in which the mandrel is the center roll, and the wall of the pipe corresponds to a sheet of metal. The cross-rolling operation produces a hole in the billet even before the mandrel is inserted. The actual function of the mandrel is to smooth the inner walls of the pipe as it emerges from the machine. Modifications of this type of mill are used to reduce the wall thickness of pipe and to increase the diameter of tubing. Tube mills are used for sizing operations, as illustrated in Fig. 16.9(b). These are used to change the diameter and wall thickness of the tube, as determined by the depth of the grooves in the rolls and the size of the plug used. Final sizing is accomplished in mills similar to the Mannesmann mill, or similar to the tube mill illustrated in Fig. 16.9(b), except that in the latter case the plug or mandrel is not used. Pipe may be produced by centrifugal casting, as described in sections 13.23–13.25. In addition, welding, extruding, sinking,

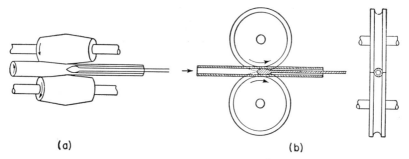

(a)   (b)

Fig. 16.9.   Steps in rolling of tubing.   (a) Cross rolling a bloom.
The top and bottom rolls are inclined slightly to the axis of the
bloom, thus tending to pull it through the mill along its length.   A
hole opens along the axis of the bloom and is smoothed by the action
of the inserted mandrel.   (b) The plan and front views of a sizing
mill for tubing.

and drawing, all of which are taken up later, are other methods
used for manufacturing pipe.

16.8.   Drawing and Cupping Operations

Hot- or cold-drawing operations are used to reduce the diameter
of rod, wire, and pipe.   In the case of pipe, the wall thickness may
also be reduced.   In order to draw pipe, the end of the pipe is
pointed, a mandrel is inserted, and the pointed end of the pipe is
forced through a die opening.   It is then gripped and pulled through
the die as shown in Fig. 16.10.   If the mandrel is not used, the outside and inside diameters of the pipe are reduced, and the operation is known as sinking.   The elongation of the pipe, rather than
change in wall thickness, compensates for the reduction in diameter.

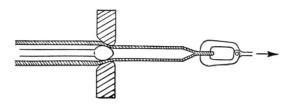

Fig. 16.10.   Drawing pipe through a die.

For wire drawing, a similar process is used.   However, since wire
can be bent and reeled, long lengths can be drawn by using a power-
driven reel called a bull block.   The bull block not only reels the

wire, but also provides the force which pulls the wire through the die. Continuous wire-drawing mills are used, in which the wire passes from one drum to another, passing through a die between each pair of drums.

Cupping is an operation which may be performed hot or cold, depending upon the metal and its thickness. As can be seen from Fig. 16.11, cupping consists of forcing a circular blank of metal through a die by means of a hydraulically operated punch or plunger. Single-action presses are used for forming thick blanks [Fig. 16.11(*a*)], while double-action presses are used for thin blanks [Fig. 16.11(*b*)]. In the double-action press, a holding-down ring prevents the formation of wrinkles or creases in the walls of the

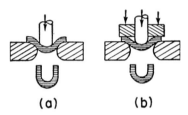

(a)   (b)

Fig. 16.11.   **Cupping operations.**   (a) Single-action press such as often used for thick stock.   (b) A double-action press in which a holding-down ring is used.   The holding-down ring exerts pressure on the stock and tends to prevent wrinkling.   Double-action presses are particularly useful for thin stock.

cup. Some double-action presses are set up to cut the blank from a strip as well as to hold and cup it. The greatest friction occurs between the metal and the die, and therefore the die surface is usually highly polished. Since there is little relative motion between the punch and the metal, it is not so essential to provide as good a surface finish on the punch as on the die. It is possible in the first cupping operation to produce a cup whose diameter is less than one-half that of the blank from which it is made. The cup may undergo additional drawing operations to adjust its height, diameter, and wall thickness. These operations may be termed redrawing operations, and in this case are similar to cupping. Two different redrawing methods are shown in Fig. 16.12. Cups are used also in the manufacture of pipe and tubing, for which the cups are subjected to drawing or sinking operations as previously described. Compressed-gas cylinders and similar closed-end objects are made by cupping.

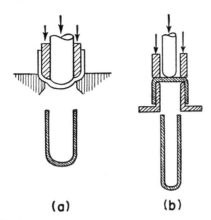

(a) **(b)**

Fig. 16.12. Redrawing operations. (a) Double-action redrawing. A holding-down ring is used. (b) Reverse redrawing. [After G. Sachs and K. R. Van Horn, *Practical Metallurgy*, p. 420. American Society for Metals, 1944.]

COLD-WORKING METHODS

The operations discussed in this section of the chapter are *predominantly,* though *not exclusively,* carried out on pieces of metal at room temperature.

16.9. Deep Drawing

A blanked sheet or cup is forced by means of a punch into or through a die. Redrawing operations are deep-drawing operations, as is also the manufacture of automobile body parts such as fenders. In deep drawing, the material undergoes rather severe deformation, and therefore it is desirable to work with a metal which has good ductility. If the blank or cup cannot be completely shaped in one draw, a series of draws is used, coupled with annealing cycles to restore ductility to the piece. In this way the metal can be deformed almost to the point of rupture, annealed, and then given appreciable additional deformation. Final hardness and strength may be controlled as described in the first portion of this chapter.

16.10. Spinning

This is usually a cold-working operation which has been applied with success to steel, tin, aluminum, and copper. Magnesium is also spun, but only at elevated temperatures. One type of spinning is schematically represented by Fig. 16.13 (*a*). The work is formed into shape in a spinning lathe under the pressure brought to bear by the spinning tool. Spinning usually does not produce a reduction in wall thickness, but rather affects only the diameter of the blank. Spinning methods are also used for necking down, bulging, flanging, expanding, and curling the ends of tubes or cylinders as shown in Fig. 16.13 (*b*)

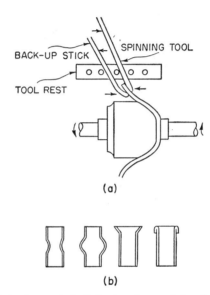

(a)

(b)

Fig. 16.13. Spinning. (a) Spinning is used for large containers such as cooking vessels. The sheet is held in a lathe and shaped over a form of desired contour. The back-up stick and spinning tool can be supported in different positions on the tool rest. (b) Spinning is also used for various shaping operations performed on tubing. [Part (b) after G. Sachs and K. R. Van Horn, *Practical Metallurgy*, p. 420. American Society for Metals, 1944.]

16.11. Stamping

There are several kinds of *stamping* operations, all of which involve similar types of equipment. The principal cold-stamping processes are shearing, embossing, and coining. Shearing consists largely of cutting blanks or punching holes in sheet metal. In these operations, the ultimate strength of the metal is exceeded. Trimming is also a shearing operation used for final sizing of partially completed pieces. Coining and embossing are similar to one another, and are shown in Fig. 16.14 (*a*) and 16.14 (*b*). The impressions of the punch and the die used for coining do not match, whereas in embossing equipment they do match. Thus, coining involves metal flow and displacement, whereas embossing is a bending operation. Both are final sizing or shaping operations, and are closely related to hot forging.

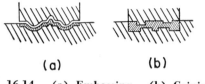

(a)   (b)

Fig. 16.14.   (a) Embossing.   (b) Coining.

16.12.   Cold Heading

In addition to coining and embossing, cold heading is sometimes called a cold-forging operation. It is an upsetting process involving deformation, as pictured in Fig. 16.15. Cold heading is used in the production of bolts, screws, rivets, and similar shapes.

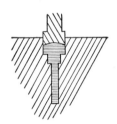

Fig. 16.15.   Cold heading.

16.13.   Impact Extrusion

The production of thin-walled tubes, having round, square, hexagonal, and other cross sections may be accomplished by impact extrusion. The principle of impact extrusion is shown in Fig. 16.16. A blank is cut which has the shape of the exterior surface of the tube. This is placed in a die, and a punch, whose shape matches that desired for the interior of the tube, strikes the blank a sharp blow. Metal flows up and around the punch. There is a lip on the bottom of the punch which produces an inside tube diameter greater than that of the punch. This reduces the area of contact between punch and formed metal, and reduces friction losses. The pressures used for impact extrusion may be as high as 150,000 psi. The temperature of the metal rises appreciably as a result of the deformation, though the blank is usually cold when placed in the die. The

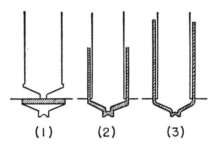

(1)   **(2)**   **(3)**

Fig. 16.16.   Impact extrusion.   Three stages in the production of a tube by means of impact extrusion.

length of tube which can be produced by this process is limited by the tendency of the punch to buckle. Buckling occurs when the ratio of length to diameter of the punch becomes too great.

HOT-WORKING METHODS

Forging, hydraulic piercing, upsetting, swaging, and extrusion (excluding impact extrusion), *are usually considered hot-working methods.* The manufacture of pipe by welding is also a hot-forming process.

16.14. Forging

There is a wide variety of forging operations and only a few are discussed here. The two major classifications of forging operations are press forging and hammer forging. In press forging, the forming pressure is applied steadily over a period of time. In hammer forging, the metal is shaped by impact. Forging presses are actuated mechanically or hydraulically. The largest ones are hydraulic presses, and they are used for forging armor plate, gun barrels, and similar heavy items of equipment. More intricate and considerably smaller parts are made by the various types of forging hammers.

Forging hammers are quick acting and deliver sharp sudden blows to the piece being shaped. Simple hammers and anvils are replaced in *drop forges* with split dies, the moving portion of which corresponds to the hammer, while the stationary portion corresponds to the anvil. The hammer or upper die is moved up and down by steam, air, or mechanical means as shown in Fig. 16.17. The *board hammer* is a mechanical device [Fig. 16.17(a)] utilizing the friction between rolls and a wooden board for raising the hammer. When the rolls are separated, the board and hammer are

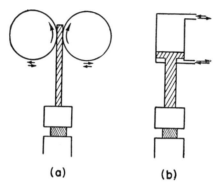

(a)   (b)

Fig. 16.17. Forging hammers. (a) A board hammer. The board to which the hammer is attached is raised by the revolving wheels when they are forced together. By opening the gap between the wheels the board and hammer are dropped. (b) Steam or air hammer in which the moving parts are raised by steam or air pressure.

dropped, and the resulting impact forms the metal. The force of the blow depends upon the height to which the board and hammer are raised before dropping. In *steam drop forges* [Fig. 16.17(b)], not only is the weight of the moving parts utilized to create the impact, but additional force is imparted by reversing the flow of steam. These forges are sometimes called double-acting forges. Air hammers use air pressure to raise the hammer, the force of the blow being regulated by the height of fall of the hammer. Steam and air drop forges are rated as high as 50,000 pounds, while board drop forges go only as high as 10,000 pounds. The steam and air drop forges have the advantages of higher speeds of operation. Connecting rods, crankshafts, and wrenches are examples of parts which are readily drop forged.

Forging machines are horizontal presses used for hot upset forging. These machines were originally used for heading bolts and similar small parts. Their capacities have been increased and they

now are used for inside and outside upsetting as shown in Fig.
16.18.   In addition to being used for upsetting tubing, they are also
used for piercing and the manufacture of gear blanks.

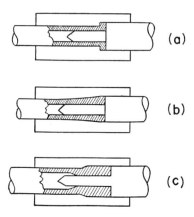

Fig. 16.13.   Forging machine.   Various types of upsetting are illustrated.   (a) Flanging of tubing.   (b) Outside upsetting of tubing.
(c) Inside and outside upsetting of tubing.   [Adapted from *Metals
Handbook*, p. 40.   American Society for Metals, 1948.]

Forging temperatures.   The energy imparted to the piece by the
impact of a drop hammer or the squeeze of a forging press or machine is converted to heat.   Unless this heat is conducted away by
contact of the piece with the dies or anvil and hammer, overheating
may result.   This danger is greater in drop forging than in press
forging.   In drop forging, the metal is in contact with the dies for
a smaller proportion of the time, and there is less opportunity for
cooling.   The initial forging temperature must take this into account.   The *forging temperature* should always be as high as can
be used without the danger of melting any of the constituents in the
alloy.   If a low-melting constituent liquefies at the grain boundaries
(the most frequent location), the piece being forged loses its
strength and commences to crack and fall apart.   In some alloys,
this occurs just slightly above the cold-working temperature.
Alloys with low-melting constituents have a very narrow forging
range, particularly when being drop forged, with resulting rapid
rates of straining and less time available for annealing.   The cold-
working temperature can be lowered by reducing the rate of straining, thereby increasing the forging range.   Certain magnesium

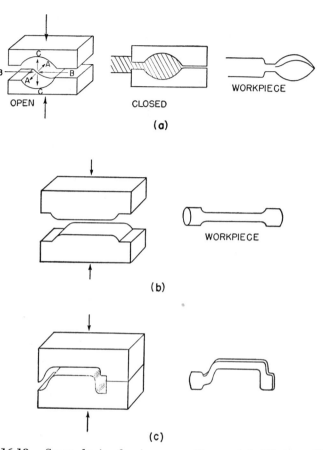

OPEN   CLOSED   WORKPIECE

(a)

WORKPIECE

(b)

(c)

Fig. 16.19. Some basic forging operations. (a) Edging. The metal flows principally in the direction *A-A*, is restricted in the *B-B* direction, and fills the die in the direction *C-C*. A 90° turn is given the workpiece between blows. (b) Fullering. In this operation the cross-section of the stock is reduced between the ends of the piece. (c) Bending. This operation is used for shaping such objects as crankshafts. [After Naujoks, Waldemar and Fabel, *Forging Handbook*, pp. 112 and 114. American Society for Metals, 1939.]

alloys are in this category, and they are more readily press forged than drop forged for this reason.

16.15. Swaging

This is usually a hot-forming process, similar to hammer forging. (Some swaging is also carried out cold.) Two or four dies are mounted in a rotating spindle, as shown in Fig. 16.20. Surrounding the die spindle are hardened steel rollers, held in a framework called a roll cage. The entering side of the die is tapered so that the work can be gradually reduced as it is fed into the swaging machine. The spindle rotates faster than the cage, and therefore

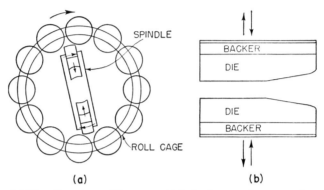

SPINDLE

BACKER

DIE

DIE

BACKER

ROLL CAGE

(a)   (b)

Fig. 16.20. Swaging. The essential features of a swaging machine, showing (a) end and (b) side views. Swaging is very closely related to forging.

the dies open and close as contact is made with the hardened steel rollers. Swaging is used for tapering and reducing the diameter of bars, rods, and tubing. It is an important step in the manufacture of tungsten rod from which tungsten wire is drawn, and is well suited to the pointing of ends of pipes or rods which are to be drawn to smaller sizes.

16.16. Hydraulic Piercing

A hot-working operation which is very closely related to the piercing operation mentioned under upsetting is known as hydraulic piercing. The principal difference lies in the magnitude of the operation. Hydraulic piercing is used for converting solid blooms or ingots into thick-walled tubes, cylinders, or shells. It is accomplished by forcing a mandrel through the solid piece of metal which is enclosed in a cylindrical vessel. Metal flows up and around the mandrel, which is operated by hydraulic pressure. This is shown in Fig. 16.21(a).

16.17. Extrusion

Hydraulic piercing is similar to the first step in certain of the *extrusion operations*. (If "impact extrusion" is not specified, the

word "extrusion" usually denotes the hot process described below.)
In one method for extrusion of tubing or hollow shapes, a hot
billet or cast shape is placed in a cylinder and a piercing mandrel
is forced through it, as shown in Fig. 16.21(b). Then a dummy
block having a smaller diameter than that of the cylinder is forced

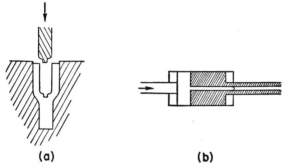

(a)   (b)

Fig. 16.21. Hydraulic piercing and extrusion. (a) In hydraulic
piercing a punch is forced into a piece of stock, causing it to flow up
and around the punch, and filling the space between the punch and
the die. This is similar to extrusion, which is shown in (b). In
this type of mechanical working, a piston forces a billet through an
orifice in a cylinder. The metal takes the shape of the orifice.

by a hydraulic ram against the pierced metal. The dummy block
squeezes the metal out of the space between the orifice and mandrel.
This forms a hollow shape having an external surface controlled by
the shape of the orifice, and an internal surface controlled by the
shape of the mandrel. The dummy block, being smaller than the
cylinder, leaves a thin wall of the original casting or billet within
the cylinder. This avoids the transfer of surface defects to the
extruded product. For the same reason, the dummy block is not
forced all the way forward, leaving the rear portion of the billet in
the press. If a mandrel is not used, solid shapes of varying cross
section can be produced. Seamless tubing, architectural details and
shapes, rods, beams, channels, and similar products are made by the
extrusion process. Extrusion was originally performed on low-
melting metals and alloys. Its field of application was soon extended to include magnesium, aluminum, and copper. More recently steel, titanium, and high-temperature alloys have been successfully extruded on a commercial basis. Steel is extruded at
much higher temperatures (2300°F or 1260°C) than aluminum.
This permits the use of much lower pressures, but at the same time
results in much higher speeds of extrusion. Molten glass is used

as a lubricant for these difficult to extrude alloys which cause much more severe die wear than aluminum, magnesium, and copper.

16.18. Welded Pipe

Since both welding and forming are involved, the manufacture of welded pipe might be considered in the chapter on welding as well as in a discussion of mechanical working. Welded pipe is made from skelp, which is simply a narrow strip of metal. To make butt-welded pipe, the hot skelp is drawn through a welding bell, which rolls the strip into tubular form and exerts sufficient pressure to butt weld the edges together. This is shown in Fig. 16.22. Larger sizes of pipe are made from skelp which has beveled edges so that a lap weld can be made. Welds may be completed by hammer forging or by other means of applying pressure and heat simultaneously.

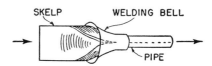

Fig. 16.22. Welded pipe. Skelp is being drawn through a welding bell, which curls it and forces the two edges together under high pressure to produce pipe having a welded seam.

Questions

16.1.   Why is the initial working of ingots carried out at elevated temperatures?

16.2.   What are *principal stresses?* Explain the numbering system and nomenclature used for the principal stresses. What basic expression relates deformation resistance, inelastic action, and the principal stresses?

16.3.   The deformation resistance of metals is a variable property. Upon what factors is this variation dependent?

16.4.   What is meant by *hot working?* Upon what does the hot-working temperature depend? Describe how the finished properties of the metal will be affected by the finishing temperature. How does hot working improve the homogeneity of the metal?

16.5.   Summarize the effects of hot working.

16.6.   What is meant by *cold working?* Describe the effects of cold work on the physical properties of the metal.

16.7. Summarize the effects of cold work on metals.

16.8. List and briefly describe the different kinds of rolling operations. What are the advantages of using small working rolls and large backing rolls? What is a cluster mill?

16.9. Describe and distinguish among drawing, sinking, and cupping.

16.10. Describe briefly how the following operations are performed: (a) forging; (b) swaging; (c) hydraulic piercing; (d) extrusion; (e) manufacture of butt-welded pipe.

16.11. Describe briefly the following operations: (a) deep drawing; (b) spinning; (c) coining; (d) embossing; (e) cold heading; (f) impact extrusion.

16.12. Why is control of the forging temperature important?

Bibliography

16.1. *The Making, Shaping, and Treating of Steel*, 6th ed. Pittsburgh: United States Steel Co., 1951.

16.2. *Forming Aluminum.* Louisville, Ky.: Reynolds Metals Co., 1952.

16.3. *Alcoa Aluminum Impact Extrusions.* Pittsburgh: Aluminum Company of America, 1948.

16.4. Burton, M. S., *Applied Metallurgy for Engineers.* New York: McGraw-Hill Book Co., Inc., 1956.

16.5. *Cold Working of Metals* (Seminar). Cleveland: American Society for Metals, 1948.

16.6. Sachs, G., and K. R. Van Horn, *Practical Metallurgy.* Cleveland: American Society for Metals, 1944.

16.7. *Metals Handbook*, 1948 ed. Cleveland: American Society for Metals.

16.8. *Metal Progress*, **66-1A** (July 15, 1954), Supplement to *Metals Handbook*, 1948 ed. Cleveland: American Society for Metals.

16.9. *Metal Progress*, **68-2A** (August 15, 1954), Supplement to *Metals Handbook*, 1948 ed. Cleveland: American Society for Metals.

16.10. Naujoks, W., and D. C. Fabel, *Forging Handbook.* Cleveland: American Society for Metals, 1939.

16.11. Kyle, P. E., *The Closed Die Forging Process.* New York: The Macmillan Co., 1954.

16.12. Evans, S. O., "Considerations for Selecting Steel Extrusions," *Metal Progress*, **67-4** (April 1955), pp. 91–95.

16.13. Crane, E. V., *Plastic Working in Presses*, 3rd ed. New York: John Wiley and Sons, Inc., 1945.

CHAPTER 17

Secondary Methods of Fabrication: Joining and Associated Operations

---

INTRODUCTORY REMARKS

17.1. Significance of Welding

It is often convenient and economical to fabricate metal structures by joining standard shapes. It may be easier to weld, braze, or solder several pieces of sheet, strip, plate, or bar stock to produce a particular shape than it is to produce the object by casting, mechanical working, machining, or a combination of these methods. Furthermore, a welded structure may be stronger than parts made by other means of fabrication. Although welding is probably the most widely used of the joining operations, brazing and soldering should not be overlooked. The strength of brazed and soldered joints is adequate for many purposes, and the comparative ease of such joining operations gives them a decided advantage for certain applications.

Features which distinguish welding methods. Many welding and joining methods have been devised. The major points of difference between these various methods are contained in the answers to the following questions:

1. How is the heat supplied?
2. What temperatures are attained?
3. What changes occur in the properties of the base metals? Can the properties of the base metal and joint be controlled?
4. What fluxes and shielding methods are used?
5. Is filler metal used?
6. Is pressure used?
7. Is the process readily adapted to automatic or semiautomatic control?

8. What is the relative cost of the process? This is a very complicated factor which depends upon the particular application. It is not discussed in this text.

The answers to these questions largely determine which process is best suited for a particular joining problem. Some of the answers depend upon the materials being joined and the effect to be achieved. The descriptions of the different joining operations center around a discussion of these questions.

In connection with joining operations, this chapter deals also with cutting and hard facing, both of which processes use methods and equipment similar to certain types of welding.

17.2. Definitions

Before proceeding with the topic of welding, a few definitions of the more common welding terms are given.

arc blow: The action of the arc playing over the surface of the metal being welded; the result of magnetic conditions.

axis of weld: The line through the weld and parallel to its route.

bare electrode: A solid uncoated metal electrode.

base metal: The metal being welded or cut.

bead: The portion of the joint which was heated to the melting temperature, in any single pass during welding.

butt joint: A joint in which the edges of the two plates to be joined lie in the same plane. [See Fig. 17.1 (*a*).]

coated electrode: A metal electrode which has a covering of appreciable thickness of some material which stabilizes the arc and improves the properties of the weld metal.

deposited metal: Filler metal, or metal which has been added by a welding process.

drawing the arc: The act of forming an arc between the electrode and the work, accomplished by touching the electrode to the work, thus completing the circuit, and then quickly withdrawing it a short distance.

filler metal: Deposited metal.

fillet weld: A joint in which the weld is made between two surfaces at right angles to one another. [See Fig. 17.1 (*b*).]

fusion zone: The portion of the joint heated to the melting temperature during welding.

heat-affected zone: That portion of the base metal whose structure or properties have been altered by the heating, or by the heating and cooling, of welding and cutting.

horizontal weld: A weld deposited so that the axis of the weld is

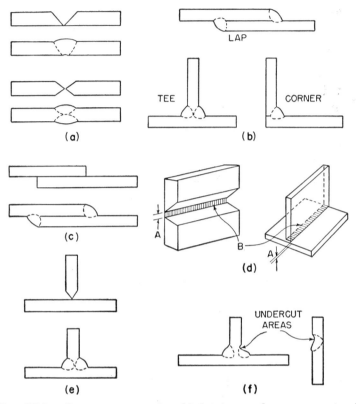

Fig. 17.1. Common types of welded joints and terms associated with them. (a) Single-V and double-V butt joints before and after welding. (b) Fillet welds in different kinds of joints. (c) Lap joint before and after welding. (d) Root of joint and root opening. The root of joint is the space between the closest approach of members being joined as indicated by B. The root opening is the distance of closest approach as shown by A. (e) T-joint before and after welding. (f) Undercutting in a T-joint and butt weld. [Part (d) adapted from *Welding Handbook*, Third Edition, p. 37. American Welding Society, 1950.]

within about 30° of the horizontal, with the electrode pointed in a general downward direction.

lap joint: A joint which is made by welding together two overlapping pieces of base metal. [See Fig. 17.1(*c*).]

overhead weld: A weld deposited so that the axis of the weld is within about 60° of the horizontal, with the electrode pointed in a general upward direction.

pass: The portion of the joint completed by one progression along the length of the weld.

penetration: The depth of fusion in the base metal of a weld.

rate of deposition: The amount of metal deposited in a unit time.

root: A section at the bottom of the cross-sectional space provided to contain a weld. [See Fig. 17.1(d).]

scarf: The chamfered surface of a joint.

spatter: The wasteful deposition of filler metal around and near the weld, but not in the zone of fusion.

tack weld: A temporary joint used for assembly purposes only.

tee joint: A joint, the cross section of which resembles the letter T. [See Fig. 17.1(e).]

undercut: A reduction in the cross section of a weld, caused by improper welding technique. [See Fig. 17.1(f).]

vertical weld: A weld deposited so that the axis of the weld is within about 30° of the vertical.

weld metal: The metal of which the weld is formed. The weld metal may consist of either filler metal, base metal, or both.

WELDING PROCESSES

17.3. Forge Welding

Although forge welding is the oldest of the joining operations, it is probably the least widely used. The equipment required is very simple, though not as convenient as that used for more modern joining methods. Essential to forge welding are a small forge, in which coke or charcoal is burned by a blast of air, a hammer, an anvil, and some tongs for holding the work. The wrought iron or steel being welded is first heated in the forge. When at the proper temperature the work is removed, and under the pressure of hammer blows the weld is completed. A borax flux is often used to prevent oxidation of the hot metal and to float impurities away from the surfaces being joined, so that a clean, sound weld results. Forge welding is limited to fairly small pieces and is not suited to the welding of long seams. It is further limited by the considerable skill required to produce a good joint.

17.4. Gas Welding

Heat is usually supplied for gas welding by an oxygen-acetylene flame. Less frequently an oxygen-hydrogen flame is used. Temperatures produced by the flames are well above the melting points of any of the common engineering metals. The base metal is invariably melted in the immediate vicinity of the joint.

In the gas welding of steel, properties of the base metal and weld may be controlled by proper manipulation of the welding torch. The temperatures in the weld and base metal vary between the melting point of steel and room temperature. Portions of steel heated above the critical range undergo recrystallization and grain growth, and upon rapid cooling, hardening of the base metal may occur. Hardening is accompanied by embrittling of the steel, and this is undesirable because the weld then loses impact strength and toughness. The rapid cooling which causes hardening can be readily prevented simply by increasing the heat input. The heat input may be increased independently of the amount of metal deposited, thus providing gas welding a distinct advantage over electric arc welding. Furthermore, by playing the flame over areas which tend to harden, slow cooling can be achieved. Thus, compared to electric arc welding, gas welding provides greater flexibility with respect to heat input and cooling rates. (When non-ferrous metals are gas welded, the effect of cooling rates on structure is usually not significant.)

Both coated and bare rods are used to provide filler metal. The coated rods supply a protective liquid slag cover. When uncoated rods are used, protection of the hot weld is achieved by adjusting the gas flame. Fluxes in the form of powders, pastes, or rod coatings are more common for gas welding of nonferrous metals, where they afford protection and also flush out impurities. Although pressure may be used in certain gas welding applications, it is not generally used.

Gas welding has been adapted to automatic or semiautomatic controls. This is practical only if there are large numbers of parts requiring the same welding sequences. One of the most successful applications of automatic gas welding is in welding sheet steel.

17.5. Resistance Welding

The resistance of the work piece to the flow of current through it is the source of heat in resistance welding. In flash welding, which is a special form of resistance welding, the heat of an electric arc is an additional source of energy. The temperatures produced in resistance welding are always above the melting point of the metal being welded. Although the properties of the metal in the weld zone are affected by the process, the effect is less important than with some other types of welding. High temperatures are produced over only a very localized area, and the amount of metal involved is fairly small. Original properties can be restored, if necessary, by suitable heat treatment. Usually the change in properties is minor and of no consequence in the types of structure fabricated by resistance welding.

Fluxes and shielding gases are rarely used, nor is filler metal needed for resistance welding. Pressure, however, is required for *all* resistance welding processes. A wide range of pressures is involved, depending upon the materials being joined and the type of resistance welding. Automatic control of resistance welding is widespread; in fact, manual operation is restricted largely to job shops, where small lots or individual pieces are to be fabricated.

There are four principal varieties of resistance welding, which are represented in Fig. 17.2. These are (1) spot, (2) seam, (3) projection, and (4) flash. In the first three, the generation of heat depends upon the square of the current flow, the time of current flow, and the resistance of the workpiece:

$$H \infty I^2Rt$$

(This simple formula is not applicable to flash welding because part of the heat is produced by an electric arc.) At the same time heat is being produced, it is also being dissipated by the electrodes and metal in the vicinity of the weld. Neglecting this loss of heat, it can be seen that doubling the current produces equivalent temperature in only one-quarter of the time. Decreasing the time requirement results in greater output and lower costs. A limit is reached when current values become excessively high and produce undesirable surface markings in the work.

For **spot welding,** the essential parts of a typical welding machine are as follows:

(1) A step-down transformer capable of delivering high currents (up to several hundred thousand amperes for heavy work) and low voltages (usually below 30 volts).

(2) Copper electrodes to conduct the current to the work. These are hollow electrodes which are prevented from overheating by cooling water circulated through them.

(3) A mechanical electrode holder which can be opened and closed quickly, and which is capable of exerting a controlled amount of pressure.

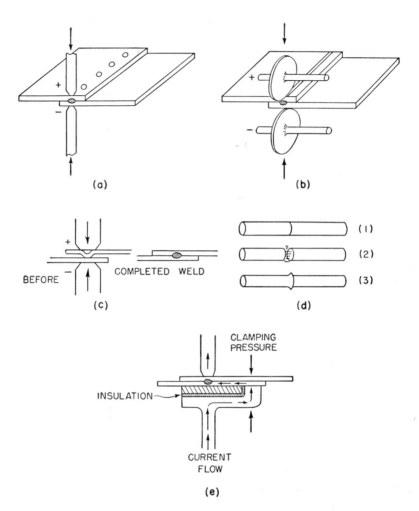

(a)

(b)

BEFORE   COMPLETED WELD

(1)

(2)

(3)

(c)

(d)

CLAMPING
PRESSURE

INSULATION

CURRENT
FLOW

(e)

Fig. 17.2. Simple sketches illustrating different resistance welding operations. (a) Spot welding. Pressure in line with the electrodes forces the work pieces together. (b) Seam welding. The electrodes are circular and may be considered to produce a series of overlapping spots. (c) Projection welding. This is a modification of spot welding, which has special application to certain combinations and thickness of metals being welded. (d) Flash welding. The sequence involves (1) making contact, (2) drawing an arc until sufficient heat is produced so that when (3), the two pieces are forced together and allowed to cool, a joint is made. (e) A special modification of spot welding where surface appearance of the part is improved by conducting the current to the weld area from a distant point. [Part (e) adapted from *Welding Handbook*, p. 382, 1950.]

(4) A timing device to regulate the time of current flow. The work is placed between the electrodes, which are then closed so as to exert the required pressure. A timing device provides the proper current flow for the desired length of time. This causes fusion of the sheetmetal workpiece, which is removed when the electrodes are opened.

Most spot welders are permanent installations to which the work is brought for joining. However, portable spot welders are also available, in which the electrodes are connected to the source of power and water by flexible cable and hose. A spot-welding gun of this design can be brought to workpieces which are too large to position between rigidly fixed electrodes. Spot welders are also provided with multiple electrodes for making multiple welds. When the appearance of an exposed surface is of extreme importance, the current may be conducted to the weld area through the work from a distant point. This is shown in Fig. 17.2(e).

Seam welders are essentially the same as spot welders. See Fig. 17.2(b). The fundamental difference is the substitution of welding wheels for spot-welding electrodes. This has the effect of producing a continuous seam weld similar to that obtained by a series of overlapping spot welds. The work is forced between the water-cooled welding wheels under controlled pressures. One or both of the wheels may be power driven. Operating speeds vary up to about 60 feet per minute.

Projection welding requires essentially the same equipment as spot welding, and embodies the same principles. For projection welding one or both of the pieces to be welded are embossed, and current flow is localized through the raised points of contact. This is shown in Fig. 17.2(c). The embossed projections are often circular in shape. Projection welders use larger electrodes, which result in longer electrode life. The pressure used for projection welding must not cause collapse of the projection during the heating cycle. Some materials having low hot strength are not readily projection welded because they cannot withstand the pressures required. Among these are bronze, brass, and copper.

Flash and butt welders are similar to one another. In butt welding the two pieces are rigidly held in a clamping device and forced together under pressure. Current flowing through the two pieces causes heating at the interface (where resistance is highest), and a weld results. Flash welders are equipped with similar clamps, but the two pieces are not in intimate contact during the initial stages of the operation. Rather, they are separated at first by a narrow gap across which arcing acts as the principal source of heat. When the proper temperature is reached, pressure is applied to the work, the current flow is stopped, and the weld is completed. Flash welding is favored over butt welding because a stronger weld usually results. Flash welding also requires less careful preparation of the surfaces to be joined, because surface irregularities tend to be burned smooth during flashing. Furthermore, flash welding is more economical from the standpoint of power consumption. Both flash and butt welding are used for welding large shafts (up to 500 square inches), bars, the ends of strips (to make a continuous length), and similar applications.

17.6. Arc Welding

The source of heat in all arc-welding processes is an electric arc. In some processes the arc occurs between a single electrode and the work, and in others it is formed between two electrodes. The temperatures produced are always well above the melting points of the common engineering metals. The base metal is almost always melted during arc welding.

There are wide variations in fluxes and shielding methods for different arc-welding processes. In a few cases, shielding is not provided nor is a flux used. In other applications one or the other may be provided. Except in the case of stud welding, pressure is not very widely used, and when it is used it is not applied simultaneously with heating. Filler metal is usually required, and it is usually supplied by the electrode itself, except in carbon-arc and inert-gas metal-arc welding.

The two principal kinds of arc welding are metal-arc welding and carbon-arc welding. Four important variations of the metal-arc processes are discussed first. This is followed by a discussion of two types of carbon-arc welding.

Probably the most common welding process is **shielded metal-arc welding.** In this process, an electric arc is maintained between a coated metal electrode and the base metal being welded. The arc provides the heat required to melt both the base metal and the electrode. The joint is formed when the molten metal solidifies.

The temperatures attained in a given weld depend upon three factors:

(1) The energy input, which is related to the current used and rate of metal deposition.

(2) The original temperature of the base metal.

(3) The heat loss from the weld to the base metal and surroundings. This depends upon plate dimensions and shape, and to some extent on the thermal conductivity of the plate.

Control of temperature is largely accomplished by means of regulating energy input, which also determines rate of metal deposition. Some control also can be achieved by preheating the base metal before welding.

Shielded metal-arc welding may affect the properties of the base metal. This is very noticeable in steels, which undergo phase changes during cooling from above the melting point. As pointed out in the chapter on heat treatment of steel, the properties of a piece of steel are altered greatly by variations in the rate of cooling of the steel through the range over which the transformations occur. Other forms of arc welding exert similar effects on the properties of the base metal. It is possible to control these effects by preheating, by controlling the speed of welding, and by annealing after welding.

The coated electrodes used for shielded metal-arc welding provide the flux and shielding gases for the weld. The coating of the electrode is melted, vaporized, or oxidized by the heat of the arc. The gases so formed provide a protective blanket which excludes the oxygen and nitrogen of the air from the molten weld metal. In addition, some of the flux reacts with impurities in the bead to produce a slag. The slag particles float to the top and form a protective cover over the molten metal. This is later chipped off. A superior coating is used on rods known as iron-powder electrodes. These electrode coatings consist mainly of a mixture of iron powder and titania. They offer the advantages of faster deposition rates and more effective use of metal. Iron-powder rods make welds with flat or concave surface, as contrasted to other rods, which tend to produce a useless convexity at the surface. Iron-powder rods also cause less spatter, but do not have as good penetration as other electrodes. Lack of penetration is advantageous when fit-up is poor, but it is otherwise considered a disadvantage.

Shielded metal-arc welding is carried on without the use of pressure.

The electrodes used for shielded metal-arc welding not only serve to conduct current but also provide filler metal. They are supplied in the form of short, coated rods for manual welding. For automatic welding the electrode is supplied as a long, coiled length.

A small amount of metal-arc welding is carried out using bare electrodes. The lack of shielding and fluxing produces in most cases a weld which is inferior in strength, ductility, toughness, corrosion resistance, and porosity. For this reason shielded metal-arc welding is usually preferred.

Submerged arc welding is largely an automatic process, although it has been adapted to some manual applications. An arc formed below the shielding material and between the electrode and base metal is the source of heat. The temperatures attained are well above the melting point of the base metal. By using large quantities of current and slow welding speeds it is possible to weld up to 3-inch plate with a single pass. The properties of the base metal are affected by this welding process in much the same way as by shielded metal-arc welding.

The flux material for submerged arc welding is supplied in the form of ground mineral matter. This material is often delivered at a constant rate just ahead of the arc. The electrode consists of bare coiled wire which is fed down below the surface of the fluxing material. The arc is thus beneath the surface of the flux, and there is no glare or spatter. The heat of the arc melts not only the electrode and base metal, but also the fluxing mineral. The flux reacts with impurities in the weld and forms a fused slag cover over the hot metal, thus protecting it from reaction with the air. Portions of the flux which are not melted by the heat of welding are collected, often by a vacuum system, so that they may be used over again. The slag is later chipped from the weld.

The electrode wire supplies whatever filler is needed for submerged arc welding. Since there is almost complete exclusion of the air from the weld, wire containing easily oxidized alloys can be used successfully. By selecting electrode wire of proper alloy content, good quality welds are possible in alloy base metals which are less conveniently welded by other methods. Pressure is not used for submerged arc welding.

The submerged arc process is readily adapted to automatic control, in which form it finds widest application. It has the limitation that it must be carried out in the horizontal or nearly horizontal position, otherwise the fluxing powder slides off the base metal. It has been quite successfully used in connection with fixtures which hold and position the work during welding.

Gas-shielded metal-arc welding is a process in which heat is developed by an arc formed between the workpiece and an electrode. There are two major versions of gas-shielded metal-arc welding. The *older* version uses a very slowly consumed ("nonconsumable") tungsten electrode which serves only to carry the current that produces the arc. In this process, if filler rod is needed, it is fed independently into the arc where it is melted. The *newer* version uses an electrode wire, which not only carries the current but also provides filler metal as it is rapidly melted. The temperatures involved are always well above the melting point of the base metal and also of the filler metal, when the latter is used.

Although the properties of the base metal and welding rod may be altered by gas-shielded metal-arc welding, the weld is in many instances superior to that achieved by other means. This is because no flux is used and hence the welds are virtually free from flux and slag entrapment. The welds are bright and clean and require no slag chipping. The oxygen of the air is almost totally excluded by the inert gas blanket which covers the work and arc. The gas is led down to the head of the welding torch, where it escapes from a nozzle near the tip of the electrode. The head of the torch is cooled by water. If the cooling water supply fails, the power is shut off automatically.

When tungsten electrodes are used the shielding gas is helium or argon. These gases were also initially used for shielding in consumable electrode welding. However, research led to the development of a successful process in which carbon dioxide is the shielding gas. Carbon dioxide can provide shielding at about one-twentieth the cost of the inert gases. Although carbon dioxide is not, strictly speaking, an inert gas, the process using it as a shielding medium is sometimes classified as an inert-gas metal-arc process.

Different effects are achieved by the use of straight polarity direct current, reversed polarity direct current, and alternating current. A brief discussion of these considerations follows. Figure 17.3

illustrates the meaning of these terms. *Straight polarity direct current* is used for those applications in which the base metal is not readily oxidizable. The electrode is held negative while the work is positive. Therefore electrons stream from the electrode to the

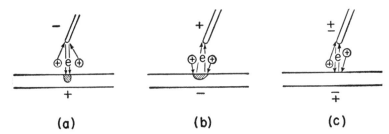

(a)   **(b)**   **(c)**

Fig. 17.3. D.c. and a.c. welding compared. (a) D.c. straight polarity. Electrons flow from electrode to work, creating intense heat and a narrow, penetrating bead. Positive gas ions flow from work to electrode. (b) D.c. reverse polarity. Positive gas ions bombard the work and break up oxides in the weld puddle. Electrode tends to overheat and must be large enough in size to permit cooling. A broad flat bead is produced. (c) A.c. welding. Actually straight and reverse polarity cycles follow each other at short time intervals in a.c. welding.

work and most of the heat is produced in the work rather than in the electrode. Positively charged gas ions flow from the work to the electrode. Because of the efficient production of heat in the work rather than at the electrode, it is possible to use a smaller electrode. With these small electrodes narrow, deep penetration of the weld is obtained. However, since the positive gas ions bombard the electrode rather than the work, there is no breakup of oxides in the surface of the weld puddle. With *reverse polarity direct current* a larger electrode is required because the electrode is held positive and the work is held negative. Thus electrons stream from the work to the electrode, and heat is generated at the latter point. At the same time, gas ions stream from the electrode toward the work and bombard the surface oxides which form in the weld puddle. The heavier or more dense the gas which is used for shielding, the more efficient is the breakup of these undesirable surface impurities. Argon, having ten times the density of helium, exerts a much greater "sandblasting" effect. Since most of the heat goes into the electrode, it is necessary to use a larger electrode which lends itself to more efficient cooling. Reverse polarity gives a shallow, wide bead. In inert-gas metal-arc welding using *alternating current,* there is actually a combination of dc straight polarity and dc reverse polarity welding. During the reverse portion of the cycle, the oxides in the weld puddle are broken up; but during the straight portion of the cycle, the oxides which momentarily exist in the surface metal serve to impede the flow of electrons from the work to the electrode and thus prevent overheating it.

Consumption of the tungsten electrode is an important consideration in inert-gas metal-arc welding. The electrode may be consumed by oxidation following a welding sequence if the gas protection is discontinued while the electrode is still very hot. The electrode also may be volatilized slowly, but this is usually considered a minor source of loss of the electrode. In dc reverse polarity welding the electrode must be held very close to the metal so that the resistance to current flow in this type of welding may be overcome. As a result of the short arc, the electrode picks up impurities unless the operator is very skilled or unless automatic welding is being used. Tungsten impurities go into the weld if the electrode becomes contaminated with base metal. If contaminated with stainless steel, the electrode must be ground clean in order to continue welding. Impurity pickup is particularly bad in working with aluminum, but not serious for magnesium.

Inert-gas metal-arc welding has been used both as a manual and an automatic process. Pressure is not used. The principal applications of the process are in the joining of aluminum, magnesium, high alloy steel, stainless steel, nickel alloys, brass, and silicon bronze. CO_2-shielded welding is particularly useful for mild steel; by this process, sound, clean, flux-free welds can be produced.

Stud welding is a highly specialized form of arc welding. It is used principally for attaching studs to plate and for similar applications. A stud is held in a welding gun [as shown in Fig. 17.4 (a)] or chuck, which positions it properly on the base plate. An arc of fairly short duration locally heats and melts both base plate and stud. Pressure is immediately applied and the joint is completed. Stud welding may be unshielded or shielded. Shielding, when used, is provided by an inert gas or by flux contained in the end of the stud. The flux is melted by the heat of welding and forms a slag which is later chipped off. This is a quick and economical means of attaching studs to plates, for it avoids the necessity of drilling, reaming, and tapping stud holes. The joint provided is a strong one.

Carbon-arc welding. The most important carbon-arc welding processes involve the use of (1) a flux or (2) an inert shielding gas, as shown in Fig. 17.4(*b*). The discussion which follows applies to these two methods. The source of heat for much carbon-arc welding is an arc drawn between the work and a carbon electrode. In twin carbon-arc welding (also known as double carbon-arc welding) the arc is drawn between two carbon electrodes. The arc is held close enough to the work to heat it. The twin carbon arc is also used for brazing and soldering, but in these applications the base metal is not melted.

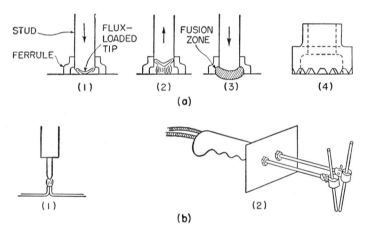

Fig. 17.4. **Miscellaneous welding processes.** (a) The sequence of stud welding. (1) Make contact. (2) Break contact and produce arc to melt base metal and end of stud. (3) Force stud into pool of molten metal and hold until solidification is complete. (4) A section through a ferrule. (b) Carbon-arc welding. (1) A carbon electrode used to edge-weld without addition of filler metal. (2) A twin carbon-arc torch.

Steels tend to change properties markedly when carbon-arc welded. Control of resulting properties is essentially dependent upon the same variables as in other kinds of arc welding, namely the balance between heat input and dissipation.

Fluxes are used in shielded carbon-arc welding. The flux performs the usual functions, such as protecting the hot metal from the air, reducing spray and spatter, and combining with impurities to form a slag cover and produce a better weld. Several types of flux are available, depending upon the particular application. For steels up to about $\frac{1}{4}$-inch thick, a paste flux may be painted on the seam before welding.   For heavier steel plate, a powdered flux is used, which forms a heavy slag.   A chemically impregnated paper cord is also commonly used for aluminum and stainless steels.   Sometimes the filler rod is coated with the fluxing material.

In inert-gas carbon-arc welding a flux is not necessarily used.   In any event, an inert-gas blanket of helium or argon envelopes the hot metal and retards or prevents oxidation.   The flux, if used with an inert-gas shield, is principally a scavenging agent.

Filler metal and pressure may or may not be used in carbon-arc welding.   When pressure is involved, it is applied after heating.

Carbon-arc welding is more readily adapted to automatic controls than to manual operation.   Because of the erratic behavior of the carbon arc, a superimposed magnetic field is often applied.   By applying the field, an arc which is of a nonpenetrating nature can be given a gouging characteristic.   In this way, deep penetration of welds can be achieved, thus making it possible to weld plates without special edge preparation.   There is also an absence of spray and spatter which produces good appearance with minimum of cleanup.   Automatic carbon-arc welding is used for producing tanks, automotive and refrigerator parts, steel barrels, and similar objects.   Carbon steel, stainless steel, aluminum, and copper and their alloys have been welded successfully by this method.

17.7. Thermit Welding

In thermit welding heat is provided by a chemical reaction between iron oxide and powdered aluminum, according to the reaction:

$$8Al + 3Fe_3O_4 \longrightarrow 4Al_2O_3 + 9Fe + \text{heat}$$

The temperatures produced by this reaction are far above the melting point of steel, which is the only metal joined by the process. Iron oxide is reduced to iron by the aluminum, to supply filler metal. Sufficient carbon is provided in the powdered mixture so that actually molten steel, rather than iron, is the filler.   Within certain limitations it is also possible to add other alloying elements to produce alloy steel welds of high strength.

Thermit welding is particularly suited to welding rather heavy sections such as rails, large crankshafts, heavy steel castings, and similar objects.   The parts to be joined are positioned in a fixture which holds them a certain distance apart. The distance separating the parts depends upon their size. This space is then filled with wax which is given the shape of the joint to be made. A form corresponding to a molding flask is placed around the joint, into which sand is rammed, as shown in Fig. 17.5. Heat is then applied to melt out the wax and leave a void of the desired shape. Additional heating serves to dry out the sand mold and preheat the pieces being joined, so that better fusion is obtained.

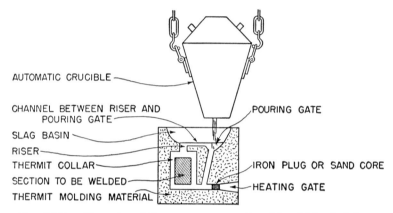

Fig. 17.5. Thermit welding apparatus and mold. [Adapted from *Welding Handbook*, p. 458, 1950.]

In the meantime, the correct amounts of iron oxide and aluminum and the necessary alloying elements are placed in a bottom-pour crucible. The powder is ignited, and after the reaction is completed the molten metal is poured into the mold. The aluminum oxide forms a light slag which floats on the surface of the molten steel.

Thermit welding is carried out also with the aid of pressure. In this operation the pieces to be joined are placed in intimate contact. The thermit reaction simply supplies the heat required. The molten steel serves as a heating medium but does not act as filler metal. Pressure is applied after the parts become hot, to complete the weld. Aluminum oxide slag coats the surfaces of the pieces being welded and thus prevents adherence of the molten steel to them.

17.8. Hard Facing

Special welding processes in which a hard alloy is deposited on the wearing surface of a metal are known as hard facing. The hard alloy can be applied by gas torch or by electric welding. This makes possible the use of lower cost, tougher materials for the major portion of the part. The expensive, wear-resistant (often brittle) alloy is restricted to those regions where it affords maximum advantage.

THE METALLURGY OF WELDING

No discussion of welding is complete without some mention of the metallurgy of welding. This is an extremely interesting topic because it involves a good many fundamental metallurgical, physical, and chemical principles.

17.9. Similarity Between Castings and Welds

Whenever a weld is made, the *zone of fusion* may be considered to be a miniature *casting*. The metal adjacent to the zone of fusion is at a relatively low temperature, thus a temperature gradient is established across the weld. This gradient, combined with fairly rapid rates of heat extraction by conduction of heat through the plate, promotes the formation of columnar grains. [See Fig. 17.6(a).] The size of these grains in many steel welds is such that they can be seen by the naked eye when macroetched.

In addition to the columnar grain structure which is typical of castings, the fusion zone may resemble castings in other ways. Slag, formed from the coating material on the welding rod or by its reaction with impurities, may be found in the bead metal. In addition to slag pockets, there may be void spaces caused by the evolution of dissolved gases from the bead, or by internal shrinkage during solidification or cooling.

17.10. Changes Produced in the Base Metal by Welding

In the base metal some interesting changes may take place as a result of the temperatures attained. In steel, and other metals undergoing phase transformations, the cooling rate and the maximum temperature are of extreme importance. The nature of the changes taking place in steel is fully described in the chapters on heat treating of steel.

First let us consider the case of a metal which exists as a single phase throughout the joining operation. If this metal is in the fully annealed condition, no changes occur. However, if the metal has been cold worked prior to welding, the portions of it which are heated to the annealing temperature undergo recrystallization and perhaps grain growth. This is shown in Fig. 17.6 (d). Relief of the residual stresses of cold working probably occurs over an even larger area. However, due to the restraint exerted by a rigidly welded body upon thermal expansion and contraction, residual stresses from welding may replace the original residual stresses. The recrystallized metal tends to be weaker and more ductile than the original metal. This is undesirable in the case of joining metals which have been intentionally hardened by cold working prior to welding.

In steels, a recrystallization occurs where the steel is heated above the critical temperature range (see chapter on heat treating of steel). At locations in the weld where the temperature is higher than this, grain growth occurs. This is shown in Fig. 17.6 (b). For temperatures below the critical points there is no recrystallization, unless previous cold work and annealing are involved.

In steels containing sufficient carbon and alloying elements, even more important changes in structure and properties result if the rate of cooling after welding is high enough. When this is the case, regions which are austenitic at the high temperature of welding may transform to the hard, brittle, martensitic structure. This structure lacks toughness. There may be other structures representing intermediate cooling rates which produce mixtures of martensite, bainite, and pearlite. Thus a steel weld may show a cast structure in the bead, with recrystallized ferrite and pearlite, and in some cases bainite or martensite in the heat-affected zone. Further away from the centerline, the unaffected structure of the base metal persists.

17.11. Factors Determining Maximum Temperatures and Cooling Rates Attained

The temperatures reached and the subsequent cooling rates determine the properties and microstructure of the bead and heat-affected zone. Therefore it is important to consider the factors upon which they depend. Disregarding heat losses to the air from the weld, the only other possibility for heat extraction is through the base metal. This being so, the temperature produced

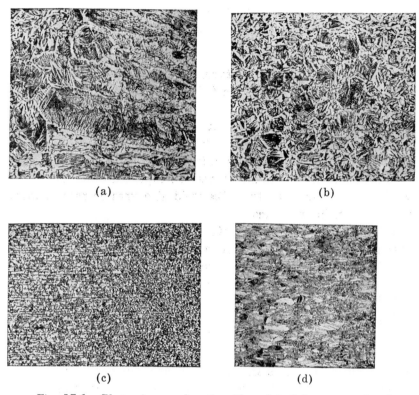

(a) (b)

(c) (d)

Fig. 17.6. Photomicrographs of welds. (a) Columnar grains in
bead of a mild steel weld. The left-hand edge of the photo shows
recrystallized base metal. (b) A portion of the base metal in a
mild steel plate which has been welded. Recrystallization and grain
growth have occurred because of the intense heat in the vicinity of
the bead. (c) Another portion of the base metal in a mild steel
plate which has been welded. This portion represents a region
somewhat further removed from the bead than the portion shown in
(b). The right-hand half of the photo shows that recrystallization
and grain refinement have occurred because of the heat of welding.
However, the heat was not intense enough to cause grain growth.
The left-hand edge of the photo shows the original structure of the
base plate, having a direction of rolling parallel to the bottom of
the page as indicated by the banded ferrite. (d) Recrystallization
in the heat-affected zone of a weld in cold-rolled alpha-brass. The
flattened grains of the cold-rolled brass are at the left of the photo-
micrograph, and the fine, equiaxed, recrystallized grains are on
the right. [Parts (a), (b), and (c) were etched in nital and photographed at 75×; courtesy of the School of Engineering, Metals
Laboratory, University of Massachusetts. Part (d) was etched in
$NH_4OH + H_2O_2$ and photographed at 75×; courtesy of Mr. I. T.
Hook and the American Brass Company.]

in the piece depends upon the balance between energy input and heat losses. Maximum temperature and cooling rates are determined by four factors:

(1) *Original plate temperature.* If the plate is cold when welded, the drop in temperature following welding is much faster than if the plate is preheated.

(2) *Plate thickness.* The heat capacity of a thick plate is greater than that of a thin plate. Thus for a given heat input, the temperature of a thick plate is raised less than the temperature of a thin plate. Since the difference in temperature produces heat flow, the heat flows away from the weld at a greater rate in thick materials than in thin ones.

(3) *Plate geometry.* This refers to comparisons such as those between tee and butt welds. (See Fig. 17.1.) The rate of heat extraction from a tee joint is higher than from a butt weld, and hence the cooling rate is higher for the tee.

(4) *Energy input.* In metal-arc welding an increase in the energy input is achieved simultaneously with an increase in the size of the deposit. (In gas welding and carbon-arc welding heat input can be controlled independently of the size of the deposit.) The energy input is expressed in terms of heat input per inch of weld. Increasing the heat input has the same effect as increasing the plate temperature, prior to welding. It therefore reduces the cooling rate.

When a weld is made by a series of overlaying passes, the first passes contribute less to embrittlement than the last one. This is because of the annealing and tempering action of each pass on every previously deposited bead.

In addition to embrittlement caused by martensite formation another factor is believed to cause loss of ductility. It has been proposed that this embrittling action is connected with what is known as strain aging in steel, which is probably a form of precipitation hardening promoted by straining. Embrittlement has been detected in areas of the plate which have been heated, by welding to temperatures in the neighborhood of 900°F. The strain necessary to induce strain aging is the result of the rigidity of the welded structure, which opposes the thermal expansion and contraction associated with welding temperatures. The most serious loss of ductility and impact strength occurs when the weld is later subjected to temperatures near 40°F.

17.12. Heat Treatment of Welds

Welds are frequently postheated for various reasons. If martensite is present, its impact strength and toughness are improved by the action of tempering. If the period of heating is sufficiently long and the temperatures attained are sufficiently high, the martensitic structure may be replaced entirely by a spheroidal or pearlitic structure. In cases where there is no martensite, postheating may be intended to relieve residual stresses. Residual stresses result from the uneven expansion and contraction of the weld during and following welding. These have an embrittling effect, and it is desirable in many cases that they be removed. In this case, postheating takes the form of a stress relief anneal. Heat treatment is sometimes used to restore corrosion resistance after welding or cutting stainless steels.

In the welding of 18-8 stainless steel containing more than 0.08 per cent carbon, there is danger of loss of corrosion resistance at the grain boundaries, followed by intergranular corrosion. Corrosion resistance is lost in those regions of the weld which are slowly cooled through a critical temperature range near 1400°F. In this temperature range, precipitation of chromium carbide is promoted. The precipitation occurs mainly at the grain boundaries, and depletes the surrounding areas of chromium, which then lose their corrosion resistance. The precipitation of carbides can be prevented by:

(1) Reducing the carbon content below 0.02 per cent.

(2) Using columbium or titanium or other elements which form stable carbides with the carbon present, thus preventing reaction between chromium and carbon.

(3) Cooling the heat-affected zone quickly through the critical range.

(4) Heating above 1750°F following welding to redissolve chromium carbides, then rapidly cooling the steel to retain chromium in solution.

BRAZING AND SOLDERING

17.13. Brazing

One of the outstanding *differences* between brazing and welding is the lower range of temperatures used for brazing. In welding operations (except in forge welding) a portion of the base metal is melted. In brazing operations, the temperatures used are well below the melting point of the base metal. The properties of the base metal may be altered by brazing, but the change is less extensive than would be caused by welding. Cold-worked metals may undergo recrystallization and softening; metals hardened by heat treatment may lose some of their hardness.

A *fluxing* material is almost always used for brazing. The flux is frequently a salt or mixture of salts applied as dry powder, paste, or solution. The composition of the flux is such that it is molten at the temperature of brazing. It melts and flows over the surfaces of the heated metal pieces which are to be joined. In this way the oxygen of the air is excluded and oxidation is prevented. If a thin film of oxide is present it is washed away by the flux. Borax is a common flux for brazing.

Filler metal is used in all brazing operations. The selection of the filler metal is usually such that it melts at least 200°F below the melting point of the base metal. Two broad classes of brazing alloys have been developed (1) the silver solders, which are essentially silver-copper-zinc alloys for use at temperatures from 1200° to 1600°F, and (2) the copper alloys, which often are copper-zinc alloys, for use at temperatures from 1400° to 2100°F. The filler metal should also have fairly good oxidation resistance and should be capable of wetting the surfaces of the metal being joined. It may be inserted in the joint in powder or thin sheet form, and then heated to its melting point. In other cases filler rod may be fed to the vicinity of the joint, where it is melted and sucked into the joint by capillary action. For capillary action to be effective, the joints must be properly fitted. In still another variation of the process, the joint may be dipped in a pot of the molten filler metal.

Heat is supplied in a variety of different ways. As already mentioned, a gas-fired or electrically heated pot of the brazing alloy may be used. Hot salt baths are also used, and in this case the filler metal is applied in a separate operation prior to dipping into the salt bath. A very common source of heat is a torch using air or oxygen in combination with acetylene, hydrogen, or other gas. Sometimes the joints are assembled, with the filler metal in place, and passed through a furnace on a conveyor belt. Resistance and induction heating also have been used successfully. A twin carbon arc is another source of heat frequently used.

The *strength* of brazed joints is often considered to be lower than that of the base metal, but this depends upon the materials being joined.   The joint itself, by proper design, may be made stronger than other portions of a brazed structure, although brazed bonds are usually weaker than similar welded joints.   The strength of brazed joints is believed to be the result of diffusion between base metal and brazing metal.

Because of wide variations in brazing problems a general statement about adaptability to automatic methods is not possible. Some operations, or at least certain phases of them, are suited to automatic controls, whereas others are essentially manual methods.

17.14. Soldering

In many respects soldering is similar to brazing.   Soldering, however, is carried out at much lower temperatures than is brazing, i.e., at about 300° to 600°F.   Because of this, there is a negligible effect on the properties of the base metal as a result of the heating cycle involved.   Fluxes are used in most soldering operations. They serve to dissolve oxides and dirt films which would otherwise prevent the solder from wetting the base metal.   The sources of heat used for soldering are essentially those used for brazing, with the important addition of the familiar soldering iron.

The soldered joint, unless reinforced by threading, crimping, or bolting, is not as strong as the metals being joined.   The function of soldering is rarely to provide high strength, but rather to provide good contact or a fluid-tight seal, or to lock together movable parts. In fact, it has been found that the thinner the solder film, the stronger is the joint.   Alloying takes place during soldering by mutual diffusion of solder and base metal.   Because of the lower temperatures, less alloying occurs than in brazing.   In some cases excessive diffusion may produce weak, brittle alloys which are undesirable.

METAL CUTTING

The equipment used for arc and gas welding has been adapted to the cutting of metals.   The greatest use for these cutting methods has been in the field of ferrous alloys.   Five means of metal cutting are summarized below.

17.15. Flame Cutting

An oxyacetylene or similar gas torch is used to preheat the metal to be cut by flame cutting. When the metal is at its ignition temperature, excess oxygen is supplied, and the metal is burned away:

$$4Fe + 3O_2 \longrightarrow 2Fe_2O_3 + \text{heat}$$

The heat liberated from the oxidation reaction is sufficient in many cases to bring nearby metal to its ignition temperature, thus continuing the cut. In some instances, preheating is continued in order to promote smoother, better cuts. In addition to removal of the metal by oxidation, erosion of the hot metal also results from the movement of the gas stream and suspended solid particles over the face of the material being cut. The same principles apply to the use of an oxygen lance. In this instance, oxygen under high pressure is conducted through an iron pipe to the preheated steel which is to be cut. The oxygen burns through the base metal and slowly consumes the pipe through which it is carried. Preheating of the base metal is accomplished by an oxyacetylene torch or by drawing an arc between work and lance.

Flame cutting is not as applicable to cast iron and high-alloy steels, particularly stainless steels, as are some other cutting methods. However, stainless steels have been cut by stacking alternate sheets of stainless and plain carbon steel. The readily oxidizable carbon steel provides the heat necessary to cut the oxidation resistant stainless steel.

Oxyacetylene flames are used for precision machine cutting of shapes, and produce surfaces comparable to rough machine cuts. Operations similar to planing, milling, and turning are successfully carried out.

A variation of oxyacetylene flame cutting which has been developed for corrosion-resistant materials is known as *powder cutting*. Iron powder is carried to a cutting nozzle by compressed air or nitrogen, or by vibratory methods. When the iron-rich powder is introduced in the oxygen-rich acetylene flame, it forms superheated iron oxide, which melts the steel being cut. Powder cutting is particularly suited to the cutting of stainless steels and other oxidation-resistant metals.

17.16. Carbon-Arc Cutting

This process uses an arc drawn between a carbon electrode and the work. Metal is removed principally by melting, and therefore the cut must be positioned to allow for drainage. However, the cut is not so smooth as that which can be made by flame cutting. It is also generally slower than oxyacetylene cutting. Carbon-arc cutting is generally considered more applicable to the cutting of cast iron and other oxidation resistant ferrous metals than is unassisted flame cutting.

17.17 Metallic-Arc Cutting

This process employs the same principles as carbon-arc methods, but has the disadvantage of the relatively high electrode cost. The coating on the electrode forms a slag which washes away the molten metal. It also provides an insulating surface on the electrode which makes possible the use of the process in closely confined spaces which cannot be entered with a carbon electrode.

17.18. Oxyelectric Cutting

Hollow carbon or metal electrodes are used for oxyelectric cutting. Oxygen is conducted through perforations to the tip of the electrode. An arc is struck which serves to preheat the metal sufficiently so that it can be ignited by the oxygen. The process is successful with cast iron and other oxidation resistant metals. Oxyelectric cutting is used also for cutting under water.

Questions

17.1. What are the distinguishing characteristics of the several welding and joining methods?

17.2. Define the following terms (a) bead; (b) heat-affected zone; (c) pass; (d) penetration; (e) undercut; (f) weld metal.

17.3. Prepare a table showing, for each of the welding methods, the following: *Source of heat; Temperature attained; Source of filler metal used, if any; Source of flux used, if any; Source of shielding used, if any; Is pressure used? Typical applications.*

17.4. Distinguish between butt and flash welding.

17.5. Explain the advantages of d-c straight polarity, d-c reverse polarity, and a-c as applied to gas-shielded metal-arc welding.

17.6. What similarities exist between casting and welding?

17.7. Describe the changes which may occur in the heat-affected zone of the base metal when (a) the base metal is incapable of phase changes; (b) the base metal is capable of phase changes.

17.8. What factors will determine the maximum plate temperature and maximum cooling rate developed in the plate following welding?

17.9. For what reasons might a weld in a medium carbon steel be heat treated? For what reason might a weld in a piece of 18-8 stainless steel be heat treated? What methods are used to prevent intergranular corrosion in welded 18-8 stainless steels?

17.10. What fundamental difference exists between welding and brazing? Describe the general features of brazing. How does soldering differ from brazing? Compare the strength and fluid tightness of soldered, brazed, and welded joints.

17.11. Describe the following processes (a) flame cutting; (b) powder cutting; (c) carbon-arc cutting; (d) metallic-arc cutting; (e) oxyelectric cutting.

Bibliography

17.1. *Welding Handbook,* 3rd ed. New York: American Welding Society, 1950.

17.2. *Welding Handbook,* 4th ed., Section 1. New York: American Welding Society, 1957.

17.3. Morris, J. L., *Welding Principles for Engineers.* New York: Prentice-Hall, Inc., 1951.

17.4. Udin, H., E. R. Funk, and J. Wulff, *Welding for Engineers.* New York: John Wiley & Sons, Inc., 1954.

17.5. *Procedure Handbook of Arc Welding Design and Practice,* 11th ed. Cleveland: The Lincoln Electric Co., 1957.

17.6. *The Oxy-Acetylene Handbook.* New York: Linde Air Products Co., 1943.

17.7. Stout, R. D., and W. D. Doty, *Weldability of Steels.* New York: Welding Research Council, 1953.

17.8. Hinkel, J., "Iron-Powder Electrodes—A Progress Report," *The Welding Journal,* **34-5** (May 1955), pp. 440–445.

17.9. Tuthill, R. W., "Fillerarc Welding Process," *The Welding Journal,* **32-8** (August 1953), pp. 703–707.

17.10. Tuthill, R. W., "New Techniques in Inert-Gas-Shielded Metal-Arc Welding," *The Welding Journal,* **34-2** (February 1955), pp. 137–143.

17.11. Bredzs, N., and H. Schwartzbart, "Metallurgy of Brazed Joints," *The Welding Journal,* **37-11** (November 1958), pp. 493–498S.

CHAPTER 18

Secondary Methods of Fabrication: Machining and Finishing

18.1. Introduction

In this text, machining is discussed from the standpoint of machinability and the factors which affect it. There is no discussion of different machining operations and machine tools, because these represent a major field by themselves. Finishing operations are included in this chapter because of the close relationship they bear to machining. Certain finishing operations are quite similar to machining, and others, though not similar, follow machining in a production sequence.

18.2. Definition of Machinability

"Machinability" is a term which has a variety of interpretations depending upon the viewpoint of the person using it. Machinability is a property of metals, but it is not a property which is readily expressed numerically. It differs in this respect from tensile strength, ductility, hardness, and other similar properties. Machinability is used in its broadest interpretation in the discussion which follows. That is to say, machinability is concerned with (1) the economy or ease of metal removal, and (2) the ability to develop a satisfactory finish on a metal.

The *economy or ease of metal removal* is dependent upon two factors. First, the power required for the removal of a given amount of metal must be considered. In addition to this, the rate at which a particular cutting tool is worn away by the machining operation is significant because excessive rates of wear result in higher tool-sharpening and replacement costs. Lowered machine output accompanies the added cost of tool maintenance and indirectly increases expenses. Therefore economical metal removal is dependent upon low power consumption and low rates of tool wear.

Machinability is concerned also with the *ability to develop an adequate finish* on the metal being machined. This, like the ease of metal removal, involves economics. It is possible to produce a high finish on most engineering metals, but the means required may involve a prohibitive cost.

A metal may be said to have good machinability if portions of it can be removed easily by machining in such a way as to produce a good surface finish. The difficulty of assigning a numerical value to such a property can be easily appreciated. Although metals have been assigned machinability ratings, the best way of finding out whether a certain metal has good machinability is actually to try the particular operation on a sample piece. Unfortunately, a metal showing good machinability for one operation may not show equally good machinability for a different operation.

18.3. The Relationship of Mechanical Properties to Machinability

Attempts have been made to correlate various mechanical properties with machinability, but no completely adequate relationship has been developed. It is difficult to isolate the effects of various properties, because a change in one property usually results in changes in other properties.

Penetration hardness is easily measured and might seem to be a good index for determining machinability. The ability of the cutting edge of the tool to penentrate the surface of the workpiece depends upon the relative hardness of tool and work. However, penetration hardness by itself cannot be used as an indication of machinability. For instance, in the machining of steels, a value of penetration hardness which is too low may predict a rough surface and a high rate of tool wear. A hardness value which is too high indicates resistance to plastic flow. Since plastic flow is involved in chip formation, great hardness usually causes an increase in power requirements for metal removal. If the penetration hardness of the work is greater than that of the tool, machining with that particular tool becomes impossible. High abrasion hardness of the work results in rapid tool wear.

Tensile strength is another easily measured property which is related to machinability. This is not surprising if it is considered that the parting of some types of chip from the workpiece involves exceeding the tensile strength over a small area. Furthermore, penetration hardness is related to tensile strength. Thus the factors which tend to relate machinability to hardness also tend to bring about a relationship of machinability to tensile strength. But again, tensile strength alone is not a reliable indication of machinability.

A third readily determined property is *ductility*. It might be expected, because high ductility is usually associated with softness and low tensile strength, that high ductility makes for good machinability. This, however, is not the case. First, excessive ductility leads to long continuous chips which tend to foul the machine tool. Second, excessively ductile materials cause rapid tool wear and a roughening of the machined surface. In the sense that a ductile material is usually soft and weak, ductility does indirectly indicate good machinability. But the effects of ductility alone are undesirable, and the ideal situation would be to have a fairly soft metal with poor ductility. This combination would promote penetration of the tool, and the ease of separation of cut metal from the workpiece. At the same time tool wear would be minimized, and finish improved.

18.4. Chip Formation and Metal Removal

Three types of chips have been observed in studies of machining. The chip types vary in their effect on surface finish and tool wear, and certain factors have been observed to favor one type of chip over another.

The discontinuous form of chip, sometimes called *type I*, is pictured in Fig. 18.1(*a*). As can be seen, when this type of chip is formed, the metal which is forced upward over the tool face is broken into short segments. Discontinuous chip formation is promoted by brittleness in the metal being machined. Thick chips, low cutting speeds, and a small rake angle also favor discontinuous chips. Surface finish is good if the pitch angle of the chips is small. Tool failure is the result of a gradual wearing away and rounding over of the cutting edge of the tool. Discontinuous chips cause the least fouling of machine tools because they are the most easily removed of the three types.

The continuous type of chip which does not produce a built-up edge on the tool face is shown in Fig. 18.1(*b*). This type of chip is often called a *type II* chip, and is promoted by ductility in the metal being machined. Thin chips, high cutting speeds, and a large rake angle are also favorable to the formation of type II chips. This type of chip seems to be encouraged by steps which reduce friction between the chip-tool interface. The use of a tool material which does not weld to the work, highly polished tool faces, and suitable cutting fluids all tend to reduce this friction. The type II chip produces the best surface finish, and yields greatest efficiency in power consumption for removal of a given amount of metal. The temperature at the cutting edge tends to rise less for this type of chip than for any other. The face of the tool is worn by the abrasive action of the chip sliding over it, and the cutting edge is slowly rounded and worn away as in the case of discontinuous chip formation.

The continuous type of chip with a built-up edge, called the *type III* chip, is shown in Fig. 18.1(*c*). The type III chip forms in metals which have good ductility. A compressed mass of metal

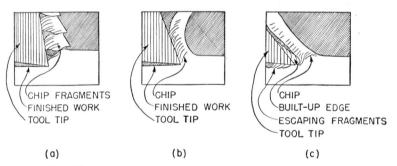

CHIP FRAGMENTS	CHIP	CHIP
FINISHED WORK	FINISHED WORK	BUILT-UP EDGE
TOOL TIP	TOOL TIP	ESCAPING FRAGMENTS
		TOOL TIP
(a)	(b)	(c)

Fig. 18.1.   Chip types formed in machining operations.

Type I	*Type II*	*Type III*

Favored by:
  brittleness in work;
  thick chips;
  low cutting speed;
  small rake angle.
Produces good finish
  if pitch angle of chips
  is small.
	Favored by:
	  ductility;
	  thin chips;
	  high cutting speed;
	  large rake angle;
	  steps with reduce friction between tool face and chip.
	Produces best surface finish and yields greatest power efficiency.
		Favored by:
		  good ductility;
		  friction at tool-chip interface;
		  welding between tool face and chip;
		  metals which gall or seize;
		  large rake angle.
		Produces poorest surface due to escaping chip fragments.

adheres to the face of the cutting tool.   Portions of the built-up edge may be broken off from time to time, and are carried away by the chip.   Still other portions of the built-up edge adhere to the workpiece and cause roughening of the machined surface.   Although friction appears to be a partial cause of the built-up edge, there is also evidence that some welding may occur due to atomic bonding.   Atomic forces become appreciable when two clean metal surfaces are squeezed together under high pressure.   Metals which show a tendency to gall or seize, such as pure iron, are particularly bad in this respect.   The type III chip, in addition to being the cause of poor surface finish, also causes severe wearing of the tool. The flank of the tool is worn by the abrasive action of the portions of the built-up edge which adhere to the workpiece.   The face of the tool is worn away by the action of the chip passing over it, producing a crater which, as it grows, moves closer to the cutting edge. This has the effect of increasing the rake angle and finally results in a breakage of the cutting edge by fracture or spalling.

18.5. The Function and Effects of Cutting Fluids on Machinability

The function of a cutting fluid is to improve machinability.   This may be achieved through reduction in power consumption, reduction of tool wear, or an improvement of finish.   How cutting fluids accomplish these results is not entirely understood.   It is well known that cutting fluids exert a cooling action which prevents overheating of the work and tool.   This may prolong tool life and improve dimensional accuracy and surface finish.   In addition, the cutting fluid may serve as a lubricant and thus reduce friction and power consumption.   It may also act in other ways, as indicated by experiments with aluminum and carbon tetrachloride.   Carbon tetrachloride (not ordinarily considered a lubricant) when applied between the chip and tool face immediately changes the chip type from III to II.   This effects an improvement in finish, and causes the built-up edge to disappear, perhaps by preventing welding between chip and tool.   The cutting fluid may improve surface finish by preventing corrosion of the workpiece, and at the same time it may prevent corrosion of the machine tool.   Finally, the cutting fluid serves to aid in chip removal.

Among the cutting fluids which have been used are air, water and alkaline solutions, oil emulsions, and sulfurized or chlorinated oils, mineral, animal, and vegetable oils. Recommended cutting oils are listed in tabular form in the literature.

18.6. The Effect of Temperature on Machinability

Low temperatures have a tendency to improve surface finish. Chips produced by turning aluminum at 200°F, 75°F, and −65°F change from type III at high temperatures to type II at low temperatures. A noticeable improvement in surface finish accompanies this change in chip type. Although loss of ductility often accompanies a decrease in temperature, such is not the case with aluminum. In this instance, improved machinability probably results from a reduced welding tendency at the lower temperature. Penetration hardness tends to rise somewhat at lower temperatures; hence there may be an increase in power requirements.

18.7. The Relationship of Microstructure to Machinability

Certain correlations between microstructure and machinability have been made. These are of much importance and are pointed out in the following paragraphs.

Grain size. Coarse grain sizes seem to be favored for rough, heavy machine cuts, perhaps because the loss of strength which usually accompanies an increase in grain size reduces the power requirements. Fine grain sizes are desirable for light cuts because of the smoother surface finish obtainable from them. This is specially true of steel. Fine grain sizes are particularly useful in the nonferrous alloys where they promote the distribution of a second phase having free-machining tendencies, such as lead in brass.

The effect of the continuous phase. Most properties of alloys are governed by the properties and amounts of the continuous phase. If the continuous phase is hard, the alloy tends to be hard. If there is only a very thin network present, the properties are less markedly influenced than if the network is broad and thick. Thus in the machining of steels having a very large ferritic matrix, difficulty is encountered because of the great ductility of the ferrite. If the carbon content is increased to about 0.3 per cent, the machinability improves. This is because of the backing given the ferrite by pearlite, which is a hard, discontinuous microconstituent, and which prevents excessive plastic flow in the ferrite. Beyond 0.3 per cent carbon, the increase in hardness, which is the result of more pearlite and less ferrite, decreases machinability by increasing tool wear and power requirements.

The effect of the discontinuous phase. The machinability of an alloy is influenced by the presence of a discontinuous phase. The extent of this influence depends upon both the nature and the distribution of this phase. These effects have been useful in developing alloys having good machinability, and in explaining the superior machinability of certain metals as compared with others.

Free-machining properties may be achieved by adding alloying elements which form a weak or brittle phase, thus assisting in the breakup of chips. Alloying elements which form low-melting constituents also may be utilized. In this case, there is a tendency for melting to occur at the temperatures of the cutting face, thus introducing a lubricant action. A low-melting, discontinuous phase is much more effective if uniformly and finely dispersed. Where segregation of low-melting constituents occurs at the grain boundaries, a fine grain size improves uniformity of distribution.

In steels, free-machining tendencies have been improved by use of sulfur and manganese. Sulfur alone produces hot shortness in steel by formation of a low-melting, weak network of iron sulfide. This produces an inferior steel. If sufficient manganese is added, the sulfur occurs in the form of pools or stringers of manganese sulfide. These serve to back up and break the chips of ductile, soft ferrite, without greatly affecting other properties of the steel. Lead is also used in steel for the purpose of imparting free-machining characteristics. Lead in a finely divided free state does not adversely affect machanical properties of heat-treated or unheat-treated steel. Lead also is used for the same purpose in copper-base alloys in which, in many cases, it is almost insoluble.

The good machinability of gray cast iron is probably due to the quantity and distribution of the graphite flakes it contains. These act as chip breakers, and also exert a lubricant effect. Since the distribution and size of the graphite flakes may vary widely, there is quite a variation in the properties of the gray cast iron, which is reflected in machinability.

The presence of an extremely hard phase in an alloy leads to a reduction in tool life. Thus in machining tool steel stock, in which there are likely to be appreciable carbides and cementite, it is desirable to have these hard phases as finely and uniformly distributed as possible. Fortunately, this condition is ideal, not only for machinability, but also for subsequent heat-treating operations.

18.8. The Effect of Defects

Castings, and less frequently, wrought metals, sometimes contain defects which have an adverse effect upon machinability. A very undesirable condition results from the fusion of sand particles to the surface of the casting. Sand has an extremely high hardness and causes excessive tool wear. Sand also may be eroded away from the mold walls and become entrapped below the surface of the casting. Improper pouring may likewise lead to slag inclusions in the casting. Slag, like sand, is very hard and produces excessive tool wear. Gas porosity may cause fairly large voids which result in tool chatter and vibration and sometimes tool breakage. On the other hand, interdendritic shrinkage which produces small, well-distributed voids may be helpful in breaking up chips. In thin or chilled sections, gray iron castings may contain cementite, which produces objectionable hard spots. In ferrous weldments, chilling adjacent to the weld may produce hardening and loss of machinability.

18.9. The Effect of Previous Cold Work

Machinability is improved by work hardening the metal, unless a hardness value is developed which is excessively high. Cold working uses up the ductility of the metal, in accordance with the Bauschinger effect, and favors formation of type I chips. It is particularly effective in improving the surface finish of annealed pure metals, which often have excessive ductility and may tend toward a chip with a built-up edge.

18.10. The Machinability of the Different Metals

Machinability ratings have been assigned to many alloys to give an indication of the relative ease or difficulty of machining. These ratings must be used with caution because of the many variables which may enter the picture. Among these is the particular operation involved, since different operations have different ratings. Furthermore, the previous history of the metal, such as degree of cold work, heat treatment, and manufacturing techniques may change its relative machinability.

The *ferrous alloys* show a wide variation in machinability, the most machinable being the leaded steels, sulfurized Bessemer steels, and malleable iron. In general, as the alloy and carbon contents of steels increase, the steel becomes less machinable. The austenitic stainless steels work harden readily, and for light cuts are rather difficult to machine. The ferritic stainless steels machine much more readily. Sulfurized austenitic stainless steels have been developed, and it is possible to improve, by suitable heat treatment (carbide precipitation), the machinability of the nonstabilized austenitic stainless steels. After machining, a solution heat treatment restores corrosion resistance.

Broadly speaking, the *nonferrous alloys* show better machinability than the ferrous alloys. Magnesium and aluminum alloys for the most part have exceptionally good machinability, magnesium alloys often being slightly superior to aluminum alloys. Some aluminum alloys offer difficulty because of excessive ductility, unusual chip length, and poor surface finish. The most machinable aluminum and magnesium alloys are almost twenty times as machinable as sulfurized Bessemer steels. The leaded brasses are also notable for machinability, the best of these being rated four times as machinable as free-cutting Bessemer stock. In general, the machinability of brasses and bronzes falls off with increasing copper content. Zinc-base alloys are often used in die-cast shapes, for which a minimum of machining is required. Zinc has good machinability, but some trouble from long chips may result. The nickel-base alloys, such as Monel metal, are about one-half as machinable as Bessemer free-machining steel. Sulfur, when introduced (R-Monel), has somewhat improved these nickel-base alloys. Bearing metals, because of the permissible tolerances, and because they often contain both hard and soft (low-melting) constituents, may pose some special machining problems. Use of carbide cutting tools which resist wear, and use of efficient cooling to prevent overheating and melting of soft constituents, are often required in the machining of bearings.

18.11. Warping

A topic of considerable importance is the change in shape which occurs upon machining pieces of metal having internal stresses. As the stressed surface layers are removed, the part adjusts its shape accordingly. Since weldments and castings which have not been annealed often have residual stresses, they may become distorted upon machining. A stress relief anneal prior to machining operations is desirable in preventing warping of this type.

18.12. Grinding

This is an operation which is similar to machining. Grinding wheels consist of small particles of abrasive bonded together by such materials as one of the resins, rubber, or fused silicates. Each particle of abrasive in the surface of the grinding wheel may be considered a small cutter. As the cutting edges of the particles become worn, the particles are pulled out of the wheel and fresh, sharp particles are exposed.

Grinding may be used as a substitute for rough machining of hard materials, although it has probably achieved its greatest value in producing a high finish on rough-machined parts. Shaped grinding wheels are fairly common for special-purpose operations such as for cutting threads.

Greater precision is possible by grinding than by cutting because of the very fine particle sizes of the chips formed. In addition, there is little deflection of workpiece and wheel, because light wheel pressures are used. Both of these factors contribute to accuracy. Superfinishing is a grinding process, used to produce an extremely high-quality surface. In superfinishing the stone is at first partly separated from the work by a suitable lubricant. Initially, therefore, the grinding action is concentrated on a few high points in the work, where the lubricant film is not able to stand up under the pressure. As the high points are finished off, the force between stone and work is spread over a larger area, causing a decrease in pressure, and a reduction in the number of locations where the lubricating film breaks down. Thus as the finish improves, so does the continuity of the lubricating film, until eventually there is no actual contact between work and abrasives, and an extremely high-grade finish is achieved.

18.13. Special Processes for Metal Removal

Several special techniques are used for metal removal. One of these is *chemical etching,* a method which is useful for almost any alloy which can be dissolved by etchant acids. Thin sheet stock is selectively etched after the areas to be protected have been masked with acid-resistant compounds. Upon immersion, the areas not protected are etched away. The process is competitive with stamping operations such as blanking or perforating, particularly if very complex shapes or a small quantity of parts are required. Chemical etching is also a useful substitute for milling, particularly milling of aluminum. The basic principles are the same as described above. By slowly immersing or removing a part from the bath, tapered sections can be made. Chemical milling offers a unique advantage in that it can be applied to components which have been formed into complicated shapes and which do not offer flat surfaces for conventional milling.

A second process, known as *electric spark machining* or *electro-erosion,* depends upon formation of an electric arc between workpiece and tool in a dielectric bath. The circuit for the process consists of a variable DC voltage across a capacitor. The capacitor is alternately charged and then discharged by an arc between workpiece and tool, both of which are submerged in a dielectric fluid such as kerosene, water, or oil. The arc causes erosion of the workpiece and the tool. The process is useful mainly for cutting materials which are very difficult to machine by mechanical means, such as cemented carbides, highly alloyed heat-resistant alloys, and hardened steel. It can be used as a substitute for most common machining operations, but is much slower than conventional machining when applied to any but alloys which are very difficult to machine.

A third process depends upon abrasion of the workpiece by *particles moving at very high speeds.* The particles are agitated by electrodynamic, magnetostrictive, or piezoelectric means. Substances to which the method is applicable include diamond, cemented carbides, tungsten, ceramics, and glass. The process, like electro-spark methods, is not competitive when applied to conventional machining problems.

18.14. Mechanical Polishing and Buffing

These are similar operations. They both produce a higher luster than grinding, and are used chiefly for decorative purposes. In mechanical polishing a wheel or belt is impregnated with fine abrasive which produces a fine finish as it is dragged across the surface of the workpiece. As the abrasive is used up, the wheel or belt must be recharged. Polishing wheels consist of abrasive bonded with glue to cloth wheels. In buffing, the abrasives are held on the buffing wheel by greases. A bar of the grease is pressed against a soft cloth wheel which picks up the abrasive. Buffing is quite expensive but gives the highest polish of the two methods. Buffing wheels tend to operate at higher surface speeds than polishing equipment.

18.15. Electrolytic Polishing

Electrolytic polishing is used for preparation of metallographic samples. It is fast and is advantageous when working with alloys which are soft or otherwise difficult to polish. Electropolishing is also applied on a commercial scale to various alloys among which are stainless steel and aluminum alloys. In these processes, the pieces to be polished are suspended as anodes in a suitable acid bath. For aluminum the process is used to produce reflectors having high reflectivity. In the case of stainless steel, the process is particularly suited to the polishing of articles which are of such size and shape that they would be difficult to polish by mechanical means.

18.16. Bright Dipping

Brightening, which is another name for bright dipping, is achieved by suspending the metal pieces in an appropriate acid bath. The temperatures and times in the baths must be controlled. The finish achieved by this process competes with a polished surface. Acetic, phosphoric, and sulfuric acids, sometimes in combination, are used for the baths. In the case of metals forming oxides which do not readily react with the above acids, nitric acid may be used to convert the surface films to a more reactive oxide.   Temperatures range from about 100°F to 225°F, and times from 1 to 10 minutes.   The process is well suited to polishing shapes of a complicated nature which do not lend themselves to mechanical finishing.   Copper, nickel, aluminum, magnesium, and their alloys have been successfully polished by this method.

18.17. Tumbling, Rolling, and Barrel Burnishing

Tumbling and rolling involve placing the work in a drum with slugs of metal or an abrasive.   Abrasive action occurs which smoothes the surfaces of the objects.   Tumbling takes place in a tightly packed barrel, while rolling is carried out in a loosely packed barrel.   Rolling produces the better finish of the two.   In barrel burnishing the parts are placed in a barrel containing hard steel balls, but no abrasive.   The surfaces of the parts are peened and smoothed over.   Burnishing often follows a tumbling or rolling operation, and produces a high luster.   It is also used to smooth and reduce the porosity of plated coatings.   All three processes are well suited to the handling of large numbers of small parts, which would be impractical to handle on an individual basis.

18.18. Cleaning Methods

The cleaning of metals is important in many cases where the workpiece is to be given a plated, painted, or similar coating.   It is sometimes a final finishing operation in itself.   There are numerous cleaning processes.   The selection of the proper one depends upon such factors as (1) the type of soil to be removed, (2) the chemical reactivity of the metal with respect to the cleaning agent, (3) the subsequent finishing operations to be used, and (4) the size and shape of the pieces to be cleaned.

There are many different kinds of *soils* encountered in metal processing, but perhaps these can be classed under two broad headings: organic-base and inorganic-base soils.   The organic-base soils include such substances as oils, greases, soap emulsions, and tars.   The inorganic substances consist principally of scales which are often metal oxides, and less frequently metal salts.   Buffing compounds, in which abrasive particles are carried in a grease, are essentially organic soils. Polishing compounds are inorganic, and may be considered as such as long as they are not suspended in an oily liquid.

There are many different *cleaning agents*. These may be classified on the same basis as the soils, namely as organic or inorganic materials. The organic cleaners include petroleum distillation products, chlorinated petroleum products, and wetting and emulsifying agents such as the sulfonated oils. In general the organic cleaners are best suited for the removal of organic soils, although there are exceptions to this. The inorganic cleaning agents are comprised of acids, bases, or strongly alkaline salts, such as sodium phosphate. The alkalies are useful in removing certain types of organic soils, and the acids are specially suited to removal of oxide scale. An important inorganic cleaning agent consists of hot molten sodium hydroxide containing sodium hydride.

There are several different *methods of applying the cleaning agents* just mentioned. Simple immersion probably requires the least elaborate equipment. The tanks must be constructed of material which resists attack by the cleaner. Means of heating, cooling, and agitating the bath may be required. Immersion may be combined with electrolysis, in which the piece is often, but not always, made anodic for a short period of time. This causes a layer of soil to be stripped from the surface of the workpiece. Spray methods utilizing the mechanical effect of high pressures are available. Probably the most ingenious means of applying the organic solvents is the vapor method illustrated in Fig. 18.2. In equipment of this type the work is suspended over heating coils which vaporize the volatile solvent. The rising pure vapors condense on the suspended workpieces, thereby washing off, or at least loosening, the soils. A combination of vapor and spray methods

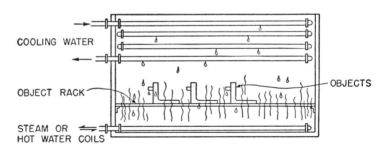

Fig. 18.2. A cross-section through a vapor degreaser showing the principle of operation.

may be used for precleaning, followed by a vapor process for final cleaning. Occasionally the cleaners may be applied by mechanical means such as brushing. Vapor cleaning alone is not generally effective in removing solid particles suspended in an oil film on the surface being cleaned.

The sodium hydride-sodium hydroxide molten salt baths for scale removal are particularly suited to steel, nickel and chromium alloys, and copper. The basic reaction is:

$$NaH + MeO \longrightarrow Me + NaOH$$

where Me represents the metal being cleaned. There is no attack of the base metal even if the treatment is carried on for too long a time. The sodium hydride is produced in the bath by reacting molten sodium with hydrogen or dissociated ammonia. The concentration of sodium hydride is less than 2 per cent. A water rinse, occasionally followed by an acid rinse, completes the process. The operation has been successfully combined with tempering so that two processing steps can be completed simultaneously.

Acid baths are very widely used for scale removal from steel. The base metal is attacked to a certain extent, and thorough rinsing is required. There is also some danger of absorption of evolved hydrogen by the steel which may cause embrittlement of the metal. In the case of enameled steel, blisters may form when the hydrogen later comes out of solid solution.

Scale also may be removed mechanically by *blast cleaning* or *scratchbrushing*. Scratchbrushing is similar to buffing, except that usually a hog-bristle or fine wire brush is used, rather than a cloth wheel. Whereas buffing requires the use of abrasives held to the wheel by grease, scratchbrushing often uses a dry powder or soapy water suspension of abrasive. Blast cleaning is particularly suited to the cleaning of castings in preparation for machining or painting. In blast cleaning, alumina, sand, or fine metal particles are directed at a high velocity at the surface of the metal. Sand particles may be propelled by high pressure or high-velocity air. Metal particles may, in addition, be propelled centrifugally, but sand is not sufficiently dense for this.

18.19. Miscellaneous Finishes for Metals

There are many other processes by which different metals may be finished to produce a variety of effects. Painting may be accomplished by brushing, dipping, spraying, or electrostatic spraying. Methods of this sort are interesting, but fit more properly into textbooks on manufacturing processes. Steel may be colored by tempering, by salt baths, by electrolytic methods, or by chemical dipping. Aluminum and magnesium can be brilliantly colored by electrolytically forming a surface oxide coating which is then dyed. (See pp. 300–301.) Copper and its alloys may be given a variety of colors such as various shades of brown, blue, or black by different chemical baths. Thus there are many finishes available for metals.

Questions

18.1. What is *machinability?*

18.2. What relationships exist between machinability and hardness, tensile strength, and ductility?

18.3. Describe the three basic kinds of chips formed by machining and the conditions which favor the formation of each. Which chip type results in the poorest surface finish? Which results in the best surface finish and economy of metal removal? What advantage is possessed by type-I chips?

18.4. What functions are performed by cutting fluids?

18.5. Describe and explain the effects of (a) temperature; (b) previous cold work on machinability.

18.6. What correlations can be made between microstructure and machinability? What are the effects of defects in metals on machinability? What is the effect of cold work on machinability?

18.7. Why must caution be exercised in the interpretation of machinability ratings? Which are the most machinable, of (a) the ferrous alloys; (b) the nonferrous alloys? Which are the least machinable of each class?

18.8. What causes warping when metals are machined? How can it be prevented?

18.9. Why is greater precision possible by grinding than by machining? Explain why the superfinishing process is successful.

18.10. Distinguish among mechanical polishing, electrolytic polishing, and bright dipping.

18.11. Distinguish between rolling and barrel burnishing.

18.12. Why is cleaning of metals important? What basic classes of soils are encountered and how may they be removed? In what ways may the cleaning agents be applied to the metal to be cleaned? What advantage is possessed by the sodium hydride method of scale removal? What is blast cleaning?

Bibliography

18.1.   Ernst H., and M. E. Merchant, *Chip Formation, Friction, and Finish.* Cincinnati: The Cincinnati Milling Machine Co., 1940.

18.2.   *Machining of Metals* (Lecture series published as book). Cleveland: American Society for Metals, 1938.

18.3.   Woldman, N. E., and R. C. Gibbons, *Machinability and Machining of Metals.* New York: McGraw-Hill Book Co., Inc., 1951.

18.4.   *United States Air Force Machinability Report,* Vol. I (1950) and Vol. II (1951). Wood-Ridge, N. J.: Curtis-Wright Corp.

18.5.   Dall, A. H., *A Review of Grinding Theories.* Cincinnati: The Cincinnati Milling Machine Co.

18.6.   *Metal Handbook,* 1948 ed. Cleveland: American Society for Metals.

18.7.   Swigert, A. M., Jr., *The Story of Superfinish.* Detroit: Lynn Publishing Co., 1940.

18.8.   Coleman, A., "Stamping Metals by Etching," *Materials and Methods,* **41-3** (March 1955), pp. 96–97.

18.9.   Sanz, M. C., "Machining Aluminum by Etching," *Materials and Methods,* **40-4** (October 1954), pp. 89–93.

18.10. *New Processes for Machining and Grinding,* National Resources Council. Washington, D. C.: U. S. Dept. of Commerce, 1953.

18.11. Hall, R. C., "Machining Hard and Brittle Materials," *Metal Progress,* **70-2** (August 1956), pp. 78–80.

18.12. "Fundamentals of Electric Discharge Machinery," *Machinery,* **62-5** (May 1956), pp. 139–145.

18.13. Bleiweis, J. L., "Simplified Methods of Cleaning Metals for Plating," *Materials and Methods,* **30-3** (September 1949), pp. 74–77.

18.14. Bergman, Adolph, "Elements of Metal Cleaning," *Metal Progress,* **57-1** (January 1950), pp. 75–78.

18.15. DuMond, T. C., "Nonferrous Metals Given High Finish by New Chemical Polishing Process," *Materials and Methods,* **31-1** (January 1950), pp. 59–61.

18.16. "Finishes for Metal Products," Staff Report, *Materials and Methods,* **42-3** (September 1955), pp. 118–132.

Index

Boldface page numbers indicate pages of major importance.